Health and Medical Care

IN NEW YORK CITY

HEALTH INSURANCE PLAN OF GREATER N.Y.

Health and Medical Care in New York City

A Report by

THE COMMITTEE FOR THE SPECIAL RESEARCH PROJECT
IN THE HEALTH INSURANCE PLAN OF GREATER NEW YORK

PUBLISHED FOR THE COMMONWEALTH FUND
BY HARVARD UNIVERSITY PRESS
Cambridge, Massachusetts · 1957

LIBRARY OF CONGRESS CATALOG CARD NO. 57-9081

MANUFACTURED IN THE UNITED STATES OF AMERICA

Published for The Commonwealth Fund

BY HARVARD UNIVERSITY PRESS, CAMBRIDGE, MASSACHUSETTS

For approximately a quarter of a century THE COMMONWEALTH FUND, through its Division of Publications, sponsored, edited, produced, and distributed books and pamphlets germane to its purposes and operations as a philanthropic foundation. On July 1, 1951, the Fund entered into an arrangement by which HARVARD UNIVERSITY PRESS became the publisher of Commonwealth Fund books, assuming responsibility for their production and distribution. The Fund continues to sponsor and edit its books, and cooperates with the Press in all phases of manufacture and distribution.

Distributed in Great Britain by Oxford University Press, London

Committee for Special Research Project

PLANNING COMMITTEE

Selwyn D. Collins, Ph.D., *Chairman*
W. Thurber Fales, Sc.D., *Vice-Chairman**
Neva R. Deardorff, Ph.D., *Secretary*

George Baehr, M.D.
Marjorie Bellows
Martin Cherkasky, M.D.
Dean A. Clark, M.D.
Edwin F. Daily, M.D.
Paul M. Densen, Sc.D.
Harold F. Dorn, Ph.D.
Jean Downes
Halbert L. Dunn, M.D.
John W. Fertig, Ph.D.
Philip M. Hauser, Ph.D.
F. W. Jackson, M.D.
Margaret Klem
Forrest E. Linder, Ph.D.
George Rosen, M.D.
Ray E. Trussell, M.D.
Theodore D. Woolsey

STEERING COMMITTEE

Responsible for research designs, collection and analysis of data, and writing of the reports

Lowell J. Reed, Ph.D., *Chairman*
W. Thurber Fales, Sc.D., *Vice-Chairman**
Forrest E. Linder, Ph.D., *Vice-Chairman*

Dean A. Clark, M.D.
Selwyn D. Collins, Ph.D.
Jerome Cornfield
Neva R. Deardorff, Ph.D.
Paul M. Densen, Sc.D.
Jean Downes
Morris E. Hansen
Philip M. Hauser, Ph.D.
Morton D. Miller
Robert Reed, Ph.D.
George Rosen, M.D.
Theodore D. Woolsey

STUDY STAFF

Jerome Cornfield, *Consultant*
Henry B. Makover, M.D., *Consultant*
Theodore D. Woolsey, *Consultant*
Nathan Goldfarb, *Administrator*

Mrs. Eve Balamuth
Medical Statistician

Mrs. Marilyn Einhorn
Statistician

Mr. John Sparks of the Research Division of the Canadian National Health and Welfare Department was loaned to assist with staff work for approximately three months in the early period.

*Dr. Fales died May 20, 1953.

Preface

THE pattern of medical care in the United States today is a fluid one. A variety of programs exist for meeting the costs of medical care, on the one hand, and, on the other, for making medical services available. However, very little factual information is available by which to judge the contributions made to the health of the population by the various programs.

The present volume is a beginning toward describing the contribution of one such program—the Health Insurance Plan of Greater New York. The word "beginning" is used advisedly for two reasons: first, H.I.P. itself is still evolving and, second, the tools with which to measure the contribution of such a plan are still crude instruments.

The need for factual data in this field was recognized from the beginning by H.I.P.'s President, Dr. George Baehr, and its former Director of Research and Statistics, Dr. Neva R. Deardorff. It was this recognition which led to a conference in the latter part of February 1951 out of which evolved a Planning Committee for the H.I.P. Special Research Project.

Many people have contributed to the study in its various stages. The basic outline for the study was prepared by the Planning Committee and the study was executed under the direction of the Steering Committee (see Chapter I).

The evolution of the Special Research Project is described elsewhere in considerable detail, except in one particular. This volume represents an instance of a highly cooperative process in which a score of persons participated. The laborious processes of study design, of supervision of data collection, of analysis of the data and preparation of the text were carried out by various members of the Steering Committee aided by a highly competent staff. Several of the committee members drafted the text of one or another of the chapters, and all of the members scrutinized and criticized the whole of the presentation.

That a flawless document has emerged from that process nobody believes. Whatever its faults, however, they are not to be ascribed to the want of a high degree of mutual helpfulness among the committee members.

Lowell J. Reed, Ph.D.

Foreword

ALTHOUGH couched in the measured terms of the objective scientist, *Health and Medical Care in New York City* describes in part the early years of one of the most imaginative ventures in medical care that has been attempted since medicine became "scientific."

When the H.I.P. in 1947 launched its operations in thirteen "uncharted fields" simultaneously, the venture was truly a pioneering one, even though sound sociological and economic engineering attested to the need for the endeavor. The basic tenet was that for families of moderate means, comprehensive medical care provided by prepayment and rendered through medical groups was an advantage. As a corollary, it was hoped that the Plan would foster emphasis upon preventive services no less than upon treatment of disease and injury, since the capitation method of compensating the medical groups gave an economic incentive for minimizing the amount and severity of illness.

All observations added up to the fact that the family doctor of the last generation, functioning in isolation from the rest of his colleagues, was as outmoded as the knight in armor. Not even the wisest physician could carry in his head all the medical knowledge his patients required, any more than he could carry in his bag all the necessary tools of modern therapy.

From the beginning H.I.P. has maintained a system of reporting all essential data on each physician's contact with each enrollee. These reports reveal the rates of utilization in each medical group, the clinical conditions presented, variations in the amounts and kinds of service utilized by each enrollee according to age, sex, type of employment, and other factors.

Valuable as these data have been, H.I.P. felt the need to compare the medical care experience of its enrollees with the experience of families in New York City who were comparable in other respects but were not enrolled in H.I.P. The studies on which this volume is based were designed to examine these two samples of the population.

The data presented in this book are of great potential value to persons concerned with developing a soundly based medical care program, because methods for the evaluation of H.I.P. service were given consideration from the outset. When the supplementary volume covering the experience of H.I.P. enrollees over a period of years has been published, the studies will be one of the significant sociological indexes of the mid-century.

As might have been expected, the present study raises almost as many questions as it answers. Having faith in the flexibility and strength of H.I.P. as an operating organization as well as in the skill of its policy makers, it seems probable to me that these unanswered questions will prove to be an advantage rather than a disadvantage to H.I.P.'s continuing program of service and scientific appraisals.

Although there has been a rapid increase in the number of prepaid medical care schemes in the United States during recent years, not even their administrative and economic aspects have been adequately studied. Even less is known regarding the impact of one or another of these schemes upon the health of the population covered. As regards that elusive problem of the quality of medical care, practically nothing is known. Indeed, it is fair to say that we are only beginning to know the criteria for measuring impact or quality.

It is for these reasons that so well planned a scientific study as that which has evaluated certain aspects of the H.I.P. operation represents a substantial addition to our meager body of knowledge and thereby contributes to the planning of public health services, particularly the medical care aspects of such services, which yearly grow more significant. In addition, studies of the type here reported contribute to the improvement of our present methodology and to the development of new and better methods for making future studies of this type.

Someday, I hope, the equally important human study of H.I.P. will be written. The driving determination and long vision of the late Mayor Fiorello LaGuardia, the statesmanship and genius for organization of Dr. George Baehr, the loyalty and enterprise of their associates—all these factors were as important as the concept itself in making it possible for H.I.P. to attain its present high stature on the American scene.

Thomas Parran, M.D.

Contents

Contents

CHAPTER I

The Research Project and H.I.P.

Launching H.I.P.

The Health Insurance Plan of Greater New York, launched early in 1947, was designed to be a practical demonstration of the values to families with moderate incomes of comprehensive prepaid medical care rendered by group practice units called medical centers. The physicians in these centers were to accent the preventive services now possible in medical practice as well as to take care of illness and injury. The group practice units were to be medical partnerships compensated by capitation payments for enrollees, and not by fees for medical services. Although the operation of the Plan was preceded by a great deal of searching for data as to the best ways to render the proffered services and as to requirements for actuarial soundness, the most diligent search brought forth comparatively little information on what was to be expected. This dearth of information arose from the complete absence of analogous experience in New York City. In other parts of this country there had been somewhat more experience with group medical practice and with prepayment, and there had been extensive experience with sickness insurance of various kinds in other countries, but there was little evidence that could be relied upon with any degree of assurance to guide the venture in New York City. The relatively meager American experience had not been acquired under the conditions projected for the Plan in this city, and had not been subjected to sufficient analysis for general interpretation.

Several uncharted fields had to be entered simultaneously. Would this community plan, based on completely voluntary group action on the part of subscribers, commend itself to them and to their employers who were to meet a part of the cost? How would labor unions regard it? No one could point to any substantial body of experience in New York City which would give a clue as to what the response would be from the many publics of which New York City is composed. On the other hand, would enough competent physicians organize themselves into medical groups to meet the conditions set forth in the insurance contract if and when a response materialized? Would it be possible to bring medical groups with well-equipped medical centers into existence? How would these resources be used by the subscribers? Would people abuse the privileges extended to them? How would the use of medical care by persons insured under this type of contract differ from what it would have been had they not been so covered? Would they avail themselves of preventive services? Would they seek medical care earlier in the course of illness than under the ordinary conditions of the private practice of medicine? How does their need for medical care vary with age and sex? How does it vary from year to year? Are there groups in the community whose need for medical care remains high year after year? If so, what is the cause of their continuing need? What, as a matter of fact, are the conditions in medical care prevailing in the community at large against which the results of the new Plan would be measured?

Since this was a venture in prepayment, knowledge about utilization was crucial to the H.I.P. for actuarial and for financial purposes. While the Plan called for a sharing by the doctors of the risk of excessive utilization, they could not carry an overload indefinitely, since the tenet had been held from the beginning that the Plan must be self-sustaining and that a medical group's compensation to its physicians must be adequate to recruit and retain competent men. The Plan had to begin without definitive answers to any of these questions relating to enrollment, need, response, and behavior. Yet these questions are decisive ones, not only for purposes of administration and finance, but also to the public, then as now deeply concerned with the problem of finding ways and means by which all members of the community may be provided with adequate medical care.

The H.I.P. Program to Accumulate Data on Comprehensive Prepaid Medical Care

Although, as has been said, the founders of the Plan and the participating physicians had mobilized all of the available data on utilization, and had made as many projections as they could from those data, and although the actual inauguration of service was largely a matter of trial, with very real possibilities of considerable error, the operation of the Plan remained in that perilous condition only during the short period necessary to acquire and begin the systematic and continuing analysis of its own experience. The Plan has from the beginning sought to know the facts of its own operation in the distribution of medical care. It has also wished to view those facts in the light of the common experience of people in New York City. Since, however, in statistical terms practically nothing is known about the private practice of medicine in this city, such a view could be had only if special means of ascertaining the relevant facts could be devised. This implied a field study of substantial dimensions.

Finally, it became evident that the administration of medical care under the conditions laid down in the contract of the new organization provided an unusual opportunity for a more searching examination of the basic *need* and *demand* for medical care than had hitherto been possible. It was thought that the careful and detailed analysis of this experience would throw light on health problems as yet unexplored by public health authorities and by administrators of prepaid medical care.

General Purposes of H.I.P. Research Program

Viewed broadly, there was need to know about the H.I.P. experience for the light that it could throw, first, on the need for medical care by population groups; second, on the volume and kind of medical service utilized by persons covered by this Plan, as compared with the services sought and received by similarly circumstanced persons not so covered; and third, on the reported conditions and services rendered to categories of enrollees over periods of years, that is, the so-called longitudinal studies. This report is concerned with the first two of these three purposes. A later series of papers will be devoted to the fulfillment of the third objective.

While these aims were established at the time the project was inaugurated, the technical means of their accomplishment were in large part still to be evolved. There were no models or designs that could be adopted immediately to serve these ends. It was expected, therefore, that an important by-product would be a contribution to methodology in the growing field of morbidity surveys and in the as yet little cultivated field of longitudinal observation and analysis of health conditions and disease in general and of medical services for care and prevention.

It was recognized from the start that the data on the general population, acquired for purposes of comparison with the H.I.P. enrollees, had values in many other connections and should be managed in such way as to conserve those values.

Inauguration of Study

The genesis of the study warrants brief review. In the summer of 1950, Dr. Lowell Reed was invited by H.I.P. to examine its primary records on utilization and to advise as to such further exploitation of them as might be profitable from the points of view of public health and the development of prepaid medical care. After his examination Dr. Reed advised the Commonwealth Fund that he considered the reports on file with the H.I.P. as basic data worthy of further study.

> The records of H.I.P. are in my opinion unique. I believe that they represent the best picture of the medical services that are desired and required by a good cross-section of urban population when these services are presented in a system that provides not only for work service but for compre-

hensive service in a pattern that is practical from the point of view of the people.

The records maintained by the groups and supplied to H.I.P. are as comprehensive as one may expect to have, and are far more complete than any records that I know of dealing with a similar problem in a population group. They are not only complete, but they give me the impression of records that are unusually accurate. Certainly the procedures followed by H.I.P. are such as to tend toward the development of accurate, consistent, and comprehensive records.

The records also offer a unique opportunity for developing a picture of medical care on the basis of the family unit. Information of this type is practically nonexistent, and yet is very definitely needed in connection with modern programs for medical service. It is probably this possibility within the records that makes them most valuable, although I should not want to minimize the desirability of a systematic study of these records from the point of view of medical services to the people on an individual basis.

In response to this suggestion, the Commonwealth Fund made it known that it would finance a conference of experts to plan a research program devoted in large part to an intensive study of the H.I.P. morbidity experience. This conference was called for the latter part of February 1951.[1] Upon completion of a three-day discussion of the purposes to be served and the methods to be used, the conferees expressed the view that these materials could be made to yield valuable contributions to knowledge of the needs for medical care and of the ability of a comprehensive plan for prepaid care to meet such needs. The conference was also agreed that such studies would warrant the expenditure of a substantial sum for special processing of the materials in preparation for the detailed analysis. It was thought that adequate knowledge of conditions and services could be derived from a sample of the experience of H.I.P. enrollees and that the analysis should be made for the period from 1948, the first full year of operation of the Plan, through 1951.

Because H.I.P. had no knowledge of the extent to which enrollees might have been using the services of physicians who were not in H.I.P., and also because there were no data on medical care in New York City with which the H.I.P. experience could be compared, this Advisory Conference recommended that a Household Survey be made both of H.I.P. families and of other families in New York City that would provide the data necessary for a clear and broad understanding of the H.I.P. experience. Thus the survey was basically designed to examine two samples of households, one drawn from the rolls of H.I.P., the other from the households in the general population. Throughout the study these will be referred to as the H.I.P. sample and the New York City sample. In the case of the H.I.P. sample, a distinction is made between those members of the household who are covered by H.I.P. and those who are not enrolled. In the latter chapters of this report the comparisons are confined to the family members in the New York City population and the H.I.P. enrollees.

Auspices of Study

For the supervision of the series of studies projected, a Steering Committee was drawn in large part from the original exploratory committee.[2] The Commonwealth Fund appropriated $156,400, including the grant for the expense of the initial exploration, toward the financing of the whole Project. This grant was matched in effect by one of $155,000 by the Rockefeller Foundation. Later these amounts were increased by $41,000 from the two foundations. With this underwriting, the Project began formal operation on July 1, 1951.

It was understood that the Steering Committee and the staff of the Research Project should have full access to all records on enrollment and utilization in the H.I.P. organization, and that the H.I.P. officials would exercise no control in the planning

[1] Attended by the following persons outside the H.I.P. staff:

Marjorie Bellows	Halbert L. Dunn, M.D.
Martin Cherkasky, M.D.	W. Thurber Fales, Sc.D.
Dean A. Clark, M.D.	John W. Fertig, Ph.D.
Selwyn D. Collins, Ph.D.	Philip M. Hauser, Ph.D.
Edwin F. Daily, M.D.	F. W. Jackson, M.D.
Paul M. Densen, Sc.D.	Margaret Klem
Harold F. Dorn, Ph.D.	Forrest E. Linder, Ph.D.
Jean Downes	Ray E. Trussell, M.D.

Theodore D. Woolsey

[2] See list of H.I.P. personnel, p. v.

of the analyses of its experience, in the conduct of the Household Survey, in the drawing of conclusions, or in the interpretation of the findings in any of the inquiries.

The Household Survey is mainly concerned with a comparison of the medical care experience of persons and families enrolled in the Health Insurance Plan of Greater New York and the experience of other families and persons in the city. To understand the purpose and results of the Household Survey it is essential that there be understanding of the Plan itself. Something must be known of its origin, history, and growth; the benefits called for in the contract; its physicians and facilities; its methods of enrollment; its premium rates; the stability of its clientele; and its methods of statistical record-keeping and compilation. These are briefly reviewed in the rest of this chapter.

Origin of H.I.P.

The Health Insurance Plan of Greater New York, generally known as H.I.P., grew out of the concern of former Mayor Fiorello LaGuardia about the inability of people of modest income to meet the rising costs of adequate and competent medical care. He was especially concerned about City employees, though his concern did not stop with them. He was seeking a community-sponsored insurance plan to which the City as an employer might turn for the purchase of such prepaid medical care. In April 1943 he appointed a committee of 16 citizens representing organized medicine, consumer groups, and the general public to investigate the subject and, if possible, to outline a plan. This committee worked during the next 16 months to find a plan that would be acceptable.

The plan proposed by the committee sought to combine the advantages of prepayment for medical care, the group practice of medicine, comprehensive service, family coverage, capitation as the basis of reimbursement to groups of physicians, and group enrollment of persons under contracts made with employers, union welfare funds, and other types of associations. Under the Insurance Law of the State of New York an insurable group must be composed of persons whose group adherence arises from conditions not related primarily to insurance; in a medical care plan this meant not related directly to the specific medical needs of its members. The Health Insurance Plan embodying these features was incorporated on September 28, 1944, over the signatures of some 80 leading citizens who signed as incorporators.

Another two and a half years were required to get the Plan into actual operation. New State and municipal legislation was required to remove legal obstacles to the group practice of medicine and to enable the City to purchase this type of insurance for its employees. Sanction by the State Insurance Department and the State Department of Social Welfare had to be obtained. Meanwhile, Mr. LaGuardia had retired from office and a new municipal administration had to satisfy itself through an independent study that the benefits offered by the Plan justified its cost to the City.

Once the Plan had been incorporated, it was possible to approach the medical profession in New York City with a concrete proposal. This stipulated that contracts would be made with groups of physicians who organized themselves and met the professional requirements of a Medical Control Board composed of a representative body of physicians to be set up by the Corporation to formulate and enforce standards of medical care. It was not difficult at that time to attract the interest of many well-qualified, excellently trained physicians who were being released from military duty and who had become habituated to a form of group practice in the Medical Corps.

When it became apparent that there would be sufficient interest among qualified physicians to insure the formation and operation of medical groups to implement the Plan, an intensive period of preparation both in developing the medical groups and in establishing the administrative headquarters of the H.I.P. followed. Premium rates had to be set. Administrative methods for premium collection and payment of capitation rates had to be worked out, enrollment and accounting procedures had to be devised, and physician efforts to form medical groups had to be encouraged and guided to assure compliance with the requirements of the Medical Control Board. These groups, in turn, had to establish partnerships, adopt names, find offices, develop administrative staffs, set up procedures of referral between general physicians and specialists, and arrange for all of the needed ancillary medical services.

Benefits and Restrictions in H.I.P. Contract

By March 1, 1947, the technical and administrative details had been sufficiently organized to enable the H.I.P. to begin operation. On that date 20 medical groups scattered throughout the four large boroughs of New York City with approximately 472 physician members were prepared to accept responsibility for the care of patients insured under the H.I.P. contract. This meant that each group had to have within its partnership or otherwise affiliated with it the requisite specialists and a staff of general physicians to enable each H.I.P. subscriber to have choice in the selection of personal or family physician.

The medical services accepted by the groups as their responsibility were described in the insurance contract as including:

Medical Services: A person while insured under this Contract shall be entitled to the following medical services provided by the Medical Group with which he is enrolled, subject to the provisions of paragraph 3 of this Section (the excluded services are described later):

a. General medical, specialist, surgical and obstetrical care.
b. Laboratory procedures, diagnostic procedures.
c. Periodic health examinations, immunizations and other measures for the prevention of disease.
d. Physical therapy, radiotherapy and other therapeutic measures.
e. Professional services for the administration of blood and plasma.
f. Eye refractions.
g. Visiting nurse service at the residence of the insured person, as prescribed by a physician of the Medical Group.
h. Ambulance service from the residence of the insured person to a hospital, when ordered by a physician of the Medical Group.

The subscriber's certificate further explained that such medical services were to be available and provided at such times as were deemed necessary and practicable by the medical group and to be in accordance with accepted medical and surgical practice and standards prevailing at the time of treatment and in accordance with standards adopted by the H.I.P. Medical Control Board. These services were to be available in the offices of the medical group, at the insured person's residence, or elsewhere within the area served by the medical group, as specified in the contract between the medical group and H.I.P. The medical group was also to furnish the services of physicians in a hospital to which the insured person was referred by the medical group. In addition, the insured person had a right to benefits consisting of medical indemnity not to exceed $150 for each instance in which such an insured person, while away from home and not able to be served by his medical group, had an accident or an emergency illness that required hospitalization.

Exclusions from the benefits included:

a. Medical services for any condition, disease, ailment or accidental injury to the extent such services are (1) covered by a workmen's compensation law or similar legislation; (2) available as a right, without respect to economic status, under the laws of the United States of America or of any state or political subdivision thereof. [Veterans Administration Services, etc.]
b. Medical services for: (1) acute alcoholism; (2) drug addiction; (3) tuberculosis, after a determination that treatment is required at a sanatorium or special hospital; (4) mental and nervous disorders, after diagnosis, for which care by a psychiatrist is required; (5) chronic illnesses in an institution other than a hospital for general care.
c. Cosmetic (other than restorative) surgery.
d. Electrolysis for epilation.
e. Services ordinarily provided by a dentist.
f. Prescribed drugs, prosthetic appliances and eye glasses.
g. Special duty or private nursing service.

It will be noted that the H.I.P. benefits do not include hospital services per se. This omission is mandatory under the State insurance law which prohibits a corporation from offering insurance for both hospital care and physicians' services. But the H.I.P. has from the beginning required all subscribers to carry Blue Cross or other hospital insurance to make sure that there will be financial provision for the H.I.P. physician to place the patient in a hospital.

Before H.I.P. came into operation the contemplated provision for comprehensive care with no physical examination as a requirement for acceptance, no waiting periods, no age restrictions, and no exclusions of pre-existing conditions was generally viewed with apprehension. Critics predicted adverse selection of risks and such excessive use of the services available as would destroy the quality of the service, if not the total functioning of the Plan. The originators of the Plan, however, depended on group enrollment to insure adequate spread of risk.

Premium Rates

The setting of premium rates was originally envisioned as a process of harmonizing the factor of the ability of families of moderate income to absorb in their budgets a regular payment for medical care (half the premium rate with the other half paid by the employer) with the expense involved in providing a comprehensive program of first-class medical care and operating an efficient insurance mechanism. The upper limit of a moderate income was placed at $5,000 for a family. Decisions and agreements as to premium rates and capitations were reached in June 1946. The following month the Office of Price Administration went out of existence and the index of the cost of living in New York City began a rapid ascent. But the Plan could not jeopardize its inauguration by trying to adjust its rates at that moment.

It was not long before another condition began to make itself felt. The rising costs of living with the ensuing wage adjustments, together with the employment of married women, carried many family incomes over the $5,000 limit. It became very difficult with such a limitation to enroll City departments as well as other employed groups. This problem was finally met by accepting families of higher income on an adjusted premium. The limits for the base premium were put at an annual income of $5,000 for a person insuring himself only and $6,500 for a family group. Premiums for persons and families with incomes above those amounts were set at 50 percent higher than the base rate.

Prior to the spring of 1952, when the Household Survey was made, the H.I.P. rates had undergone one revision and provision had been made for the enrollment of persons with higher incomes at the higher rates. The premiums paid at the various periods are shown in Table I–1.

The first premium rate revision was required to meet the general rise of the cost of living in New York City together with the effect of family

Table I–1. Annual premium rates in H.I.P., March 1947 through date of survey[1]

TIME PERIODS	BASE PREMIUM RATE[2]			RATE FOR PERSONS WITH INCOMES IN EXCESS OF $5,000 AND FAMILY INCOMES IN EXCESS OF $6,500[2]		
	1 person	*2 persons*	*3 or more persons*	*1 person*	*2 persons*	*3 or more persons*
March 1947–December 1949	$29.04	58.08	87.00	$ —	—	—
January 1950 through date of survey	34.56	69.12	103.68	—	—	—
April 1950 through date of survey	—	—	—	53.40	106.80	160.20

[1] The contract and the certificate issued to each subscriber have from the beginning specified that there is to be no charge by the medical group for these services, except that it may charge "not exceeding two dollars ($2.00) for each visit requested and made between 10 P.M. and 7 A.M. to such insured person at his residence." The medical groups' agreement with H.I.P. provides that physicians are to receive no fees or gratuities from or on behalf of H.I.P. patients for services rendered under the insurance contract.

[2] These rates are for H.I.P. benefits only; they do not cover hospital costs.

sizes larger than had been expected. A second rate revision, which took place after the survey (July 1953) grew out of the further advance in prices and from the additional costs occasioned by the operation of the new medical centers, which involved heavy capital investment and higher operating costs than were originally estimated. An additional element of expense arose from the conviction held by most of the medical groups that family physicians and pediatricians should have offices away from the medical center and scattered throughout the neighborhoods in the city. Neither rate increase was occasioned by utilization in excess of the expectation, and neither increase was followed by a loss of enrollment.

H.I.P. Medical Groups and Subscriber's Choice of Physician

Before the H.I.P. offers the services of a group of physicians to H.I.P. subscribers, the medical group has to meet the standards of the H.I.P. Medical Control Board and enter into a formal contract with H.I.P. to supply the services set forth as guaranteed to subscribers through medical groups. These standards relate to the qualifications of the physicians, their group organization, and the facilities and equipment of the group's medical center. Each group must be a medical partnership composed of family physicians and representatives of the twelve basic medical specialties.[3] Each group defines the area from which subscribers are accepted by it. Some medical groups provide all of the office services at the medical center, while others decentralize the family physicians (and in a few instances the pediatrician's services) and use the medical centers largely for the specialist services.

When a person has signified an intention to join H.I.P., he is supplied with a directory of medical groups that lists their names and addresses, gives the names of the physicians composing the group, indicates which are family physicians, and gives the address of any office they may have away from the medical center at which they are prepared to see patients. The person is not enrolled until he has chosen a medical group. Beginning with his effective date, that medical group receives semi-monthly capitations for the subscriber and each of his dependents. New subscribers are instructed to visit their medical groups promptly in order to select their family physician from the several who are in the medical group, to arrange for check-ups, and to become acquainted with their doctors and the H.I.P. system before an emergency occurs. Subscribers are free to choose any medical group that serves their area of residence and to change their family physicians and, in some groups, their pediatricians at any time. When a subscriber moves out of the area served by his medical group, he transfers to a group serving his new location.

From the beginning, the H.I.P. subscriber has been urged to think of his affiliation with the H.I.P. medical group as the election of a team of doctors engaged in medical group practice and designed to meet, with very few exceptions, all of his medical needs. Utilization data show that about half of all the physician services rendered are those of specialists. H.I.P. subscribers are free to use outside physicians, but such physicians will receive no compensation from H.I.P. or the medical group for assistance in diagnosis and treatment. Subscribers who are devoted to a family physician they have had prior to joining H.I.P. may continue with him and use their medical group only for X-ray, laboratory, and other specialist services. Conversely, some subscribers may continue with a specialist they have previously had and use their H.I.P. affiliation for any other medical needs that they or their dependents may develop. Women pregnant at the time of enrollment often continue with the obstetrician they have previously engaged.

Development of Medical Centers

The original plan called upon each medical group to equip itself with a medical center from which to serve the H.I.P. enrollees who had chosen the group for their medical needs. Because of the acute shortage of suitable office space in the early years of the Plan's operation, the re-

[3] A medical group organized by a hospital or a university may be composed of a salaried staff.

quirement that such groups establish a medical center was temporarily suspended, but all groups were required to set up administrative offices which arranged appointments of subscribers with the physicians, who used their private offices. In a few instances, however, groups were able to centralize their services from the beginning, either for all services or for all the specialist services. Since that time, the H.I.P. requirement for medical centers has been gradually enforced. The operation of a medical center entails considerable initial outlay and some operating expense. Its advantages are conditioned in large measure by the size of the enrollment—small enrollments entail excessive overhead charges—and by the extent to which the physicians on the staff can concentrate their offices in the center and thus free themselves of the expense of private offices elsewhere.

By the end of 1952 there were 927 doctors on the staffs of the 30 groups. Of these, approximately 520 were specialists—80 of them pediatricians—and 407 general physicians. As has been said, a large majority of the medical groups arrange for their general physicians and in some cases their pediatricians to maintain private offices scattered throughout the area served by the respective groups. These physicians have some hours at the center for patients who are also seeing specialists. The opinion held by these groups is strongly to the effect that this extension of family service into neighborhoods is preferred by their subscribers.

Enrollment in H.I.P.

On March 1, 1947, the H.I.P. enrolled 2,643 persons. Almost all these were members of a labor union, Local 89, A. F. of L., the Chefs, Cooks, Pastry Cooks and Assistants. On April 1 the enrollment of City employees began with several of the smaller municipal departments. The United Nations covered its staff on May 15, 1947. By the late summer of that year the employees of the Board of Education had been enrolled. In the autumn the Parks Department came in and in January 1948 the employees of the Sanitation Department began to come under coverage. Late in 1948 the Board of Transportation entered into contract with H.I.P. for the enrollment of its employees. This occurred during the first five months of the following year. In 1952 the Police Department arranged for the coverage of its uniformed force. Meanwhile, other labor unions' welfare funds and many small business concerns, social and civic agencies, private schools, the employees of some local units of the State and Federal governments, and the tenants of some housing projects had made contracts with H.I.P. Among the latter was a veterans' cooperative housing project in the Borough of Queens. Several other housing projects were later enrolled.

In total, the H.I.P. enrollment advanced from 2,643 on March 1, 1947, to 376,413 on December 31, 1952. The details of the growth of enrollment are shown in Table I–2.

From this table it will be seen that there has

Table I–2. Enrollment experience for all persons insured by H.I.P. each year, 1948–1952 and ten months 1947

ITEM	MARCH 1–DEC. 31, 1947	1948	1949	1950	1951	1952
Opening enrollment	—	76,106	122,405	229,208	255,980	287,659
Additions to enrollment[1]	82,279	59,330	126,951	56,962	64,732	132,631
Terminations[2]	6,173	13,031	20,148	30,190	33,053	43,877
Closing enrollment	76,106	122,405	229,208	255,980	287,659	376,413
Net gain	76,106	46,299	106,803	26,772	31,679	88,754
Percentage gain	—	60.8	87.3	11.7	12.4	30.9

[1] Additions to enrollment include: Newly enrolled subscribers and their eligible dependents; persons who renewed their insurance coverage; persons who converted from group to individual coverage; net gain of dependents arising from changes in the size of enrolled families.

[2] Terminations include all subscribers and their dependents who are suspended from coverage. The number of persons who converted from group to individual enrollment is included in "Additions to Enrollment."

been a high degree of stability in the H.I.P. enrollment through the several years of its operation. The losses it has sustained arise from many causes; children become 18 years of age and go away to school; death occurs; persons are admitted to institutions; there are resignations and loss of jobs in covered employment; some contracts are cancelled for a variety of reasons; and indifference or dissatisfaction with the program lead to terminations of individual coverages. In the earlier years enrollees leaving New York City had to terminate, but since January 1, 1950, they have been able to have coverage by an indemnity plan limited to members of insured groups who live out of the area served by medical groups.

H.I.P. System of Records and Statistics

In order to record in some detail and to analyze its experience, the H.I.P. has maintained from the beginning a system of reporting which shows the essential data on each physician's contact with each enrollee in the Plan. Through a one-line entry on a daily roster of visits, designating the physician and the group, each patient is fully identified, as is the contract group under which he is covered, the place at which he was seen (office, home, or hospital), the nature of the services rendered (preventive, obstetric, surgical, and other), and an indication of the diagnosis.

Underlying these data on utilization are those on enrollment, which show currently for each person his status at any given time. Very careful registration is maintained and communicated to the medical groups so that they will be prepared to serve their registered enrollees under the H.I.P. contract. The medical groups must know precisely who is covered at any given time and the precise dates of the enrollee's coming on and going off of the rolls. Although this body of enrollment data changes constantly, it is so devised as to yield at all times an accurate population base with which to compute utilization and other rates.

Out of these comparatively few basic records the H.I.P. has built a statistical system that has lent itself to many uses beyond the primary one of providing an actuarial base for its operation. Both the medical group administrators and H.I.P. staff, medical and other, constantly use the statistical data which emerge from this reporting system for a wide variety of purposes.

The obvious products of such a system are the rates bearing on enrollment experience and the basic utilization rates—utilization rates for persons enrolled in the different medical groups, rates for persons in different contractor groups, and rates for persons with variant characteristics of age and sex. Only a few figures will be cited here to indicate the major facts on utilization that came out of this system in the years prior to the inauguration of the Special Research Project. They are listed in Table I–3.

Table I–3. Measures of general utilization for total H.I.P. population, 1948–1951

RATE	1948	1949	1950	1951
Physicians' services per enrollee year of coverage	4.7	4.7	5.2	5.3
Highest rate reported for any medical group	7.1	5.8	9.1	6.7
Lowest rate reported for any medical group	2.8	2.9	4.2	4.0
Estimated proportion of enrollment served	48.0	56.0	75.0	81.0
Major operations per 1,000 years of coverage	12.0	12.9	14.9	15.7
Deliveries per 1,000 years of coverage	6.6	8.2	12.1	13.4
Radiological services per 1,000 years of coverage	[1]	[1]	261	282

[1] Services by radiologists were not tabulated prior to 1950.

Potentialities of H.I.P. Materials for Further Research

While the ongoing program of H.I.P. has required many data which the reporting system has supplied,[4] the administrative needs of the organization did not exhaust the possibilities for information on health conditions and medical care which the system provided. For instance, only rarely was it necessary for administrative purposes to compile statistical data on the patients' diagnoses, and then only for small groups of patients;[5] yet the filing of such material by the physicians presented an excellent opportunity to see the general morbidity conditions of this growing

[4] See "Memorandum on Work of the Division of Research and Statistics, 1946 Through June 1954."

[5] The diagnostic notes on the utilization reports have served many other than statistical purposes.

population as it came under systematic medical observation. It was the realization of these possibilities for seeing health conditions as revealed in the current practice of medicine and for answering more searching questions as to the effect of the H.I.P. services that led the H.I.P. officials to turn outside their own ranks for advice as to the exploitation of these materials for other than immediate administrative purposes. Conceivably such exploitation could not only contribute to thorough statistical evaluation of the H.I.P. program, but it could also serve even broader uses than those of the H.I.P. itself. The design of the Household Survey as one of the means for the pursuit of these ends is described in the chapter which follows.

CHAPTER II

Objectives and Methods of the Household Survey

Objectives of the Household Survey

The Special Research Project officially began on July 1, 1951. Eight months of intensive work in developing the sample design, the schedule, and other procedures preceded the field work of the Household Survey. Interviewing of the households in the samples began on March 3 and ended on June 27, 1952.

The specific objectives of the Household Survey were the following:

Insurance

To examine the extent to which the New York City population is covered by insurance for hospitalization and for medical care, and the extent to which persons are covered by more than one insurance plan.

To study the demographic and social characteristics of the New York City population, of the H.I.P. population, and of the population covered by other insurance plans.

Health Conditions and Medical Care

To compare the medical needs of the population of New York City and of the H.I.P. population.

To compare the amount of medical care, including preventive services, received by the general population and by the H.I.P. population in comparable social groups.

To compare the amount of unattended illness in the general population and in the H.I.P. group.

To attempt to develop broad indexes of quality of medical care received by the general population and by the H.I.P. population.

To picture the medical care needs, the services received, and the quality of the care received by the New York City population.

To learn of the extent to which medical care is sought by the H.I.P. enrollees outside the H.I.P. system.

To determine whether it is possible to estimate from the H.I.P. experience, on a continuing basis, the total morbidity and the needed services for the total population of New York City.

In addition to the acquisition of substantive data bearing on these questions, it was hoped, as said above, that the survey would yield experience of value in the development of an improved methodology for inquiries into these several fields of interest. (See Appendices describing in detail the method employed.)

Size of Samples

At the close of the interviewing, data had been collected on 3,235 households with one or more persons enrolled in H.I.P. at the time of the survey and on 4,190 New York City households not in H.I.P. The H.I.P. households contained 10,981 members of whom 8,040 had H.I.P. coverage. The New York City households had 13,558 persons as members.

The 3,235 H.I.P. households are 2.7 percent of the New York City resident households with one or more members enrolled in H.I.P. on December 31, 1951, when the sample was drawn. The 4,190 households in the New York City sample are 0.2 percent of those reported in the 1950 Census minus those in H.I.P. at the end of 1951.

The comparisons in matters of health and medical care will be confined to H.I.P. enrollees and persons in the New York City sample, except in the chapters dealing with the comparability of the two samples in respect to demographic and socioeconomic characteristics, where the characteristics of members of H.I.P. households who were not covered by the Plan will also be examined. Before making such comparisons a brief description of the methodology of the survey is in order.

Methods of Survey

Sample Designs

The Household Survey was based on a sample design that would result in a sample of 5,000 H.I.P. families and another sample of 5,000 families from the general population within the five boroughs of Greater New York. The H.I.P. sample was drawn from a straight 10 percent sample of all families that had ever been enrolled—the 10 percent whose enrollment, utilization, and morbidity experience were to form the basis of the longitudinal studies. By drawing the 5,000 families from the larger sample it became possible to relate the survey data to the longitudinal findings on these families. It was known at the time that of the H.I.P. families, approximately 20 percent would no longer be on the rolls by December 1951, the end of the longitudinal study period, and would therefore not be in the Plan at the time of the Household Survey in the following spring. In effect, the persons and families in the H.I.P. sample consisted of two groups: those in H.I.P. at the time of the Household Survey and those who were no longer on its rolls. The latter group presented distinctive problems in the collection and analysis of data and since the data on it served no important objective of the study, it was omitted.

The families in the New York City sample were chosen on the basis of area probability sampling. After the schedule to be used by the interviewers had been drafted, Alfred Politz Research, Inc. was commissioned to conduct the field work. The sample design and the interviewing process are discussed in detail in Appendices C and D.

Schedule of Questions

The schedule of questions which was largely self-explanatory both to the interviewer and the respondent and, insofar as possible, was self-coding, called for general demographic data, including any insurance for medical care, for each member of the household and some items on the family. It asked about the illness status of each person in the household on the day previous to the interview, about all illnesses that had occurred within an eight-week period previous to the interview, and about illnesses in 1951 that required hospitalization over at least one night or a period of seven days at home in bed. It inquired about defects, minor chronic conditions, and some physical problems not ordinarily thought of as "illness." Upon learning of an illness or of these other conditions at any of the specified times, the interviewer prepared a special supplementary schedule which gave the details on each episode or condition, including the disability involved, the medical care received, and the insurance coverage for that specific condition. There were also questions on preventive health services received and on prenatal care. All together there were 14 items on the family as a whole, 14 items on each person, 24 items on the illness memorandum for episodes in the eight-week period, and 23 for episodes in 1951. (See Appendix A for Survey Schedules.)

Ideally, when the objectives and general plan of the survey have been spelled out, the construction of an interview to obtain the desired information and a schedule on which to record the responses and other necessary data should be a routine matter. In practice, of course, this is seldom the case. It is in designing and pretesting the interview that one begins to come face to face with realities.

The interview for the Household Survey part of the Special Research Project and its embodiment in the schedule were developed over a period of several months. The schedule underwent half a dozen revisions and was subjected to two pretests in the field before interviewing in the sample households began in March 1952.

The schedule as it finally took shape contained a number of the improvements in schedule design that had been worked out in surveys outside the field of public health. The schedule used in this survey and the one used in the San José phase of the California Morbidity Research Project were developed simultaneously.[1]

They were the first illness survey schedules to

[1] Field work in San José actually started about two weeks earlier than in New York City, but the schedules were being prepared at the same time during the fall of 1951. Both showed the influence of Census Bureau research and experience in schedule design.

make use of the columnar form, that is, with one column for each member of the household. A format of this sort permits the use of space in the left-hand margin for printing out in detail the questions to be asked. This has been found to lead to greater uniformity in the wording of questions by the interviewers.

While the use of a check list of chronic diseases in an illness interview dated back to the National Health Survey of 1935–1936, the check list of symptoms (used both in San José and in New York City but with somewhat different inclusions) had been used only once before in a large-scale survey (the survey in the State of Michigan in 1948).

Field pretesting had not been a prominent feature of most of the earlier illness surveys, either, but in this survey a great deal of effort went into achieving a naturalness in the wording of questions.

Problems of Recording Morbidity Data

Perhaps the most important innovation introduced by this study was the use in the interview of a battery of questions approaching the matter of illness in the family from several points of view in order to probe the memory of the respondent. It was apparent to those designing the interview that previous surveys attempting to measure both nondisabling and disabling illness had suffered from a considerable degree of underreporting. A rate of 1,800 illnesses per 1,000 persons per year was considered very high in general illness surveys; yet it was known from studies of the common cold that the average person had two to four colds a year. Hence, for all forms of illness, a rate of 5,000 per 1,000 per year should not be considered too high.

As has been said, the schedule includes a set of questions relating to illness yesterday, a set relating to illness during the last eight weeks, and a set for illness during the calendar year 1951. It should be noted that the respondent was given at least four opportunities to mention illness or injury yesterday—first, a question on sickness yesterday; next, a question on the effects yesterday of any injury, whether incurred yesterday or previously, as long as the effects lasted more than 24 hours; third, a question on symptoms of any sort that lasted at least 24 hours; and, finally, a question to bring out any other medical or dental condition for which a person may have had cause to see a doctor or dentist yesterday. Any mention of illness, injury, symptom, or medical attention led to the opening up of a column on the Illness and Medical Care Memorandum (Schedule 2).

A similar pattern of questions is followed in the set relating to the last eight weeks except that a check list of specific symptoms was used instead of a general question about symptoms, and two additional questions were asked, one to obtain information on check-ups and routine health examinations and the other to get a total of doctor and dentist visits in the past eight weeks.

Questions dealing with the calendar year 1951 are restricted to hospitalization, illnesses resulting in bed stays of seven or more days, and the total number of times a doctor was seen during the year. A "yes" response to either of the first two of these led to the opening up of a column on the second type of Illness and Medical Care Memorandum (Schedule 3).

Finally, a separate question was asked regarding a set of nine chronic diseases, providing one more opportunity for the reporting of disease conditions existing at present in members of the household. In this case, however, no effort was made to ascertain whether the condition caused symptomatic illness yesterday, in the last eight weeks, or in 1951, nor was a sickness Memorandum opened up during the interview when one of these diseases was reported. This last aspect of the schedule design led to some difficulties in the diagnostic coding of the data. It was possible, for example, for a respondent to report asthma in a member of the household as an illness occurring in the past eight weeks and then to fail to report asthma in the check list question. Likewise, a household member could be reported as having one or more of the ailments on the check list though no associated illness or medical care was reported for yesterday, the past eight weeks, or the year 1951. A coding procedure, described in Appendix D, was adopted to take care of such situations.

While experience with the schedule brought

out other weak spots, which are also discussed at some length in Appendix D, there is no doubt about the general success of this battery of illness questions in picking up illness. In surveys in which illness is measured by means of an interview, with one member of a household speaking for the other members, it is generally believed that the more intensive the questioning the more illness will be reported. But as the intensity increases the additional reports tend to be of less and less interest from the standpoint of the severity and medical significance of the illnesses. The interview must be designed to bring out, as a minimum, illness of all the degrees of severity needed for the purposes of the survey. Thereafter, the characterization of the illness by means of later questions and the tabulation of the various categories must be used to distinguish the trivial from the significant ailments.

The per capita amount of illness of all degrees of severity brought out by this interview probably exceeds that in any prior survey. In the New York City sample a total of 7,486 illnesses, injuries, and other medical conditions was reported for 13,558 persons in the eight-week period preceding the interviews. No exact comparison of this frequency with other surveys is possible, since it includes illnesses beginning prior to the eight-week period as well as those having their onset during the period; yet it appears to be greater than the amount found in general illness surveys conducted prior to 1950.

The chief concern of the Household Survey was the provision of a comparable measure of the medical needs in the two populations—the population of H.I.P. enrollees and the population of the City of New York not enrolled in the Plan. Another basic purpose of the survey was to compare the amount and kinds of medical services received under H.I.P. with those received in the general population of New York City, the overwhelming part of this latter population having no extensive medical care insurance coverage of the type provided by H.I.P. This comparison could not be intelligently analyzed, it was believed, without knowledge of the medical care needs of the H.I.P. and non-H.I.P. populations.

For the purpose of measuring medical care needs the planners decided to stick to the idea of using illness as the index. While other methods of measuring these needs might have been discovered, none had ever been tried, and the difficulties of devising such methods are formidable.[2] At least morbidity had been used on numerous other occasions for this same purpose, and a good deal had been learned about how to measure and classify illness.

It might be supposed, however, that whichever of the two populations received the greater amount of medical care might report certain conditions as illnesses which otherwise would not be considered as such. Among these conditions are acne, sterility, obesity, menopausal complaints, cysts, etc. These conditions are not all minor and some are quite common. Such conditions might be reported much more completely when medical care had been received. Consequently the use of morbidity as an index of medical care needs might be biased in this comparison owing to a differential in completeness of reporting.

The first suggestion for avoiding this difficulty was that comparison of illness in the two groups might be confined to that illness which involved interruption of the sick person's usual activities (disability) or confinement to bed. But even here it was felt that there was a possibility of bias. It is known, for example, that staying home from work or going to bed as a result of an illness may often be an action taken at the doctor's orders. Was it not likely, therefore, that an illness might sometimes be disabling simply because a doctor had been seen?

There was no doubt that this might happen at times, and it was believed that the only solution was to use as many safeguards as could feasibly be included in the study design. The safeguards actually built into the plan were of five types:

1. Since the receipt of medical care might be the key to remembering an illness it was decided to include a set of questions dealing with illness

[2] The "symptom schedule" used in the Michigan study of medical care needs is actually a measure of morbidity. It was, in fact, designed to be one answer to the same conceptual difficulty encountered in the H.I.P. project.

yesterday. The problem of recall should certainly be less when dealing with such recent events.

2. Similarly, the problem of recall could be expected to be diminished and the intervention of the doctor less of a determinant of interruption of usual activities in the case of illnesses of a more severely disabling nature. However, such illnesses are less frequent; even the number occurring in a period of eight weeks would be hardly sufficient for an analysis in samples of the size planned. This suggested including a question about severely disabling illnesses (taken to be those causing the sick person to remain in bed for seven or more days) occurring in the preceding calendar year.

3. The effects of H.I.P. coverage might be more pronounced for illnesses at the other end of the severity scale, because the emphasis in H.I.P. is placed upon early treatment and prevention of serious disability. Hence, it was desirable to include some questions that probed for the less serious illnesses experienced during the eight-week period, particularly those that might go untreated in fee-for-service experience. The very fact that such illnesses might often go completely untreated meant that respondents would frequently be ignorant of the nature of the condition, no diagnosis having ever been made. This led to the inclusion of a question on symptomatic complaints yesterday and a check list of nine selected symptoms. Respondents were asked whether any member of the household had experienced one of these nine symptoms during the last eight weeks.

4. There was actually as great an interest in knowing about the *kind* of medical care received as in measuring the *amount* received in relation to an index of needs. Therefore, an effort was made, in three sections of the schedule particularly, to get at differences in the kind of medical care received. At one point respondents were asked to report whether anyone in the household had had "a physical check-up or a routine health examination by a doctor during the last eight weeks." If so, the respondent was asked a question regarding the reason for this examination (particularly to determine whether it was undertaken as a preventive measure) and what tests and procedures it included. At another point the following question was asked about each condition for which a doctor or dentist had been seen: "How long after the development of this condition did . . . wait before calling the doctor (or dentist)?" At a third point in the schedule a series of seven questions was asked about medical care during pregnancy and the puerperium for all instances where a pregnancy followed by delivery had been reported.

5. Finally, an additional safeguard against the bias of differential incompleteness of reporting lay in the planning of appropriate tabulations. Here principal reliance was originally to be placed upon including a classification by income in a number of the important tabulations comparing illness and medical care in the H.I.P. and non-H.I.P. populations. The hypothesis was that completeness of reporting of illness was related to the accessibility of medical care. Hence, it was felt that the appropriate comparison for the H.I.P. group as a whole might be found in one of the higher income strata of the non-H.I.P. households. In any case it would be important to examine the relationship of illness of various degrees of severity to income in order to interpret the H.I.P. versus non-H.I.P. findings. Since no more than 80 percent of the households reported this item completely, however, the educational attainment of the head of the household was substituted for income as a major axis of classification in the tabulations.

Another safeguard that was available in the tabulations was the comparison of illness at a number of different levels of severity and the comparison of particular classes of illness selected as those likely to be reported whether attended by a physician or not.

Thus, it may be seen that the conceptual issue that arose in planning the comparison of medical care received in relation to an index of needs was particularly influential in planning the schedule and the tabulations, as well. Aside from this consideration, the contents of the schedule were determined with the following purposes in mind: (1) to measure, using an identical measuring instrument, the morbidity, the amount and type of medical care, and the insurance coverage and availability of sick leave in two populations, asking the questions in such a manner that the ordinary household respondent could be expected to answer them with reasonable accuracy; and (2) to learn sufficient facts about the demographic, economic, and social characteristics of the populations to permit, primarily, comparisons of morbidity and medical care, holding constant certain sources of variation, and, secondarily, study of the characteristics of the population enrolled in H.I.P.

Interviewers and Respondents

Interviewers were instructed to seek the data from a responsible adult member of the family. For 84.9 percent of the persons in the H.I.P. group and 77.6 percent of the persons in the New York City families, the informant was reporting on himself—more frequently herself—her spouse, or her child. For 4 percent and 7 percent, respectively, the informant was reporting on another relative. For 10.5 percent of the subjects in the H.I.P. households and 13.7 percent of the other group, the relation of the informant to the subject was not reported. In the remainder of the cases the subject for whom the informant gave information was a lodger, servant, or friend who lived in the household.

The details of the response rates and the extent to which replication was used are fully described in Appendices C and D. It is sufficient here to report that the response from the families containing active H.I.P. members was such that it can be accepted as covering 81 percent of the original sample drawn, and that the New York City families with no H.I.P. members who were interviewed reflected 86 percent of the original sample for the non-H.I.P. population. A total of 3,235 households with 10,981 persons, of whom 8,040 were current H.I.P. enrollees, composed the responding H.I.P. sample; and 4,190 households with 13,558 persons, that of the general population. (See Appendix E for comparative data from the two samples and from other sources dealing with the base populations from which the samples were drawn.)

Revisiting was required to make contact with a responsible member in more than 50 percent of households in both the H.I.P. and the New York City samples. In 25 percent of the cases three or more visits had to be made before the mission was accomplished.

General Quality of Data

No categorical statement can be made as to the quality of the total aggregation of data returned on these schedules. Obviously, the quality of the response varies as the questions vary in their demands upon the knowledge, memory, intelligence, and cooperation of the respondent. In some instances the quality of the data can be assessed through comparison with the data from the 1950 Census and the enrollment data maintained by H.I.P. In a few instances comparisons can be made with the findings of other inquiries which have employed acceptable sampling techniques. Wherever possible, the data sought in this inquiry have been processed in such a way as to facilitate such comparison. On the whole, the materials have stood up very well when such comparisons have been possible. But each body of data must be scrutinized for its own quality.

In the chapters which follow the data are set forth in relation to the broad objectives of the survey. Since it was known in advance that the H.I.P. enrollee population differed in some respects, notably in age distribution, from that of the city, the populations in the two samples, that of New York City and of the H.I.P. enrollment, are, at the start, compared for a number of demographic characteristics. Thereafter, demographically comparable groups are used in the examination of insurance status, contacts with physicians in 1951, and use of family physicians and pediatricians, as well as in the examination for the three time periods—previous day, eight-week period, and preceding year—of health and medical care experience of H.I.P. enrollees and the New York City population not covered by H.I.P.

CHAPTER III

Demographic Characteristics of Households and Their Members

THREE questions are at issue when the data from the two samples are aligned for comparison of the socioeconomic characteristics of the two groups of households. First, are these samples good reflections of the larger groups for which they stand in respect of a given characteristic? Second, how do the H.I.P. households differ from those with no members thus covered? Third, in what respects are H.I.P. enrollees different from the other persons in their households who are not enrolled? In other words, what is the effect of selection among members of households when some but not all members become H.I.P. enrollees?

The first question is answered briefly in Chapter II and at some length in Appendices C and D. In Appendix E, the data for the two samples are checked against other information for the respective populations, notably, in the case of the New York City sample, the data from the 1950 Census. A close correspondence is shown there between each of these two samples and the population it was designed to represent. This chapter sets forth the ways in which the H.I.P. population deviates from that of the city sample and from the persons not so covered in H.I.P. households, that is, it deals with the second and third of the three questions listed above.

Comparisons between H.I.P. and non-H.I.P. households will be made on the basis of family size and composition, race, birthplace and religion of head of family, marital status and labor force status of persons over the age of 14 years, education of persons over the age of 24 years, occupation and industry of those in the labor force, family income and selected housing conditions, and, finally, the age and sex of the persons in the sample populations. In a few instances households as such will be the units used, but in most of the comparisons the units will be persons who are characterized by given demographic and family conditions.

To simplify the analysis and further sharpen the values of the two samples as a means of comparison of medical care experience, all households in the general population sample found to contain H.I.P. members were transferred to the H.I.P. sample. At the time of the survey H.I.P. had on its rolls about 3.7 percent of the New York City population; it was to be expected that some families in a sample of the general population of this size would be found to have members covered by H.I.P. A total of 3.3 percent of the persons and 3.0 percent of the households for which data were secured in the New York City sample were so found and were transferred to the H.I.P. sample. Since, as will be seen later, the H.I.P. families (not the enrollees within them) do not differ markedly in demographic characteristics from those in the general population sample, this transfer of a small segment of households from the New York City sample to the H.I.P. sample does not impair the representative quality of the former other than in this one respect of having no families with at least one member belonging to H.I.P.

Household Membership and H.I.P. Coverage

A comparison of households having H.I.P. members with households having no H.I.P. members presents some difficulties that are not at once apparent.[1] The requirements of the Insurance Law of New York State for group insurance of families are such as to make it practically impossible to cover under the family contract all the members of many households and even all the blood relatives in some types of families. According to this law, a family consists only of spouses and their unmarried children, own or adopted, under the age of 18 years. A stepchild and one committed by a court to the family are also in the accepted category. But the parents of the insured person and all relatives by blood or marriage other than the spouses and the unmarried children under 18 are not eligible as family members in group insurance. Moreover, H.I.P. does not require every subscriber to cover his eligible dependents, though in group contracts for family coverage (as distinguished from contracts for employee-only coverage) 75 percent of the enrollees with eligible dependents are expected to cover them. In those instances in which the H.I.P. contract is for employees only, there can be no coverage of dependents. Several of the early H.I.P. contracts with labor unions were of this type.

Since, for the purposes of this study, any household with even one member covered is classified as in the H.I.P. group, there is no uniformity among these units as to the extent to which members are covered or the family position of the covered members. In all analyses of medical care, distinctions must be made between the covered members of the H.I.P. families and those who are not enrollees. But for the purposes of establishing the demographic characteristics of the population from which the H.I.P. enrollees have been recruited, the fact that some of the H.I.P. families were only partially covered can be ignored. The term *H.I.P. households* will be used to designate these in their entirety; *H.I.P. enrollees* will refer to the covered members only.

In the H.I.P. households, heads of families were covered in 88.8 percent of the cases; in 11.2 percent of the households the H.I.P. enrollees were subsidiary members. Even when heads of families were covered, not all the eligible dependents were necessarily members of H.I.P. There was no consistency between the position of the covered member in the family and the extent of family coverage. The covered part of the household might consist of the legally eligible family, or the head, or any other adult member alone. In some instances the family members were all covered, even though some were not eligible for family coverage; they were covered under separate contracts.

[1] The survey used the standard definitions of "household" employed by the Census Bureau. In the case of the definition of "families," slight modification from the Census definition was made in order to be able to show the number of primary families in a single dwelling unit.

Table III–1. Persons in H.I.P. and New York City samples, by size of household and H.I.P. status

SIZE OF HOUSEHOLD	H.I.P. SAMPLE						NEW YORK CITY SAMPLE	
	Total		*H.I.P enrollees*		*Others*			
	Number	Percent	Number	Percent	Number	Percent	Number	Percent
Total	*10,981*	100.0	*8,040*	100.0	*2,941*	100.0	*13,558*	100.0
1 member	178	1.6	178	2.2	—	—	398	2.9
2 members	1,648	15.0	1,330	16.5	318	10.8	2,302	17.0
3 members	2,433	22.1	1,737	21.6	696	23.6	3,087	22.8
4 members	3,216	29.3	2,464	30.6	752	25.6	3,496	25.9
5 members	1,875	17.1	1,290	16.1	585	19.9	2,170	16.0
6 members	912	8.3	588	7.3	324	11.0	1,074	7.9
7 members	392	3.6	259	3.2	133	4.5	406	3.0
8 members	136	1.2	80	1.0	56	2.0	232	1.7
9 members	108	1.0	72	0.9	36	1.2	135	1.0
10 members	50	0.5	20	0.3	30	1.0	100	0.7
11 members	33	0.3	22	0.3	11	0.4	33	0.2
12 members	—	—	—	—	—	—	60	0.4
13 members	—	—	—	—	—	—	65	0.5

Size of Households

The households in the H.I.P. sample were distributed over a range of from one to 11 members; the New York City households, over a range from one to 13 members (Table III–1). The membership of H.I.P. households had a somewhat larger proportion in the four-person family groups and a comparative deficit in the one- and two-person households. But outside of these divergencies the proportion of persons in households of various sizes was almost parallel in the two groups.

Under the conditions of family coverage described above, it is not surprising to find that in families of all sizes there were some persons who were not covered. Thus, in the 824 instances of two-person families, 318 had but one person in H.I.P. In the case of the larger families, the persons covered might be one or all.

Composition of Households

For the analysis of family composition two approaches are made: (1) persons in families of given types (i.e., husband and wife only, or husband, wife, and child or children, etc.) are set forth, and (2) persons in specified relationships to the head of the family (i.e., spouse, child, grandchild, parent, brother, sister, etc.) have been counted. The two samples are aligned for the first of these types of analysis in Table III–2. These data on type of family are consonant with those on size of family.

While there are some differences between the sample of H.I.P. and the sample of New York City families, they are comparatively small. Couples with no children in the household comprised 11.5 percent and 12.3 percent of the persons in the H.I.P. and the New York City samples, respectively. In both groups, 56.3 percent of the population were in families with children under 18; 35.8 percent of the population in H.I.P. households, and 38.5 percent of that in the New York City sample lived in households with one or more children under the age of 6 years. About 16 percent of the persons in H.I.P. households and approximately 15 percent of those in the city sample were housemates in various combinations of friends, lodgers, and relatives of different types. As is to be expected, the H.I.P. enrollees themselves show a slightly greater concentration in families consisting only of parents and children at least one of whom is under 18 years.

When the family members are classified by the relationship to the head of the family, there is again a close resemblance between the population in the H.I.P. households and those in the city sample (see Table III–3).

Table III–2. Persons in H.I.P. and New York City samples, by type of household

TYPE OF HOUSEHOLD	H.I.P. SAMPLE						NEW YORK CITY SAMPLE	
	Total		*H.I.P. enrollees*		*Others*			
	Number	Percent	Number	Percent	Number	Percent	Number	Percent
Total	*10,981*	100.0	*8,040*	100.0	*2,941*	100.0	*13,558*	100.0
Single person alone	178	1.6	178	2.2	—	—	398	2.9
Husband and wife alone	1,268	11.5	1,108	13.8	160	5.4	1,670	12.3
Husband, wife, and at least one child under 18	5,406	49.3	4,669	58.1	737	25.0	6,315	46.6
One parent with at least one child under 18	125	1.1	85	1.1	40	1.4	510	3.8
Parent(s) with all children over 18	1,349	12.3	641	8.0	708	24.1	1,563	11.5
Two or more families with at least one child under 18	643	5.9	288	3.6	355	12.1	801	5.9
Two or more families with no children or none under 18	174	1.6	77	0.9	97	3.3	180	1.3
All other groups	1,793	16.3	976	12.1	817	27.8	1,996	14.8
Not reported	45	0.4	18	0.2	27	0.9	125	0.9
Households with child or children born after March 1946 (i.e., under 6 years)	3,930	35.8	3,201	39.8	729	24.8	5,217	38.5

Table III–3. Persons in H.I.P. and New York City samples, by relationship to head of household

RELATIONSHIP TO HEAD OF HOUSEHOLD	H.I.P. SAMPLE						NEW YORK CITY SAMPLE	
	Total		*H.I.P. enrollees*		*Others*			
	Number	Percent	Number	Percent	Number	Percent	Number	Percent
Total	*10,981*	100.0	*8,040*	100.0	*2,941*	100.0	*13,558*	100.0
Head	3,235	29.5	2,874	35.7	361	12.3	4,190	30.9
Wife	2,650	24.1	2,115	26.3	535	18.2	3,112	22.9
Child	4,023	36.6	2,829	35.2	1,194	40.6	4,950	36.5
Parent or parent-in-law	300	2.7	26	0.3	274	9.3	256	1.9
Other relatives	616	5.6	161	2.0	455	15.5	730	5.4
Unrelated persons	127	1.2	29	0.4	98	3.3	242	1.8
Not reported	30	0.3	6	0.1	24	0.8	78	0.6

About 90 percent of the persons in H.I.P. households consisted of heads of households, spouses, and children; 8.3 percent were other relatives; and 1.5 percent, unrelated persons or of unknown relationship. In the general population sample the proportions were 90.3, 7.3, and 2.4, respectively.

While the distribution of the total persons in the H.I.P. households by family status conforms closely to the proportions found in the sample of the general population, there are a few notable departures when the H.I.P. enrollees are singled out. More of them were in the position of head or spouse and fewer in other relations. About 30 percent of the "children" in these families were not covered by H.I.P. (see Table III–4). In approximately half of these instances these children of the person considered to be the head of the family were over 18 years of age. They therefore could not be covered by their parents, and H.I.P. coverage was not automatically available to them. Although some of these older children were covered by reason of their having been brought into H.I.P. by the parent while they were still under 18 years, through the exercise of the conversion privilege on reaching that age, and through coverage on independent contracts, it is known that the H.I.P. population is deficient, when compared with the New York City population, in young persons aged 18 to 29 as well as in persons over 65 years of age—conditions which will be made more explicit in a later section. A few of these older children, together with parents and parents-in-law, brothers and sisters and their spouses, nephews and nieces, grandparents and grandchildren, aunts, uncles, cousins, and foster children not legally within the custody of the family who were found in these households, though ineligible under the subscriber's contract, were covered by reason of independent access to H.I.P. coverage. In some instances such persons were subscribers living in families with neither the head of the family nor the spouse covered.

In terms of size and composition, there would

Table III–4. Persons in H.I.P. households, by relationship to head and H.I.P. coverage

RELATIONSHIP TO HEAD OF HOUSEHOLD	TOTAL		H.I.P. ENROLLEES		OTHERS	
	Number	Percent	Number	Percent	Number	Percent
Total	*10,981*	100.0	*8,040*	73.2	*2,941*	26.8
Head	3,235	100.0	2,874	88.8	361	11.2
Wife	2,650	100.0	2,115	79.8	535	20.2
Child	4,023	100.0	2,829	70.3	1,194	29.7
Parent or parent-in-law	300	100.0	26	8.6	274	91.4
Other relatives	616	100.0	161	26.1	455	73.9
Unrelated persons	127	100.0	29	22.8	98	77.2
Not reported	30	100.0	6	20.0	24	80.0

Table III–5. Persons 14 years of age and over, H.I.P. and New York City samples, by marital status

MARITAL STATUS	H.I.P. SAMPLE						NEW YORK CITY SAMPLE	
	Total		*H.I.P. enrollees*		*Others*			
	Number	Percent	Number	Percent	Number	Percent	Number	Percent
Total	*8,397*	100.0	*5,926*	100.0	*2,471*	100.0	*10,253*	100.0
Married	5,688	67.7	4,671	78.8	1,017	41.2	6,664	65.0
Widowed	510	6.1	164	2.8	346	14.0	808	7.9
Divorced	60	0.7	25	0.4	35	1.4	118	1.1
Separated	107	1.3	68	1.2	39	1.6	192	1.9
Never married	1,843	21.9	884	14.9	959	38.8	2,183	21.3
Not reported	189	2.3	114	1.9	75	3.0	288	2.8

appear to have been nothing that especially distinguished the households with H.I.P. members from those in the general family population. But it is apparent that the H.I.P. enrollee population, as such, shows some selection due to the operation of the definition of a family in group enrollment. The group of H.I.P. enrollees was weighted with heads of families and spouses and fell slightly below the city sample in the proportion of other types of household members. But again, the differences come within a relatively narrow range.

Marital Status

Although the distribution by marital status of the total persons in the sample of the H.I.P. households did not differ markedly from that of the persons in the sample of households in the city, the H.I.P. enrollees did differ, again owing to the legal definition of a family for the purpose of insurance coverage. Among the H.I.P. enrollees there were considerably more married persons and fewer in all of the other marital classes than in the city population (see Table III–5).

Race of Informant and Birthplace of Household Head

Because there were some families with members of different races, a condition which, it was thought, informants might be reluctant to discuss, the schedule called for the race of the informant only. It has been assumed that the other members of the household were usually of the same race, though that is not invariably true in this community. Tabulations on this basis (see Table III–6) show a slight preponderance of white persons in the H.I.P. households (91.9 percent) over those in the New York City sample (89.2 percent). This difference is corroborated by other social and economic data.

H.I.P. households show 70.0 percent of their members living in families headed by a person born in continental United States, while in the New York City sample, 62.1 percent of the members fall in that category (Table III–7). Thus there was a somewhat higher proportion of United States-born persons in the H.I.P. households. Approximately 26 percent of all members of H.I.P. households were in families headed by a person born in Europe, as compared with 29.2 percent of those in the sample of New York City households. Only 1.2 percent of members of H.I.P. households were persons whose family head was born in Puerto Rico, as compared with 3.1 percent in the city group.

Table III–6. Persons in H.I.P. and New York City samples, by race of informant

RACE OF INFORMANT	H.I.P. SAMPLE						NEW YORK CITY SAMPLE	
	Total		*H.I.P enrollees*		*Others*			
	Number	Percent	Number	Percent	Number	Percent	Number	Percent
Total	*10,981*	100.0	*8,040*	100.0	*2,941*	100.0	*13,558*	100.0
White	10,089	91.9	7,428	92.4	2,661	90.5	12,095	89.2
Non-white	845	7.7	582	7.2	263	8.9	1,380	10.2
Not reported	47	0.4	30	0.4	17	0.6	83	0.6

Table III–7. Persons in H.I.P. and New York City samples, by birthplace of head of household

BIRTHPLACE OF HEAD OF HOUSEHOLD	H.I.P. SAMPLE						NEW YORK CITY SAMPLE	
	Total		*H.I.P. enrollees*		*Others*			
	Number	Percent	Number	Percent	Number	Percent	Number	Percent
Total	*10,981*	100.0	*8,040*	100.0	*2,941*	100.0	*13,558*	100.0
Continental United States	7,690	70.0	6,153	76.5	1,537	52.3	8,426	62.1
Puerto Rico	129	1.2	45	0.6	84	2.9	419	3.1
Other Western Hemisphere	236	2.2	118	1.5	118	4.0	428	3.2
Europe	2,811	25.6	1,651	20.5	1,160	39.4	3,966	29.2
Other	47	0.4	22	0.3	25	0.8	160	1.2
Not reported	68	0.6	51	0.6	17	0.6	159	1.2

Comparison of nativity between the persons in the New York City sample and the H.I.P. enrollees themselves shows an appreciably higher proportion of the latter than of the city group reported from households headed by persons born in continental United States—76.5 percent as compared with 62.1 percent. Correlatively, the H.I.P. household members who were not covered came in greater ratios from families headed by foreign-born persons. Only 20.5 percent of the H.I.P. enrollees as compared with 39.4 percent of the non-covered relatives and housemates and 29.2 percent of persons in the New York City sample were in families with heads born in Europe. There were also fewer among the H.I.P. enrollees than among the New York City sample in all the other categories of birthplace outside the United States and Europe.

Educational Status

The educational status of the persons aged 25 or over in H.I.P. households ran the gamut, as did that of the members in the New York City households, from no formal education to more than high school graduation. But considerably more of the members in the H.I.P. households than in the general population were in the latter class—23.3 percent as compared with 14.2 in the city sample (Table III–8). For H.I.P. enrollees the proportion rose to 27.1 percent. How much of this came about from the factors operating in the selection of groups that had been enrolled, and how much from factors operating in the selection of persons within those groups, there is no way of determining.

Differences of such magnitude make it necessary to use education as one of the factors in establishing later comparisons between the two groups in respect to health conditions and use of medical resources. As will be explained later, the data on income present difficulties which make it desirable to use another index of socioeconomic level. Education of the head of the household has been selected for that purpose.[2]

[2] See *United States Census of Population: 1950*, Special Report, P-E No. 5B (Education), Washington, D.C., U.S. Government Printing Office, for data on the correlation of income and education, especially for persons aged 30 and over.

Table III–8. Persons 25 years of age and over, H.I.P. and New York City samples, by education

YEARS OF SCHOOLING COMPLETED	H.I.P. SAMPLE						NEW YORK CITY SAMPLE	
	Total		*H.I.P. enrollees*		*Others*			
	Number	Percent	Number	Percent	Number	Percent	Number	Percent
Total	*6,941*	100.0	*5,233*	100.0	*1,708*	100.0	*8,062*	100.0
None	185	2.7	73	1.4	112	6.5	387	4.8
Less than 9	2,237	32.2	1,539	29.4	698	40.9	2,912	36.1
9 to 12	2,681	38.7	2,081	39.8	600	35.1	3,242	40.2
More than 12	1,620	23.3	1,419	27.1	201	11.8	1,143	14.2
Not reported	218	3.1	121	2.3	97	5.7	378	4.7

Religio-Cultural Affiliation

There was little or no tangible evidence that the H.I.P. enrollees tended to come from one or another of the three large religio-cultural groups in New York City—Catholic, Protestant, and Jewish. The question was asked about the head of the family: was he or she Catholic, Protestant, Jewish, or of other religious affiliation? Other members of the household were assumed to belong to the same sectarian group. This assumption is not invariably correct, but for the purposes of this survey it was safe, since there was no reason to believe that as between the two groups of households the proportion of those with mixed affiliations would vary or that the representative character of the head of the family would differ as between the two populations sampled.

The results of the canvass for this item are shown in Table III–9.[8] It is evident from this that there was little if any religio-cultural bias among the H.I.P. samples. It would appear now that if it existed, it was in the direction of having a larger proportion of Catholic and Jewish people and a relative shortage of Protestants. The fact that the H.I.P. sample had proportionately fewer non-white households may account in part for this deficiency.

Summary of Social Characteristics

Before going on to the economic data, it may be well to summarize the findings of the preceding sections and of the material set forth in detail in Appendix E.

It would first appear that the New York City sample did reflect with considerable fidelity the New York City population in respect of size and composition of families, marital status of persons 14 years of age and over, racial origin, nativity of white persons, educational status of persons 25 years of age and over, and religious affiliation. This would seem to lay down a fairly firm foundation for the comparisons which follow in the later sections of this report between the H.I.P. population and that for the city as a whole.

The H.I.P. households did not depart widely from these same patterns for size of family except as fewer persons lived in the one-person households and more in the larger families, notably the four- to six-person family groups. In family composition, relationship of members to the head of the family and marital status, there were no outstanding differences. There were fewer non-white persons in this sample than in that of the city as a whole, but the difference is not of such magnitude as to cause concern beyond making allowance for it at appropriate points in subsequent analyses. There is reason to believe that the nativity data show considerable similarity between the H.I.P. and non-H.I.P. households. In the education of persons 25 years of age and over an appreciably higher proportion of the persons in the H.I.P. households had had more than high school education—23.3 percent as compared with 14.2 in the New York City sample—but among the H.I.P. households were many headed by per-

[8] For a brief account of the efforts in New York City to determine the size of the three religio-cultural groups, see Neva R. Deardorff, "The Religio-Cultural Background of New York City's Population," *The Milbank Memorial Fund Quarterly*, Vol. XXXIII, No. 2, pp. 152–160, April 1955.

Table III–9. Households and persons, H.I.P. and New York City samples, by religion of head of household

RELIGION OF HEAD OF HOUSEHOLD	HOUSEHOLDS				PERSONS			
	H.I.P. sample		*New York City sample*		*H.I.P. sample*		*New York City sample*	
	Number	Percent	Number	Percent	Number	Percent[1]	Number	Percent
Total	*3,235*	100.0	*4,190*	100.0	*10,981*	100.0	*13,558*	100.0
Catholic	1,576	48.7	1,890	45.1	5,781	52.7	6,461	47.6
Protestant	599	18.5	984	23.5	1,857	16.9	3,088	22.8
Jewish	962	29.7	1,159	27.7	3,053	27.8	3,579	26.4
Other	44	1.4	80	1.9	132	1.2	214	1.6
Not reported	54	1.7	77	1.8	158	1.4	216	1.6

[1] Tabulation of H.I.P. enrollees shows a distribution closely resembling this.

sons of very modest educational attainment. Finally, no marked differences are discernible in religio-cultural affiliation.

When the data on H.I.P. enrollees themselves are reviewed, a few of the differences between them and the people in the city sample are accentuated. More of them were in families with children under 18 years of age; more were heads of families and spouses; and, naturally, more were married. The proportion of white persons rose a little higher, as did the proportion in families headed by a person born in continental United States. Among those 25 years of age and over, the fraction with more than a high school education rose to 27.1 percent. This is the kind of weighting in a group insured for prepaid medical care that might be expected under the rules now operative in the group insurance field in respect of eligibility of dependents and under the economic and social conditions that obtain in New York City. The H.I.P. program was designed for people who wish to pay their way as regards medical expense but who can do that only if there is a method by which they can budget for it.

The more specific data on the economic condition of the people in the two samples follow.

Labor Force Status of Household Members

While it is highly desirable to examine the data on labor force in the two samples as a means of assessing their economic characteristics, it must be remembered that these present problems both of a technical and an interpretive kind. The labor force status of a given person is not immediately apparent in some cases. The Census defines the labor force as consisting of "all persons classified as employed or unemployed [i.e., looking for work] . . . and all members of the armed forces."[4]

When the two survey samples are compared (see Table III–10), it is found that the H.I.P. households had a higher proportion of persons 14 years of age and over who were in the labor force than did the New York City families—60.7 percent as compared with 55.0 percent. This condition is consistent with what is to be expected when a group of families is selected largely on the basis of the employment status of a family member, usually the head of the family but in some instances the employed wife.

When the figures on H.I.P. enrollees and on other members of their households are examined, it is found again, as might be expected, that the proportion of H.I.P. enrollees in the labor force was higher than that of other family members; 64.2 percent of all H.I.P. enrollees over 14 years were thus classified. Of the other members in these households, the proportion was approximately the same as in the sample of New York City households, 52.3 percent as compared with 55.0 percent of the New York City sample. In other words, those persons in H.I.P. households

[4] *United States Census of Population: 1950,* Vol. III, Chapter 37. In this survey, family members away from home in the armed forces were not enumerated.

Table III–10. Persons 14 years of age and over, H.I.P. and New York City samples, by labor force status

LABOR FORCE STATUS	H.I.P. SAMPLE						NEW YORK CITY SAMPLE	
	Total		*H.I.P. enrollees*		*Others*			
	Number	Percent	Number	Percent	Number	Percent	Number	Percent
Total	*8,397*	100.0	*5,926*	100.0	*2,471*	100.0	*10,253*	100.0
In labor force	*5,095*	60.7	*3,804*	64.2	*1,271*	52.3	*5,634*	55.0
Working	4,851	57.8	3,637	61.4	1,214	49.2	5,278	51.5
Looking for work	111	1.3	52	0.9	59	2.4	247	2.4
Other[1]	133	1.6	115	1.9	18	0.7	109	1.1
Not in labor force	*3,224*	38.4	*2,069*	34.9	*1,155*	46.7	*4,474*	43.6
Keeping house	2,276	27.1	1,524	25.7	752	30.4	3,204	31.2
Going to school	657	7.8	444	7.5	213	8.6	737	7.2
Unable to work	136	1.6	32	0.5	104	4.2	269	2.6
Other[1]	155	1.9	69	1.2	86	3.5	264	2.6
Not reported	78	0.9	53	0.9	25	1.0	145	1.4

[1] This category includes persons who are on leave or are employed in seasonal occupations, who are neither working nor looking for work.

who were not covered by H.I.P. did not include an undue proportion of dependents. As explained earlier, these persons were an erratically constituted group. They might be the primary family whose older child or other relative was the only member covered, or the dependents of a subscriber who had elected not to cover them or was on a contract that covered only employees, or the ineligible relatives living with a primary family that was on the rolls.

Women and Girls in Labor Force

When the data on the marital status of women and girls 14 years of age and over in the sample of H.I.P. enrollees and the New York City sample are examined to see the proportion of each marital category that was in the labor force, wide differences between the two samples appear. They are what could be anticipated from the selected nature of the H.I.P. population in respect of employment status. Married women as well as those who were widowed, divorced, or separated were in the labor force in greater proportions in the H.I.P. sample than in the New York City sample (Table III–11). These proportions would not characterize the total group of women and girls in H.I.P. households, irrespective of H.I.P. enrollment. But it is noteworthy that among the female enrollees a higher proportion were in the labor force, particularly the married women.

Table III–11. Percentage of women and girls 14 years of age and over in labor force, H.I.P. enrollees and New York City sample, by marital status

MARITAL STATUS	H.I.P. ENROLLEES		NEW YORK CITY SAMPLE	
	Number	*Percent in labor force*	*Number*	*Percent in labor force*
Total	*2,791*	35.9	*5,554*	31.8
Married	2,176	29.0	3,372	20.2
Widowed, divorced, or separated	144	84.8	892	36.8
Never married	416	56.5	1,135	60.9
Not reported	55	23.6	155	41.9

Occupational and Industry Groups of Household Members

As might be anticipated from the data on education as well as from knowledge about the sources of H.I.P. enrollment, there were wide differences in the occupations to which the employed members of the two groups of households belonged.

Among the H.I.P. enrollees in the labor force the proportion of persons in professional and semiprofessional pursuits was over twice that found among the members of the New York City families in the labor force (Table III–12). There was also a slightly larger proportion in service occupations, other than domestic, than was found among the New York City families. Fewer members were engaged as proprietors and managers, as clerical and sales workers, and as domestic helpers.

The representation of persons in the various industry groups among the labor force members in the H.I.P. and New York City households shows the marked differences that were previously known to exist. As compared with the industry distribution for the city as a whole, the H.I.P. households were short on persons engaged in manufacturing and in the wholesale and retail

Table III–12. Persons in labor force, H.I.P. and New York City samples, by occupational group

OCCUPATIONAL GROUP	H.I.P. SAMPLE						NEW YORK CITY SAMPLE	
	Total		*H.I.P. enrollees*		*Others*			
	Number	Percent	Number	Percent	Number	Percent	Number	Percent
Total	*5,095*	100.0	*3,804*	100.0	*1,291*	100.0	*5,634*	100.0
Professional, semiprofessional workers	1,072	21.0	931	24.5	141	10.9	566	10.0
Proprietors, managers, and officials (including farm) and farmers	290	5.7	217	5.7	73	5.6	638	11.3
Clerical and sales	1,128	22.1	657	17.3	471	36.5	1,458	25.9
Craftsmen, foremen, operatives, and laborers	1,822	35.8	1,417	37.2	405	31.4	2,085	37.0
Domestic service	48	0.9	15	0.4	33	2.6	67	1.2
Other service	523	10.3	422	11.1	101	7.8	527	9.4
Not reported	212	4.2	145	3.8	67	5.2	293	5.2

Table III–13. Persons in labor force, H.I.P. and New York City samples, by industry in which employed

INDUSTRY	H.I.P. SAMPLE						NEW YORK CITY SAMPLE	
	Total		*H.I.P. enrollees*		*Others*			
	Number	Percent	Number	Percent	Number	Percent	Number	Percent
Total	*5,095*	100.0	*3,804*	100.0	*1,291*	100.0	*5,634*	100.0
Construction	273	5.4	232	6.1	41	3.2	250	4.4
Manufacturing	606	11.9	229	6.0	377	29.2	1,364	24.2
Transportation, communication, public utilities	1,306	25.6	1,230	32.4	76	5.9	507	9.0
Wholesale and retail trades	347	6.8	199	5.2	148	11.5	1,036	18.4
Finance, insurance, real estate, and service trades	1,381	27.1	1,024	26.9	357	27.6	1,375	24.4
Government, not elsewhere classified	772	15.2	688	18.1	84	6.5	231	4.1
Other	2	[1]	1	[1]	1	0.1	11	0.2
Not reported	408	8.0	201	5.3	207	16.0	860	15.3

[1] Percentage less than 0.05.

trades (Table III–13). They had marked excesses of workers in transportation and of governmental workers.

Even wider differences from the New York City population appear for the group of H.I.P. enrollees. Only 6 percent of their labor force members were in manufacturing, a quarter of the proportion among the labor force members in the New York City households. The H.I.P. enrollees had a very much smaller proportion engaged in wholesale and retail trades, and were even more heavily weighted with persons in transportation and in governmental service. Table III–13 displays the distribution for the two samples.

Distribution by employer status shows corresponding differences between the various groups. More than half of all labor force members of H.I.P. households and over 71 percent of the labor force members among H.I.P. enrollees were in governmental service, while in the New York City families 73.4 percent of the labor force members worked for private employers and only 8.4 percent were in public employment (Table III–14). All of these data for the H.I.P. group conform to what was already known about them.

Family Income and Housing

The belief that health conditions and medical care are significantly associated with family income is widely held, although in New York City there are both highly developed public health services and a system of medical care intended to prevent persons and families in the low income brackets from being deprived of good care.

In this survey, it was thought that data on family income had to be included even though it was known in advance that these might prove to be difficult to elicit in this city. The cooperation of the informant was purely voluntary. The interviewer did not enjoy the official status with which the enumerators of the United States Census are clothed. In general it may be said that the income data obtained may be usable for some purposes but are far from satisfactory for the purposes of

Table III–14. Persons in labor force, H.I.P. and New York City samples, by type of employer

TYPE OF EMPLOYER	H.I.P. SAMPLE						NEW YORK CITY SAMPLE	
	Total		*H.I.P. enrollees*		*Others*			
	Number	Percent	Number	Percent	Number	Percent	Number	Percent
Total	*5,095*	100.0	*3,804*	100.0	*1,291*	100.0	*5,634*	100.0
Private employer	1,869	36.7	913	24.0	956	74.0	4,138	73.4
Government	2,891	56.8	2,725	71.7	166	12.9	473	8.4
Own business	180	3.5	103	2.7	77	6.0	704	12.5
Without pay in family business	1	[1]	1	[1]	—	—	21	0.4
Not reported	154	3.0	62	1.6	92	7.1	298	5.3

[1] Percentage less than 0.05.

this survey. As has been said, the education of the head of the family was substituted for income as an index of socioeconomic status.

The method used to collect income data followed one which had been pretested in the Current Population Survey in April 1948. This required that the Census enumerator ask the respondent to indicate on a card the broad class interval into which the total money income fell for each primary family and for each person not a member of a primary family. It was there found that in terms of median income the returns did not differ widely from those resulting from inquiries of a much more intensive kind.[5]

The technique of showing the respondent a card with the income class intervals was used in this survey, but nothing was said about distinguishing between the income accruing to members of the primary family and that received by other related and unrelated persons in the household. It was thought that a broad characterization of income levels would serve the purposes here embraced, and that a more meticulous and elaborate inquiry would only add to the demand upon the patience and cooperation of the informant and to the cost of collection and analysis, without a corresponding increment in the value of the data. When the results are viewed solely as a survey of income, however, it must be emphasized that there is considerable uncertainty about the precision of these returns.

The concept of family income itself is subject to varying meanings and interpretations. When all income received by family members is pooled and expenditures are made from a common purse, it is much easier for a family to have a clear idea of its income than when some of the income is regarded as personal to one or more members who think of themselves merely as purchasing lodging and board from the head of the family. The problem is aggravated when the household includes persons who are not related to the family, and when two or more families are sharing living quarters in a single household. But, for the purposes of this survey, it was thought that even though there would be variant family mores in the pooling of the income, a rough grouping of families according to economic levels could be obtained, and that the method used would provide adequate comparative data for these samples. The outcome of these efforts is shown in Table III–15.

In both the H.I.P. and the New York City households the number of persons for whom no data on family income were returned was high, 15.4 percent for H.I.P. and 21.9 percent for the city household members, and to that extent the picture is obscured. In the H.I.P. group, 28.4 percent of the persons were living in households reported to have incomes of $5,000 or over as compared with 21.4 percent of the persons in the city households. It may be noted in this connection that in the H.I.P. households the proportion of persons 25 years of age and over with more than high school education exceeded the proportion of such persons in New York City families by about 9.1 percentage points.

[5] Herman P. Miller, "An Appraisal of the 1950 Census Income Data," *Journal of the American Statistical Association*, Vol. 48, No. 261, p. 29, March 1953.

Table III–15. Persons in H.I.P. and New York City samples, by annual family income

ANNUAL FAMILY INCOME	H.I.P. SAMPLE						NEW YORK CITY SAMPLE	
	Total		*H.I.P. enrollees*		*Others*			
	Number	Percent	Number	Percent	Number	Percent	Number	Percent
Total	*10,981*	100.0	*8,040*	100.0	*2,941*	100.0	*13,558*	100.0
$2,000 or less	201	1.8	108	1.3	93	3.2	1,102	8.1
2,001–$3,000	925	8.4	623	7.8	302	10.3	1,763	13.0
3,001– 4,000	2,723	24.8	2,179	27.1	544	18.4	2,793	20.6
4,001– 5,000	2,322	21.2	1,904	23.7	418	14.2	2,035	15.0
5,001– 6,500	1,449	13.2	1,064	13.2	385	13.1	1,328	9.8
6,501– 8,000	805	7.3	559	7.0	246	8.4	779	5.8
8,001 and over	867	7.9	547	6.8	320	10.9	786	5.8
Not reported	1,689	15.4	1,056	13.1	633	21.5	2,972	21.9

Table III–16. Persons in H.I.P. and New York City samples, by housing conditions

HOUSING CONDITIONS	H.I.P. SAMPLE						NEW YORK CITY SAMPLE	
	Total		*H.I.P. enrollees*		*Others*			
	Number	Percent	Number	Percent	Number	Percent	Number	Percent
Toilet facilities	*10,981*	100.0	*8,040*	100.0	*2,941*	100.0	*13,558*	100.0
Shared	483	4.4	347	4.3	136	4.6	795	5.9
Not shared	10,358	94.3	7,592	94.4	2,766	94.1	12,591	92.8
Not reported	140	1.3	101	1.3	39	1.3	172	1.3
Central heating	*10,981*	100.0	*8,040*	100.0	*2,941*	100.0	*13,558*	100.0
Yes	9,956	90.6	7,312	90.9	2,644	89.9	11,866	87.5
No[1]	681	6.2	463	5.8	218	7.4	1,159	8.6
Not reported	344	3.2	265	3.3	79	2.7	533	3.9

[1] Includes "not heated."

Of the H.I.P.-covered persons themselves, 13.8 percent were reported to be members of households with incomes over $6,500, as compared with 11.6 in the New York City population.[6] According to Table III–15, members of families with incomes of $3,000 to $5,000 constituted at least 46.0 percent of the H.I.P. group, and 35.6 percent of the city families; and 50.8 percent of the H.I.P. enrollees were found to be living in families within that income range.

Of special concern are the persons in the households with very low incomes. Only 1.8 percent of the persons in the H.I.P. households were living on family incomes reported to be $2,000 or less, while 8.1 percent of those in the city families were reported as thus circumstanced.

Further supporting the conclusion that the H.I.P. groups had fewer persons living under grossly adverse economic conditions are the data on housing. Only two items clearly reflecting defective housing conditions were included in the survey: the presence or absence of central heating and the sharing of toilet facilities by more than one family. In both cases the H.I.P. households had slightly smaller proportions of persons living in homes with the lower housing standards than were reported for the New York City sample (Table III–16).

It is clear that although both groups had families in all of the social and economic levels for which classifications were made, the H.I.P. population had somewhat more persons in families whose heads had enjoyed the advantages of better education, fewer families with very low incomes and substandard housing, less unemployment, more people in the labor force and in the employable ages. When the H.I.P. enrollees are considered as a separate population group, these advantages appear in even higher proportions.

Age and Sex of Household Members

It remains to give the basic attributes—age and sex—of the persons who are the subjects of this survey. A rough picture of the age distribution of the persons in the two groups of families is presented in Table III–17.

Table III–17. Percentage distribution of persons in H.I.P. and New York City samples, by age

AGE	H.I.P. SAMPLE			NEW YORK CITY SAMPLE
	Total	*H.I.P. enrollees*	*Others*	
Total	100.0	100.0	100.0	100.0
Under 5	9.0	9.9	6.7	10.3
5 to 14	15.8	17.8	10.1	15.4
15 to 44	43.6	43.5	44.1	42.5
45 to 64	25.0	25.9	22.5	21.8
65 and over	5.1	2.4	12.5	6.7
Not reported	1.5	0.5	4.1	3.3

Although there were no marked differences in the age distribution of the members of H.I.P. and the New York City households, it is to be noted that the H.I.P. households, including both enrollees and others, were slightly deficient in children under five and persons over 65 years of age.

[6] This cannot be checked by the H.I.P. figures on subscribers with incomes over that figure because there are two upper-income limits, one for single-person coverages and one for families. According to State regulations, when a person elects to cover himself alone his own income only is the criterion for him. His family may have an income of any size.

Table III–18. Persons in H.I.P. and New York City samples, by age and sex

AGE AND SEX	H.I.P. SAMPLE						NEW YORK CITY SAMPLE	
	Total		*H.I.P. enrollees*		*Others*			
	Number	Percent	Number	Percent	Number	Percent	Number	Percent
			Male and Female					
Total	*10,981*	100.0	*8,040*	100.0	*2,941*	100.0	*13,558*	100.0
Under 5	996	9.0	798	9.9	198	6.7	1,392	10.3
5 to 14	1,732	15.8	1,435	17.8	297	10.1	2,095	15.4
15 to 44	4,785	43.6	3,489	43.5	1,296	44.1	5,757	42.5
45 to 64	2,743	25.0	2,082	25.9	661	22.5	2,961	21.8
65 and over	562	5.1	195	2.4	367	12.5	903	6.7
Not reported	163	1.5	41	0.5	122	4.1	450	3.3
			Male					
Total	*5,396*	100.0	*4,229*	100.0	*1,167*	100.0	*6,446*	100.0
Under 5	549	10.2	432	10.2	117	10.0	730	11.3
5 to 14	868	16.1	735	17.4	133	11.4	1,109	17.2
15 to 44	2,212	41.0	1,684	39.8	528	45.2	2,589	40.2
45 to 64	1,418	26.3	1,220	28.9	198	17.0	1,417	22.0
65 and over	283	5.2	143	3.4	140	12.0	413	6.4
Not reported	66	1.2	15	0.3	51	4.4	188	2.9
			Female					
Total	*5,585*	100.0	*3,811*	100.0	*1,774*	100.0	*7,112*	100.0
Under 5	447	8.0	366	9.6	81	4.6	662	9.3
5 to 14	864	15.5	700	18.3	164	9.2	986	13.9
15 to 44	2,573	46.1	1,805	47.4	768	43.3	3,168	44.5
45 to 64	1,325	23.7	862	22.6	463	26.1	1,544	21.7
65 and over	279	5.0	52	1.4	227	12.8	490	6.9
Not reported	97	1.7	26	0.7	71	4.0	262	3.7

The group aged 45 to 64 was disproportionately large among members of H.I.P. households. These findings are in harmony with those reported above on proportion of persons in the labor force and related data. The shortage of older persons was accentuated in the case of the insured members in the H.I.P. families. Although the children were better covered than the aged, there were still some families in which they were not insured. The reasons for this have been given above.

In the H.I.P. total sample population (10,981 persons), the males and females were almost equal in number (see Table III–18). The 5,396 males constituted 49.2 percent and the 5,585 females, 50.8 percent of the total. But in the

Table III–19. Persons in H.I.P. sample, by age, sex, and coverage status

AGE AND SEX	TOTAL		H.I.P. ENROLLEES		OTHERS	
	Number	Percent	Number	Percent	Number	Percent
Total	*10,981*	100.0	*8,040*	73.2	*2,941*	26.8
Males—total	*5,396*	100.0	*4,229*	78.4	*1,167*	21.6
Under 5	549	100.0	432	78.7	117	21.3
5 to 14	868	100.0	735	84.7	133	15.3
15 to 44	2,212	100.0	1,684	76.1	528	23.9
45 to 64	1,418	100.0	1,220	86.1	198	13.9
65 and over	283	100.0	143	50.5	140	49.5
Not reported	66	100.0	15	22.7	51	77.3
Females—total	*5,585*	100.0	*3,811*	68.2	*1,774*	31.8
Under 5	447	100.0	366	81.9	81	18.1
5 to 14	864	100.0	700	81.0	164	19.0
15 to 44	2,573	100.0	1,805	70.2	768	29.8
45 to 64	1,325	100.0	862	65.1	463	34.9
65 and over	279	100.0	52	18.6	227	81.4
Not reported	97	100.0	26	26.8	71	73.2

sample of New York City families, the females outnumbered the males by 5 percentage points—52.5 to 47.5 percent. The probable reasons for this are discussed in Appendix E, in which the New York City sample is compared with the 1950 Census returns.

Owing to the operation of the rules in the group enrollment of families, it is to be expected that certain age-sex classes will be covered better than others. Within the H.I.P. households 78.4 percent of all males and 68.2 percent of all females were covered (Table III–19). The age-sex groups best covered by H.I.P. were the children and the men 45 to 64 years. Over 80 percent of the children under 15 were covered, as were 86.1 percent of the men aged 45 to 64. But only half of the men of 65 and over and 18.6 percent of the women of that age were covered.

It is against these broad socioeonomic and demographic backgrounds that the comparisons of health conditions and needs of medical care and the provision for care in the two samples will be made in the chapters which follow. Because the two groups of households show some significant differences, and these differences are further accentuated for the H.I.P. enrollees themselves, it will be necessary to make these comparisons for subgroups with similar characteristics.

Duration of Coverage of H.I.P. Enrollees

As a further preliminary before setting forth the data on the illness reported and the provision of medical care, it was necessary to consider briefly the length of time that the members of H.I.P. families had been covered. Obviously health conditions and habits in hygienic living and the use of medical care are not subject to immediate and drastic change by reason of a group decision to purchase prepaid medical care. At the time of the survey—the spring of 1952—a total of 78.5 percent of the enrollees had been in the Plan for at least two years; 33.5 percent since January of 1948 or earlier; 4.7 per cent had entered in 1948; 40.3 percent in 1949; 15.7 percent in 1950; 5 percent in 1951; and 0.8 percent in 1952. These latter two groups could have become members only by virtue of marriage, birth, or adoption in families whose initial enrollment had been earlier, since no families or persons were included in the sample who enrolled after December 31, 1950, except as added family members. Of the 2,941 members of H.I.P. families who were not covered, 206 were former members who had lost status for various reasons. These were mainly older children who had passed the age of 18.

Not all of the 8,040 H.I.P. enrollees had been covered uninterruptedly since their enrollment; 266 or 3.3 percent had some break in their coverage after their original enrollment.

Before comparisons of health and medical care are undertaken, attention will be directed in Chapter IV toward the extent to which the New York City families and the members of H.I.P. families who were not covered by H.I.P. were reported to have other types of prepaid medical care.

CHAPTER IV

Insurance Status of Household Members

Problems of Recording Insurance Status

People rarely have a precise knowledge of the conditions of the insurance contracts into which they have entered or of those purchased for them by their employers, unions, or other agents. Some people do not even know whether they are covered at all as of a given day, and one representative of a household may not be able to report fully and accurately at a single interview on the insurance coverage of all of its members. In spite of these difficulties it was thought advisable to include in the schedule some questions bearing on this subject. It was believed that even though the data should prove to be defective, an effort should be made to bring further enlightenment to this confused subject.

Several conditions contribute to the obscurity and complications that beset this subject. These in turn create technical difficulties in conducting an inquiry such as this. As has been said earlier, in New York State full coverage for medical care requires at least two kinds of insurance, one for hospital care and one for the services of physicians and auxiliary personnel. Even the most comprehensive general programs offered in these two fields will not meet every kind of medical expense with which a family may be confronted, and indemnity types of insurance make no pretense of doing so. With no barriers to duplicating coverages, supplementary types of coverage have been devised to meet the additional expense entailed by diseases, notably poliomyelitis, that may require extended hospitalization and special forms of treatment. Thus, a person wishing to make sure that he and his dependents were fully covered might carry three or more kinds of insurance with which to meet expense for medical care.

A second problem inheres in the fact that, because prepaid medical care is relatively new and hospital costs and physicians' fees are often bracketed together in people's minds, many persons use one name to designate all the insurance they may have, whatever the type or types. The popular term "Blue Cross" has taken on a generic character to cover not only hospital insurance of all types, but also, to some persons, some coverages for physicians' services, especially for Blue Shield.

Prepaid medical care, as a benefit often linked with employment and the other insurance carried by employed groups, frequently covers only the employed member of the family. When the household has more than one employed member and they work for different employers, their insurance coverage may differ widely, and the family may present a complicated insurance picture. The fact that Workmen's Compensation and commercial accident policies may pay for hospital care and medical services is also a factor in this complexity.

And lastly, these insurance coverages are currently carried often on a month-to-month basis and are subject to termination in various ways. A person may lose status completely without the informant for the household knowing about it.

In the case of this inquiry, a check on some of these difficulties was afforded by the fact that the H.I.P. status of all enrollees was known in advance, as was the fact that all of them were required to have hospital insurance as well. About 70 percent of the enrollees at the time of the survey were covered by joint contracts which combined H.I.P. with the Associated Hospital Service, the local Blue Cross.

In the interview with the informant for the household, the subject was approached from two directions. First, a series of general questions about each person's insurance status was recorded on Schedule 1; later in the interview questions as to insurance pertaining to each illness and hospitalization reported were recorded on Schedules 2 and 3 (see Appendix A).

In asking the general question about insurance status, the interviewer inquired first about Blue Cross, then about other hospital insurance, next about H.I.P., then "other insurance for doctor's care" for each member of the household. Each of these four questions called for a "yes" or "no" answer. If other insurance for doctor's care was claimed, the respondent was asked to specify. Coverage for Workmen's Compensation was not to be included. In the case of each illness within the previous eight-week period and each illness reported for 1951, inquiry was made as to whether or not there was any insurance coverage and, if so, whether it covered (1) doctor's care only, (2) hospitalization only, (3) hospitalization and surgery only, (4) hospitalization, surgery, and other doctor's care, or (5) any other kind of coverage. If the last category was selected, the respondent was asked to specify.

It was thought that this should give a rough picture of the extent to which various segments of the population were insured for any part of their medical care, and should indicate the major components of their coverage.

Contrary to expectation, considering the complications besetting this subject, the informants reached in this survey disclaimed precise knowledge of health insurance coverage for only 0.3 percent of the H.I.P. enrollees, 1.5 percent of the other members in H.I.P. families, and 0.7 percent of the members of families in the New York City sample. But this readiness to answer did not always signify accuracy of information, as will be shown later. Moreover, the reporting as returned by the interviewers was technically incomplete for 16.4 percent of the H.I.P. enrollees, 11.6 percent of other H.I.P. family members, and 10.9 percent of the members of the New York City families. This incompleteness consisted for the most part in having left blank the spaces requiring categorical answers regarding additional insurance after a given type had been recorded. For 3.4 percent of H.I.P. enrollees, 43.9 percent of other members of H.I.P. families, and 45.1 percent of members of the New York City sample, it was either specifically stated that the person was not insured or all of the insurance questions were left unanswered. In the latter case it has been assumed that there was no insurance but that the interviewer failed systematically to check all of the "no" answers.[1] As will be seen later, the figures for the New York City sample on the proportion of persons with some kind of insurance do not depart widely from the data derived from other sources.

The returns for the H.I.P. enrollees will be presented first (Table IV–1). The insurance status of the persons in H.I.P. households, not enrollees, and of the persons in the New York City sample will follow (Tables IV–2, IV–3). Because Blue Cross and H.I.P. were the insurance organizations given the leading positions in this study, the situation will be described in terms of coverage (*a*) by Blue Cross, (*b*) by all other types of hospital insurance, (*c*) by H.I.P., and (*d*) by all other types of prepaid medical care.

Insurance Status Reported, H.I.P. Enrollees

The first question that arises relates to the extent to which the informants in H.I.P. households reported correctly on the H.I.P. status of their members. Of the 8,040 H.I.P. enrollees, the informants gave accurate data as concerns H.I.P. status on 7,328 or 91.1 percent. For an additional 4.7 percent, Blue Cross or other hospital insurance only was reported, while for 3.7 percent of the covered persons the informant reported no insurance or no knowledge of any. In a very small number of cases the informant reported insurance for medical care other than H.I.P. It is conceivable that they had such coverage. The cases in which the H.I.P. enrollees are reported as having only Blue Cross or other insurance for hospital care illustrate the tendency to include insurance for both hospital and physician's care under one

[1] See Appendix D for a description of the editing of the insurance data.

term. The same tendency is much more conspicuously displayed by the 34.7 percent of the H.I.P. enrollees for whom the informants gave H.I.P. as their only coverage, although, as has been said, H.I.P. requires contractors to provide hospital insurance so that hospital care will be immediately available should it be needed.

Table IV–1 summarizes in some detail the answers received in respect of the 8,040 persons known in advance to be H.I.P. enrollees and required to have hospital coverage of some type.

Table IV–1. H.I.P. enrollees, by type of medical care insurance reported

TYPE OF MEDICAL CARE INSURANCE REPORTED	*Number*	*Percent*
Total in sample	*8,040*	100.0
Total reported as H.I.P. enrollees	*7,328*	91.1
H.I.P. only	2,792	34.7
H.I.P. and Blue Cross	4,323	53.8
H.I.P., Blue Cross, and other hospital	10	0.1
H.I.P., Blue Cross, and other doctor's care	84	1.0
H.I.P., Blue Cross, other hospital, and other doctor's care	2	[1]
H.I.P. and other hospital	10	0.1
H.I.P., other hospital, and other doctor's care	14	0.2
H.I.P. and other doctor's care	93	1.2
H.I.P. enrollees not so reported	*712*	8.9
Blue Cross only	359	4.5
Blue Cross and other hospital	3	[1]
Blue Cross and other doctor's care	24	0.3
Other doctor's care	15	0.2
Other hospital only	18	0.2
Other hospital and other doctor's care	2	[1]
No insurance reported	270	3.4
Insurance stated as unknown	21	0.3

[1] Percentage less than 0.05.

Besides their H.I.P. coverage, 234 enrollees (2.9 percent) were reported to have other insurance for physicians' services. It is known that such insurance is held, for H.I.P. physicians are asked from time to time to fill out papers for enrollees enabling them to collect indemnity after they have had surgical and sometimes other care.[2] In only 15 instances were two kinds of hospital coverage reported. In absence of data from other sources, it is impossible to arrive at any final conclusion as to duplication of insurance coverage among H.I.P. enrollees, but it would seem that only a small number had additional coverage for physicians' care or more than one type of hospital insurance.

Insurance Status of Unenrolled Members of H.I.P. Households

Data on the insurance status of the persons other than enrollees in the H.I.P. households could be checked only to the extent of establishing the number of those persons who mistakenly thought that they were covered by H.I.P. This amounted to the substantial proportion of 13.2 percent. Some wives of men insured on employee-only contracts thought that they, too, were covered. In other cases the person may have previously been a member but had lost status by outgrowing eligibility for family coverage or for other reasons. Since each family or single person covered is provided with an identification card which lists all insured persons under the contract, and since new cards are sent immediately when coverage changes occur, it is difficult to ascribe this discrepancy to anything other than sheer confusion or misconception in the mind of the informant.

There is, however, one small class of persons about which the insurance rules themselves breed some temporary confusion. These are the infants. The H.I.P. family contract specifies that a child born into an H.I.P. family is forthwith covered from birth; medical groups provide service to them without question. But delays often occur in the reporting of births to the H.I.P. Registrar so that central records are sometimes in arrears in the adding of new children to the subscribers' records and identification cards.

Table IV–2 sets forth all of the combinations of types of insurance that were claimed for the 2,941 non-H.I.P. persons in H.I.P. households. All together, 40.6 percent were reported as covered at least by Blue Cross and 3.2 percent by other hospital insurance without Blue Cross, giving a total of about 44 percent with hospital coverage. Very few cases of duplicating hospital insurance appeared. Aside from the erroneous

[2] Since H.I.P. contracts with medical groups prohibit any payment to an H.I.P. physician for services rendered to an H.I.P. enrollee, except $2.00 for a late night call, this indemnity accrues to the patient.

claims for H.I.P. coverage, slightly less than 8 percent of these persons were reported as covered for some type of doctor's care.

Table IV–2. Persons in H.I.P. sample, not H.I.P. enrollees, by type of medical care insurance reported

TYPE OF MEDICAL CARE INSURANCE REPORTED	*Number*	*Percent*
Total—Summary Analysis	*2,941*	100.0
Total persons with any type of insurance for medical care	1,605	54.6
Blue Cross only	914	31.1
Blue Cross with other types	280	9.5
Other types only	411	14.0
Total with no insurance for medical care reported or insurance stated as unknown	1,336	45.4
Total—Detailed Analysis	*2,941*	100.0
Blue Cross only	914	31.2
Blue Cross and other hospital insurance	4	0.1
Blue Cross and H.I.P.	192	6.5
Blue Cross, H.I.P., and other hospital insurance	1	[1]
Blue Cross, H.I.P., and other insurance for doctor's care	4	0.1
Blue Cross and other insurance for doctor's care	76	2.6
Blue Cross, other hospital insurance, and other insurance for doctor's care	1	[1]
Blue Cross, H.I.P., other hospital insurance, and other insurance for doctor's care	2	0.1
Other hospital insurance only	71	2.4
H.I.P. only	188	6.4
H.I.P. and other insurance for doctor's care	2	0.1
Other insurance for doctor's care	127	4.3
Other hospital insurance and other insurance for doctor's care	23	0.8
No insurance reported	1,291	43.9
Insurance stated as unknown	45	1.5

[1] Percentage less than 0.05.

All together, the data would indicate that about 55 percent of these 2,941 persons in H.I.P. households were thought to have some kind of insurance against the cost of hospital or physician's care, or both. Of those percentage points, 6.4 represent cases in which the informant mistakenly thought there was coverage for H.I.P. care and for nothing else. This reduces the percentage with any kind of insurance to about 49.

Insurance Status Reported, New York City Sample

In examining the insurance status claimed for the persons in the New York City sample, it must be remembered that when households in the original area probability sample were found to have bona fide H.I.P. members, such households were transferred to the H.I.P. sample. No H.I.P. enrollees are, therefore, to be expected in the group of New York City residents. Yet 2.5 percent of these were erroneously reported as H.I.P. enrollees, for 1 percent of whom the coverage was reported as H.I.P. only. Some of these persons may have had coverage previously but may have lost status by the time of the survey.[3]

The elimination of the H.I.P. households from the original New York City sample resulted in the transfer of 3.3 percent of the persons out of the New York City sample as originally designed. Not all of these persons belonged to H.I.P., since the whole household was thus transferred irrespective of H.I.P. status of the individual members. The removal of this relatively small segment of the families, however, does not materially affect the proportion of the otherwise insured as they were reported to the enumerators. These are shown in Table IV–3.

In the New York City sample a total of 54.3 percent of all of the 13,558 persons were reported to have some type of insurance coverage for medical care, including the 1 percent who were erroneously reported to have H.I.P. only and the 1.5 percent erroneously reported to have H.I.P. plus some other coverage. If the H.I.P.-covered persons—3.3 percent of the sample as originally drawn—who were transferred out were restored to this sample, the proportion of those having some kind of prepaid coverage for the medical expense of illness would be brought to approximately 56 percent. The 54.3 percent in the New York City sample with some kind of reported coverage break up into 42 percent who actually had hospital insurance only (40.5 percent who so reported, plus 1.5 percent who erroneously claimed H.I.P. also); and 11.3 percent who were covered for doctor's care, with or without hospital care (this figure excludes the 2.5 percent erroneously reported to have H.I.P., either alone or with other coverage). Of the 11.3 percent, 7.1 percent had coverage for both hospital and doc-

[3] Because of changes of names through marriage and for other reasons, it was impossible to trace these persons in the H.I.P. files.

tor's care (other than H.I.P.). A total of 115 persons, less than 1 percent, were reported as having two kinds of hospital insurance.

Table IV–3. Persons in New York City sample, by type of medical care insurance reported[1]

TYPE OF MEDICAL CARE INSURANCE REPORTED	*Number*	*Percent*
Total—Summary Analysis	*13,558*	100.0
Total persons with any type of insurance for medical care	7,354	54.3
Blue Cross only	4,942	36.5
Blue Cross with other types	984	7.2
Other types only	1,428	10.6
Total with no insurance for medical care reported or insurance stated as unknown	6,204	45.8
Total—Detailed Analysis	*13,558*	100.0
Blue Cross only	4,942	36.5
Blue Cross and other hospital insurance	82	0.6
Blue Cross and H.I.P.	192	1.4
Blue Cross, H.I.P., and other hospital insurance	2	[2]
Blue Cross, H.I.P., and other insurance for doctor's care	4	[2]
Blue Cross and other insurance for doctor's care	673	5.0
Blue Cross, other hospital insurance, and other insurance for doctor's care	28	0.2
Blue Cross, H.I.P., other hospital insurance, and other insurance for doctor's care	3	[2]
Other hospital insurance only	464	3.4
H.I.P. only	131	1.0
H.I.P. and other insurance for doctor's care	1	[2]
H.I.P. and other hospital insurance	10	0.1
Other insurance for doctor's care	568	4.2
Other hospital insurance and other insurance for doctor's care	254	1.9
No insurance reported	6,112	45.1
Insurance stated as unknown	92	0.7

[1] All persons drawn from households containing no H.I.P. enrollees.

[2] Percentage less than 0.05.

There are no figures issuing from other sources against which those deriving from this survey can be checked. Neither organizations engaged in insurance of this type nor the bodies that in recent years have been studying the spread of voluntary insurance of this kind have compiled any figures on the persons resident in New York City who are covered. The leading insurance organizations are chartered for more extensive boundaries, and no analyses of their enrollments for residents versus non-residents of this city are reported. The group contracts into which they enter with employers, unions, and other organizations usually cover non-resident members among the insured. But some intimations as to the probable accuracy of these figures may be had from such figures as have been released.

The Blue Cross membership in the State of New York at the end of 1952 was reported to be 47.7 percent of the total population.[4] That figure roughly approximates the 43.7 percent for members of the families in the New York City sample plus the H.I.P. cases that were removed from it. The United Medical Service, which operates in 17 counties in New York State, reported that as of April 1952 it had approximately 2,600,000 members. It is estimated that about two-thirds of these members, or 1,733,000, lived in New York City.[5] This yields a proportion of 22 percent of the city's population. In addition to these, there are the persons insured by other carriers. This study indicates that only 11.3 percent of the New York City sample actually had coverage for physicians' care in any degree. It is conceivable that the charging by the United Medical Service of claims against contracts may cause some of this discrepancy, with the suburban enrollees of New York City contractors charged as city enrollment. It also is highly probable that in this study there were some instances of coverage for some forms of medical care, notably surgical service, which were bracketed with hospital care or were not known to or not mentioned by the informant.

The President's Commission on the Health Needs of the Nation estimated as of the end of 1951 that "about 57 percent of civilian population of the United States had some insurance against the cost of medical care . . . about 13 percent of the population had hospital insurance only and another 25 percent of the population was also covered for surgical expenses. In addition, about 16 percent of the American people had limited medical insurance, which in many

[4] Blue Cross Fact Sheet, December 31, 1952, issued by the Blue Cross Commission of the American Hospital Association, Chicago 11, Illinois.

[5] See 1951 *Blue Shield Annual Report* in respect of benefit payment.

cases provides physician care only in the hospital. Only a handful of the population, less than 3 people out of every 100, had prepaid comprehensive medical service."[6]

The recently published bulletin of the Health Information Foundation, *National Family Survey of Medical Costs and Voluntary Health Insurance*, resulting from an analysis of a national sample of 2,809 families with 8,846 persons, surveyed in June and July 1953, reported 57 percent of these persons covered by some type of insurance. It also reported that 70 percent of the 1,803 urban *families* had "some coverage."

If data from the New York City sample give a very rough approximation of the situation—and there is some reason to believe that they do—they indicate that in this community about the same proportion of people had some kind of coverage as obtained throughout the nation. It contains, however, a smaller proportion with some insurance for doctor's care, though the small fraction with comprehensive care is about the same. For the sheer fact of some insurance or none at all, the returns from this survey appear to be reasonably accurate. The figures on the persons with and without insurance will, therefore, be further analyzed for a few outstanding demographic characteristics of the population in the New York City sample. The cases known to have been erroneously reported have been segregated. Later the data reported on insurance for specific illnesses will be presented.

Insurance Status, New York City Sample, by Age, Sex, and Labor Force Status

When all of the persons in the New York City sample are classified by age (over and under 14 years), by labor force status, and by sex, some fairly wide variations appear as to their insurance coverage. All of the cases (3.2 percent) in which the informant disclaimed knowledge of insurance status and all in which the return was obviously in error have been segregated.[7] In Table IV–4 it is brought out that children under 14 years were covered to a slightly greater extent (54.3 percent) than were adults (50.9 percent). The way in which family coverage is defined and the premiums set may lead to a selection of large families, and this in turn may account for the slightly better showing among children than among adults.

Table IV–4. Percentage of persons in New York City sample, over and under 14 years of age, by labor force status, sex, and insurance status

LABOR FORCE STATUS AND SEX	TOTAL	PERCENTAGE WITH		
		Some insurance	*No insurance*[1]	*Insurance reported as unknown or incorrectly given*
Total persons	*13,558*	51.7	45.1	3.2
Total persons 14 years and over	*10,248*	50.9	45.7	3.4
Male	4,695	52.1	44.5	3.4
Female	5,553	49.8	46.8	3.4
In labor force	*5,635*	56.6	39.6	3.8
Male	3,869	55.9	40.5	3.6
Female	1,766	58.3	37.6	4.1
Not in labor force	*4,474*	44.2	52.9	2.9
Male	791	35.1	62.7	2.2
Female	3,683	46.1	50.9	3.0
Labor force status not reported	*139*	36.7	59.7	3.6
Male	35	[2]	[2]	[2]
Female	104	39.4	55.8	4.8
Children under 14 years	*3,310*	54.3	43.1	2.6

[1] Includes those reported specifically as not insured and those for whom no information on insurance status (539 of 6,112 persons) was reported.

[2] Percentage not calculated, base less than 50.

Among the adults, the females in the labor force—a smaller and on the average a younger group—were found insured in a slightly larger proportion than were males in the labor force. Men and boys who were not in the labor force had the smallest proportion with insurance (35.1 percent). Of the 791 males in this group, 418 were reported as attending school, while 170 were permanently unable to work. The close relationship of coverage to employment doubtless accounts for the fact that the males who are not in the labor force are poorly represented among the insured.

[6] These figures derive from the reports of the insurance organization and not from canvasses of the population itself. *Summary Volume* by Health Publications Institute, Raleigh, N.C., May 1953, p. 120, *et seq.*

[7] This serves to reduce the percentage reported as having some insurance, as does the elimination of all H.I.P. households in the New York City sample.

Insurance Status, New York City Sample, by Education of Household Head

The spread of insurance throughout the various social levels in the population is indicated in considerable degree by a distribution of insured and uninsured persons in terms of the education or schooling of the head of the household of which they are members. The results of this distribution for persons over and under 14 years of age appear in Table IV–5. A marked progression upward appears in the proportion of insured persons as the number of completed years of schooling of the head of the household advances. Persons with insurance were half again as numerous in families headed by a person with more than 12 years of schooling as they were in families headed by persons with less than nine years of school attainment. An intermediate position but nearer the proportions in the more fortunate groups appears for the group of persons in families headed by persons with at least some secondary education.

Table IV–5. Percentage of persons in New York City sample, over and under 14 years of age, by education of head of household and insurance status

YEARS OF SCHOOLING COMPLETED BY HEAD OF HOUSEHOLD	TOTAL	PERCENTAGE WITH		
		Some insurance	*No insurance*[1]	*Insurance reported as unknown or incorrectly given*
Total persons	*13,558*	51.7	45.1	3.2
Persons 14 years and over	*10,248*	50.9	45.7	3.4
Less than 9	4,547	41.5	55.4	3.1
9 to 12	3,572	59.2	37.8	3.0
More than 12	1,517	65.3	29.7	5.0
Not reported	612	36.1	59.6	4.3
Persons less than 14 years	*3,310*	54.3	43.1	2.6
Less than 9	1,151	42.4	54.8	2.8
9 to 12	1,496	57.9	39.7	2.4
More than 12	554	69.9	26.7	3.4
Not reported	109	51.4	48.6	—

[1] Includes those reported specifically as not insured and those for whom no information on insurance status was reported.

Insurance Status, New York City Sample, by Occupational Group

Over the broad occupational groups in the labor force, the percentage of the insured shows a fairly wide range. Clerical and sales personnel were reported as insured to the extent of 66.1 percent, while only about 20 percent of the domestic service workers, a very small group, were so reported. The professional people and proprietors of business enterprises approached the clerical and sales group, but craftsmen and service workers fell considerably lower in the proportion covered. Table IV–6 indicates for each group the distribution of those with and without insurance and the proportion for whom the report was defective.

Table IV–6. Percentage of persons in New York City sample in labor force, by occupational group and insurance status

OCCUPATIONAL GROUP	TOTAL	PERCENTAGE WITH		
		Some insurance	*No insurance*[1]	*Insurance reported as unknown or incorrectly given*
Total	*5,635*	56.6	39.6	3.8
Professional, semiprofessional workers	566	60.8	31.8	7.4
Proprietors, managers, officials (including farm) and farmers	638	61.5	37.3	1.2
Clerical and sales	1,459	66.1	30.6	3.3
Craftsmen, foremen, operatives and laborers	2,083	52.9	44.4	2.7
Domestic service	67	19.4	76.1	4.5
Other service	527	48.6	46.1	5.3
Not reported	295	39.7	50.5	9.8

[1] Includes those reported specifically as not insured and those for whom no information on insurance status was reported.

Insurance Status of Persons Hospitalized during 1951, New York City Sample

Because illness sufficiently serious to require hospitalization is apt to entail considerable expense, the insurance status of persons who were hospitalized at any time during 1951 was given special attention. In Table IV–7 the insurance data for the 911 hospitalized persons in the New York City sample are set forth with detail as to the length of stay of persons with and without insurance and the number of hospital days in each of the several categories of duration. It will be seen from this that progressively fewer people had insurance as the length of stay grew longer. The figure declined from 52.2 percent to 32.8 percent

Table IV–7. Hospitalized persons in New York City sample, 1951, percentage distribution by insurance status, and hospital days by duration of stay

DURATION OF HOSPITALIZATION	TOTAL	PERCENTAGE WITH		
		Some insurance	*No insurance*	*Insurance status not reported*
Total persons	*911*	43.7	50.6	5.7
Total days	*10,133*	33.9	62.6	3.5
Under 3 days				
Persons	115	52.2	45.2	2.6
Days	142	50.7	47.2	2.1
3 to 9 days				
Persons	489	46.2	47.5	6.3
Days	2,921	46.6	47.4	6.0
10 to 20 days				
Persons	159	40.9	55.3	3.8
Days	2,075	39.9	56.4	3.7
21 days and over				
Persons	110	32.8	64.5	2.7
Days	4,995	23.5	74.4	2.1
Not reported				
Persons	38	34.2	42.1	23.7
Average length of stay	11.12	8.59	13.79	6.82

of the persons with the given durations. The persons without insurance were without coverage at any time during their stay. The days of care that were insured declined from 50.7 percent for persons who stayed less than three days to 23.5 percent for persons who stayed 21 days or over. All together, 911 individuals were reported to have had 10,133 days in the hospital but only 3,439 of these days (33.9 percent) were reported for persons with hospital insurance.

Among children under 15 years of age in hospitals in 1951, the boys not only greatly outnumbered the girls but apparently stayed longer on the average; 91 boys stayed 1,111 days (average 12 days), while the 54 girls stayed only 318 days (average 6 days). Only 26.5 percent of the hospital days of these children were covered by insurance. In the age group 15 to 44, the females greatly exceeded the males (407 females to 117 males), but the males remained in the hospital longer. Their average stay was 11 days as compared with the 8 days for women. In this group 30 percent of the hospital days of men and 40 percent of the hospital days of women were covered by some insurance. The maternity cases in this group doubtless contributed to these results. Among people 45 to 64 the number of men and women hospitalized was approximately the same (5.2 percent of the men and 5.6 percent of the women), with an average stay of 19.2 days for men and 17.6 for women. But only 25.9 percent of the days' stay of women were covered by insurance as compared with 44.9 percent of the days' stay of men. Among persons 65 and over, 7.5 percent of the men and 6.1 percent of the women were in hospitals in 1951, the men with an average of 16 days' stay and the women with 11.7 days. Only 23 percent of the hospital days of these men were covered by insurance, but slightly over half of the older women's days were so covered. The number of such old persons in the sample was small (903), with no institutionalized population included. Insofar as these figures indicate the relative amount of hospitalized illness among the aged, they may suffer somewhat both from sampling error and from factors of selection.

Insurance Status of Persons Hospitalized during 1951, H.I.P. Enrollees

Of the 8,040 enrollees in the H.I.P. sample, 594 were reported to have been in a hospital or hospitals during 1951; for 502 of these persons (84.5 percent) the stay in the hospital (4,613 days) was reported as covered at least in part by hospital insurance; for 70 persons the stay (1,322 days) was reported as not covered; and for 22 persons (140 days) this detail was not reported.[8] The bulk of the days of those not covered (1,035 days) was in stays of 21 days or longer. These days not covered by hospital insurance were almost equally divided between males and females and appeared in all age groups, but were more frequent among older persons than among children. They were about twice as frequent among persons in families with heads who had less than nine years of schooling as among persons in families with heads who had more than 12 years of schooling.

Conditions Insured for Medical Care, Eight-Week Period, New York City Sample

It was thought that perhaps a better picture of the extent of insurance coverage for medical care

[8] The status of the H.I.P. enrollees was established as of the end of 1951. Not all of them had been covered by H.I.P. throughout the entire year.

could be obtained by asking, in the case of each illness or medical condition, whether or not such physician's care as was received was covered by insurance. Even those with insurance are not necessarily covered for the specific conditions from which they were suffering. It was also thought that people in practical situations would be better informed about their insurance status than would those with no occasion to seek medical care or insurance services in connection therewith.

Within the eight-week period a total of 7,485 medical conditions were reported as found in

Table IV–8. Medical conditions, New York City sample, eight-week period, by diagnosis, receipt of doctor's care, and insurance coverage for medical services

DIAGNOSTIC GROUP	TOTAL CONDITIONS	RECEIVED DOCTOR'S CARE		
		Total	*Covered by some insurance*	
			Number	Percent
Total cases	*7,485*	*3,270*	*233*	7.2
Infective and parasitic diseases	*375*	*290*	*10*	3.4
Tuberculosis	28[1]	14	—	
Other	347	276	10	
Neoplasms	*64*	*58*	*15*	25.9
Allergic, metabolic, endocrine, and nutritional diseases	*623*	*208*	*6*	2.9
Asthma	189	42	1	
Other allergies	81	49	2	
Diabetes	133	32	1	
Obesity	191	57	1	
Other	29	28	1	
Diseases of blood and blood-forming organs	*36*	*32*	*2*	[2]
Mental, psychoneurotic, and personality disorders	*60*	*35*	—	
Diseases of nervous system and sense organs	*232*	*144*	*3*	2.1
Vascular lesions and inflammatory disorder of C.N.S.	88	46	—	
Diseases of ear	79	58	1	
Diseases of eye	65	40	2	
Diseases of circulatory system	*1,282*	*259*	*12*	4.6
Heart disease	364	125	5	
Hypertension	382	72	6	
Other	536	62	1	
Diseases of respiratory system	*1,799*	*1,002*	*64*	6.4
Acute upper respiratory infection	1,101	461	30	
Other	698	541	34	
Diseases of digestive tract	*506*	*206*	*22*	10.7
Ulcer of stomach and ulcerative colitis	42	28	2	
Gastroenteritis	13	11	4	
Functional disorder of stomach and intestines[3]	307	88	4	
Other	144	79	12	
Disorder of genito-urinary tract	*367*	*164*	*16*	9.8
Disorder of menstruation and menopause	287	93	4	
Other	80	71	12	
Deliveries and complications of pregnancy	*64*	*60*	*11*	18.3
Delivery without complication	46	45	9	
Other	18	15	2	
Diseases of skin and cellular tissue	*270*	*116*	*5*	4.3
Diseases of bones and organs of movement	*1,232*	*301*	*33*	10.9
Arthritis and rheumatism	669	126	10	
Disorders of back and symptoms referable to limbs or back	312	110	10	
Other	251	65	13	
Accidental injuries	*260*	*199*	*27*	13.6
All other	*316*	*196*	*7*	3.6

[1] Seven arrested cases.
[2] Percentage not calculated, base less than 50.
[3] Includes gastritis and symptoms referable to gastrointestinal tract.

5,180 of the 13,558 persons in the New York City sample (Table IV–8). Of these medical conditions, 3,270 (43.6 percent) were reported as having received attention and care from physicians at some time during the eight-week period. Some of the conditions without medical care doubtless had had care prior to that time, and some conditions that had just appeared would probably have care later. Of the treated cases, 233 (7.2 percent) were reported as covered to some degree by insurance, including that for hospital care. About equal numbers of illnesses in males and in females were thus covered (Table IV–10). Approximately the same number (248) were given free treatment,[9] and for another group of about the same size (239) the insurance status was unknown. For 2,550 of these medical conditions (77.9 percent) there was a definite report that the medical care for the condition was not covered by insurance (Table IV–10).

These 7,485 medical conditions were classified by diagnosis into 74 categories. The insured illnesses fell into 43 of the 74 diagnostic groups, but in only 27 of these had benefits been received in more than one case. The insurance factor in the specific illness picture of the people in the New York City sample for the eight-week period is summarized in Table IV–8. The high proportion of neoplasms that were reported as covered by some insurance probably reflects the greater likelihood that these cases would receive some hospital care and would be covered by hospital insurance. In fact, the variation in the percentages shown in Table IV–8 may simply reflect different rates of hospitalization for the various conditions.

Treated Conditions Reported Not Insured for Medical Care, H.I.P. Enrollees

The returns for the H.I.P. sample (8,040 persons) for the eight-week period gave a total of 4,648 instances involving 3,311 persons in which a medical condition was reported. Of these conditions, 2,445 were in receipt of physician's care (52.6 percent) and of the treated conditions, 1,826 (74.7 percent) were reported as having some insurance coverage. For 148 medical conditions the insurance status was reported as unknown, and in 51 instances the doctor's care involved no costs (see footnote 9); in 420 instances the informant reported that there was no insurance covering the medical care received. Several kinds of circumstances probably account for this substantial number of instances (17.1 percent) in which the medical care of these H.I.P. enrollees was reported as not covered by insurance. First, some informants did not report accurately. It will be recalled that for 8.9 percent of the H.I.P. enrollees the informant failed to report H.I.P. coverage. Second, there are doubtless other instances in which the care received was not covered by the contract, that is, the patient sought care from outside physicians in New York City[10] or, if elsewhere, was not hospitalized, in which event the indemnity for illness away from home was not applicable. Third, all Workmen's Compensation and Veterans Administration cases are excluded from H.I.P. coverage, and the interviewers were instructed not to include Workmen's Compensation as insurance.

The distribution of the medical conditions of H.I.P. enrollees among the various diagnoses appears in Table IV–9, together with the data on receipt of medical services and insurance coverage.

Treated Conditions, by Sex, Age, and Medical Care Insurance, Eight-Week Period, Both Samples

Insurance coverage for physician services varied among the age and sex groups in the New York City sample from 11.5 percent for the medical conditions of males aged 15 to 44 down to 1.6 percent for those of women 65 or over (Table IV–10). In all age groups the conditions found in males were covered in higher proportions than were those among females, but the difference in the coverage of the sexes was greatest among the elderly. Conditions receiving medical care in men

[9] Such free care was available in various ways: free clinics in public and voluntary hospitals, in industrial medical services, and from physicians related to the patients.

[10] The extent of the use of outside physicians is reported in a later chapter of this report. See also Chapter I, section on H.I.P. medical groups and subscriber's choice of physician.

Table IV–9. Medical conditions, H.I.P. enrollees, eight-week period, by diagnosis, receipt of doctor's care, and insurance coverage for medical services

DIAGNOSTIC GROUP	TOTAL CONDITIONS	RECEIVED DOCTOR'S CARE		
		Total	*Not covered by insurance*	
			Number	Percent
Total cases	*4,648*	*2,445*	*420*	17.1
Infective and parasitic diseases	*221*	*180*	*33*	18.3
Tuberculosis	10[1]	2	—	
Other	211	178	33	
Neoplasms	*29*	*28*	*7*	[2]
Allergic, metabolic, endocrine, and nutritional diseases	*431*	*192*	*31*	16.0
Asthma	115	34	10	
Other allergies	100	73	3	
Diabetes	65	27	6	
Obesity	131	44	8	
Other	20	14	4	
Diseases of blood and blood-forming organs	*24*	*23*	*3*	[2]
Mental, psychoneurotic, and personality disorders	*33*	*23*	*8*	[2]
Diseases of nervous system and sense organs	*172*	*144*	*29*	20.1
Vascular lesions and inflammatory disorder of C.N.S.	41	27	6	
Diseases of ear	68	59	16	
Diseases of eye	63	58	7	
Diseases of circulatory system	*573*	*129*	*44*	34.1
Heart disease	135	45	18	
Hypertension	158	37	10	
Other	280	47	16	
Diseases of respiratory system	*1,311*	*815*	*105*	12.9
Acute upper respiratory infection	795	398	49	
Other	516	417	56	
Diseases of digestive tract	*351*	*156*	*28*	17.9
Ulcer of stomach and ulcerative colitis	40	22	8	
Gastroenteritis	21	7	—	
Functional disorder of stomach and intestines[3]	194	65	3	
Other	96	62	17	
Disorder of genito-urinary tract	*211*	*114*	*19*	16.7
Disorder of menstruation and menopause	155	61	5	
Other	56	53	14	
Deliveries and complications of pregnancy	*33*	*131*	*4*	3.1
Delivery without complication	18	18	2	
Other	15	13	2	
Diseases of skin and cellular tissue	*193*	*113*	*15*	13.3
Diseases of bones and organs of movement	*684*	*207*	*46*	22.2
Arthritis and rheumatism	272	47	11	
Disorders of back and symptoms referable to limbs or back	221	91	22	
Other	191	69	13	
Accidental injuries	*158*	*133*	*24*	18.0
All other	*224*	*157*	*24*	15.3

[1] Three reported as arrested.
[2] Percentage not computed, base less than 50.
[3] Includes gastritis and symptoms referable to gastrointestinal tract.

aged 65 years and over were reported as covered to the extent of 7.6 percent.

Among the H.I.P. subscribers and their dependents over the age of 5 years the proportion of treated medical conditions reported as *without* insurance for doctor's care (total 420) rose progressively with the age of the patients suffering the conditions (Table IV–11). All were, of course, eligible to receive the services of their medical groups without charge, but within the limitations

Table IV–10. Percentage distribution of treated medical conditions, New York City sample, eight-week period, by age, sex, and insurance status in respect of condition

AGE AND SEX OF PATIENT	TREATED CONDI-TIONS	PERCENTAGE WITH			
		Some insur-ance	*No insur-ance*	*No costs*	*Insurance status unknown*
All ages	*3,270*	7.2	77.9	7.6	7.3
Male	1,363	8.3	74.4	9.6	7.7
Female	1,907	6.3	80.6	6.1	7.0
Under 5	*447*	5.8	77.4	11.7	5.1
Male	246	6.1	76.0	12.2	5.7
Female	201	5.5	79.1	10.9	4.5
5 to 14	*565*	5.5	81.2	9.2	4.1
Male	308	5.8	79.5	10.1	4.6
Female	257	5.1	83.2	8.2	3.5
15 to 44	*1,119*	9.3	76.4	5.1	9.2
Male	415	11.5	72.8	7.2	8.5
Female	704	8.0	78.6	3.8	9.6
45 to 64	*737*	6.8	78.2	7.4	7.6
Male	250	8.4	69.6	8.8	13.2
Female	487	5.9	82.6	6.8	4.7
65 and over	*306*	3.9	80.4	8.5	7.2
Male	118	7.6	76.3	11.9	4.2
Female	188	1.6	83.0	6.4	9.0
Not reported	*96*	10.3	70.9	6.3	12.5
Male	26	[1]	[1]	[1]	[1]
Female	70	11.4	74.3	2.9	11.4

[1] Percentage not calculated, base less than 50.

Table IV–11. Percentage distribution of treated medical conditions, H.I.P. enrollees, eight-week period, by age, sex, and insurance status in respect of condition

AGE AND SEX OF PATIENT	TREATED CONDI-TIONS	PERCENTAGE WITH			
		Some insur-ance	*No insur-ance*	*No costs*	*Insurance status unknown*
All ages	*2,445*	74.7	17.1	2.1	6.1
Male	1,192	73.2	18.2	2.6	6.0
Female	1,253	76.1	16.2	1.6	6.1
Under 5	*334*	80.5	13.2	—	6.3
Male	196	76.5	15.3	0.5	7.7
Female	138	85.5	10.2	—	4.3
5 to 14	*463*	82.3	12.7	1.1	3.9
Male	265	78.1	15.8	1.9	4.2
Female	198	87.9	8.6	—	3.5
15 to 44	*893*	74.9	16.1	2.5	6.5
Male	330	75.2	16.7	3.3	4.8
Female	563	74.8	15.8	1.9	7.5
45 to 64	*660*	70.0	20.6	2.9	6.5
Male	334	69.5	19.8	3.0	7.7
Female	326	70.6	21.5	2.7	5.2
65 and over	*80*	50.0	37.5	5.0	7.5
Male	64	54.7	32.8	6.2	6.3
Female	16	[1]	[1]	—	[1]
Not reported	*15*	[1]	[1]	[1]	[1]
Male	3	[1]	[1]	[1]	[1]
Female	12	[1]	[1]	[1]	[1]

[1] Percentage not calculated, base less than 50.

described above, which may apply with greater frequency—Workmen's Compensation cases, for instance—among some ages than in others. Treated conditions among girls aged five to 14 reported as not covered came to 8.6 percent, while those among elderly men reached the figure of 32.8 percent. It is probable that the informants were better informed about the insurance covering the children in the family than they were about the insurance of the adults, especially the elderly males. It is also conceivable that the H.I.P. families were more likely to turn to the H.I.P. medical groups for their children's care than were the older persons whose habits, attitudes, and medical affiliations had become fixed. Finally, the number of treated conditions of elderly persons was so small as to be subject to sizable sampling error.

Treated Conditions, by Medical Care Insurance and Education of Household Head, Eight-Week Period, Both Samples

By tabulation of treated medical conditions as insured or uninsured at each educational level in the two samples, two hypotheses were tested: that persons in families the head of which had more schooling would be more likely to have prepaid medical care, and, in the case of those in the H.I.P. sample, that they would be more likely to avail themselves of the medical groups' services. The results appear in Table IV–12.

Table IV–12. Percentage distribution of treated medical conditions, H.I.P. enrollees and New York City sample, eight-week period, by education of head of household and insurance status in respect of condition

YEARS OF SCHOOLING COM-PLETED BY HEAD OF HOUSEHOLD	TREATED CON-DITIONS	PERCENTAGE WITH			
		Some insur-ance	*No insur-ance*	*No costs*	*Insurance unknown*
	H.I.P. enrollees				
Total	*2,445*	74.7	17.1	2.1	6.1
Less than 9	660	72.1	20.2	1.8	5.9
9 to 12	916	73.8	19.0	2.7	4.5
More than 12	825	79.4	12.1	1.2	7.3
Not reported	44	43.2	29.5	9.1	18.2
	New York City sample				
Total	*3,270*	7.2	77.9	7.6	7.3
Less than 9	1,259	4.5	79.2	10.0	6.3
9 to 12	1,276	9.6	74.6	7.4	8.4
More than 12	548	8.6	79.7	4.4	7.3
Not reported	187	3.2	87.7	2.1	7.0

From this it would appear that there were at least some families for which these assumptions held true, since the New York City sample showed evidence of less insurance for physician's service among those in families headed by persons with the minimum of schooling.[11] Similarly, among the H.I.P. enrollees there was some correlation between education and the proportion of those who made use of their insurance privileges.[12] But the difference was not great. It is true that these persons in H.I.P. with the better education and the higher incomes were in a better position to use outside physicians if they felt so inclined. It is also true that those with less education and lower incomes had greater access to free medical care (see Table IV–12).

Sick Leave Benefits as Insurance

Employers who continue the salaries or wages in full or in part of employees who become ill are in effect insuring these workers in some measure against loss of income through illness. It was therefore thought advisable to inquire in this survey as to the extent of such provisions for sick leave. While it is true that since July 1950 New York State has required employers to make provision for employees totally disabled for causes beyond those covered by Workmen's Compensation, it was not such situations toward which this inquiry was directed. (Disability coverage by State law was specifically excluded.) In the survey the informant was asked whether the employed member received any pay for the "days when he (the employee) stays away from work because of illness," with a distinction between full and part pay. It was thought that sick leave allowance might have a significant effect on the use of medical care. An employee with income uninterrupted by reason of absence for illness is in a better position to take the necessary time to seek medical care and to follow medical advice than is one who must sacrifice wages for these purposes. An employee without provision for sick leave may very well keep going until serious illness or discomfort forces him to see a physician and to undergo treatment at home or in the hospital.

Striking differences were found in the extent to which persons in the labor force in the H.I.P.-covered group and those in the general population were reported to have sick leave on full pay. Whereas 70.2 percent of the H.I.P. enrollees in the labor force had sick leave on full pay, only 37.1 percent of the persons in the New York City sample were definitely reported as enjoying this benefit. Among non-H.I.P.-covered persons in H.I.P. households, the percentage who enjoyed sick leave provisions extended voluntarily by their employers approximated that found in the general population. In Table IV–13 will be found the full tabulation of these data.

Table IV–13. Persons in labor force with and without paid sick leave, H.I.P. and New York City samples

EMPLOYER'S SICK LEAVE POLICY	H.I.P. SAMPLE				NEW YORK CITY SAMPLE	
	H.I.P. enrollees		*Others*			
	Number	Percent	Number	Percent	Number	Percent
Total	*3,804*	100.0	*1,271*	100.0	*5,634*	100.0
Full pay	2,669	70.2	530	41.7	2,091	37.1
Part pay	397	10.4	125	9.8	503	8.9
No pay	471	12.4	383	30.1	1,758	31.2
Inapplicable[1]	107	2.8	77	6.1	724	12.9
Not reported	160	4.2	156	12.3	558	9.9

[1] Own business or without pay in family business.

As of January 1952, the Bureau of Labor Statistics, United States Department of Labor, conducted its Occupational Wage Survey in New York City. It reported on formal sick leave policies in terms of establishments in industry groups, and differentiated between office and plant workers. Its findings raise no serious question as to the essential accuracy of the distribution shown in Table IV–13, though the returns for the New York City sample would indicate a somewhat more favorable situation than is disclosed by the Bureau of Labor Statistics study. This is probably due to the fact that the Bureau of Labor Statistics study recognized only formal provisions for such a benefit. Small establishments and those

[11] A marked difference was found between the education classes in having "some" insurance (Table IV–5), but this was largely for hospital care.

[12] In later chapters there are further data bearing on this question.

with informal arrangements would augment the figures as found in that inquiry. (See data in the Bureau of Labor Statistics Occupational Wage Summary, January 1952.)

Sick Leave Status, by Occupational Groups, Both Samples

In addition to the different levels of paid sick leave indicated in Table IV–13 for those in the labor force in the New York City sample and among the H.I.P. enrollees, some fairly wide differences among occupational groups appear within both samples. The range in the New York City sample for persons with some sick leave allowance was from 66.8 percent for clerical and sales personnel to 23.9 percent for employees in domestic service (Table IV–14). Only about 33 percent of the persons in the large group of craftsmen and laborers were reported as enjoying provision for pay during illness.

In the groups of professional persons and proprietors there were substantial numbers of persons to whom the question was inapplicable. When these are eliminated from the base population of professional people in the New York City sample, the proportion of persons with sick leave rises from 53.5 to 68.1 percent and that of proprietors and managers is more than doubled to 84 percent.

The sick leave status of H.I.P. enrollees was conditioned by the policies in the various branches of public employment from which about 70 percent of the H.I.P. enrollees had come. The differences between the proportions of persons with sick leave were considerably less than appeared for occupational groups in the city generally, but, as was said above, there still were some differences among these groups.

Sick Leave Status, by Education of Household Head, Both Samples

As might be expected from the data on the sick leave status of persons in the several occupational groups, consistently higher proportions of persons with sick leave benefits appear as the education of the head of the family advances (Table IV–15).

The difference widens when the persons to whom this question is inappropriate are withdrawn from the base of calculation. In the New York

Table IV–14. Percentage distribution of persons in labor force, H.I.P. enrollees and New York City sample, by occupational group and sick leave pay status

OCCUPATIONAL GROUP	TOTAL	PERCENTAGE WITH			
		Sick leave pay	*No sick leave pay*	*Sick leave pay status not reported*	*Question inapplicable*
		H.I.P. enrollees			
Total	*3,804*	80.6	12.4	4.2	2.8
Professional, semiprofessional workers	929	87.2	6.5	2.2	4.1
Proprietors, managers, and officials (including farm) and farmers	217	77.0	2.3	5.5	15.2
Clerical and sales	655	86.4	9.5	2.7	1.4
Craftsmen, foremen, operatives, and laborers	1,417	75.6	20.0	3.0	1.4
Domestic service	15	[1]	[1]	—	—
Other service	421	84.1	10.7	3.8	1.4
Not reported	150	60.3	4.6	34.4	0.7
		New York City sample			
Total	*5,634*	46.0	31.2	9.9	12.9
Professional, semiprofessional workers	566	53.5	17.5	7.6	21.4
Proprietors, managers, and officials (including farm) and farmers	638	41.1	4.7	3.1	51.1
Clerical and sales	1,459	66.8	19.6	7.5	6.1
Craftsmen, foremen, operatives, and laborers	2,083	33.6	52.0	7.3	7.1
Domestic service	67	23.9	35.8	28.3	12.0
Other service	527	49.3	37.8	8.5	4.4
Not reported	294	26.4	12.9	57.3	3.4

[1] Percentage not calculated, base less than 50; 6 reported having sick leave pay.

Table IV–15. Percentage distribution of persons in labor force, H.I.P. enrollees and New York City sample, by education of head of household and sick leave status

YEARS OF SCHOOLING COMPLETED BY HEAD OF HOUSEHOLD	TOTAL	PERCENTAGE WITH *Sick leave pay*	*No sick leave pay*	*Sick leave pay status not reported*	*Question inapplicable*
		H.I.P. enrollees			
Total	*3,804*	80.6	12.4	4.2	2.8
Less than 9	1,295	76.2	17.6	4.3	1.9
9 to 12	1,326	82.6	11.1	3.8	2.5
More than 12	1,074	85.0	7.6	3.0	4.4
Not reported	109	64.5	12.7	21.0	1.8
		New York City sample			
Total	*5,634*	46.0	31.2	9.9	12.9
Less than 9	2,416	41.7	37.0	11.8	9.5
9 to 12	2,005	50.3	29.4	7.1	13.2
More than 12	868	56.8	14.5	8.3	20.4
Not reported	345	24.3	42.5	17.6	15.6

City sample the following increases in the proportion of persons with sick leave benefits occur when this adjustment is made:

	CRUDE PERCENTAGE	ADJUSTED PERCENTAGE
Less than 9 years of schooling	41.7	46.1
9 to 12 years of schooling	50.3	57.9
More than 12 years of schooling	56.8	71.3

If it can be assumed that families with heads who have received the lesser amounts of education have less income, it would follow that they would have less financial reserve with which to meet the burden of expense for illness. When there are no provisions for sick leave, the illness of a breadwinner carries with it not only the added expense for medical care but the loss of income as well. More families headed by persons with less education have neither insurance for medical care nor sick leave benefits.

Sick Leave Status, by Age and Sex, New York City Sample

The broad situation in respect of sick leave benefits for the age-sex groups in the labor force in the New York City sample is set forth in Table IV–16.

Table IV–16. Percentage distribution of persons in labor force, New York City sample, by sex, age, and sick leave status

SEX AND AGE	TOTAL	PERCENTAGE WITH *Sick leave pay*	*No sick leave pay*	*Sick leave pay status not reported*	*Question inapplicable*
Male	*3,868*	43.9	30.8	9.2	16.1
14 to 44	2,207	47.1	31.1	9.0	12.8
45 to 64	1,326	39.8	29.8	8.3	22.1
65 and over	181	38.1	39.8	5.0	17.1
Not reported	154	41.3	24.5	24.5	9.7
Female	*1,766*	50.6	32.1	11.5	5.8
14 to 44	1,161	54.5	30.3	11.7	3.5
45 to 64	442	43.5	37.1	7.9	11.5
65 and over	35	[1]	[1]	[1]	[1]
Not reported	128	42.9	26.6	22.7	7.8

[1] Percentage not calculated, base less than 50; numbers are 13, 16, 3, and 3, respectively.

When the inapplicable cases are eliminated from the base, for the males and the females, the percentage of those with sick leave in each of the three age groups stands at:

Male	
14 to 44	54.0
45 to 64	51.1
65 and over	46.0
Female	
14 to 44	56.5
45 to 64	48.8

Again the differences are considerably reduced, but the pattern of age differentials is not changed.

Summary

1. The collection of data on coverage by insurance for medical care through a single interview with one representative of a household is beset with technical difficulties, some of which have tended to obscure the findings of this study. However, there is reason to believe that the conditions reported broadly approximate those which prevailed in New York City in the spring of 1952. In the case of the H.I.P. enrollees, the statements of the informants could be checked against the records of the Plan. In all cases of medically at-

tended illness and of hospitalization, the answers to the general question of insurance status were repeated and further detail was solicited.

2. For 8.9 percent of the H.I.P. enrollees the informant failed to report that the person was so enrolled. In 39.8 percent of the cases there was a failure to report hospital coverage though such insurance is required by H.I.P. as a prerequisite to enrollment. It is thought that the latter deficiency arose from the tendency of many persons to confuse the names of the several types of coverage.

3. The persons in H.I.P. households who were not covered by H.I.P. were reported to have some kind of medical care insurance to the extent of about 55 percent. But of these, 6.4 percent were reported as H.I.P. enrollees with no report of any other type of insurance. When these are deducted, about 49 percent were given as covered by some other type of medical care coverage. Of these, 31.2 percent were reported as covered only by Blue Cross.

4. The persons in the general population other than the households with one or more H.I.P. enrollees were reported to be covered by some type of insurance for medical care to the extent of 54.3 percent. Accepting this figure for the moment and restoring the H.I.P. families to the sample, a proportion of approximately 56 percent is arrived at; 42 of the 56 percentage points were for persons with insurance for hospital care only. This approximates the figure of 57 percent reported by the President's Commission on the Health Needs of the Nation for coverage by insurance for any type of care and the 57 percent for the nation reported by the Health Information Foundation for 1953.

5. After correction of the figures for detectable inconsistencies, the percentage of persons in the general population, not in H.I.P., with any kind of insurance for medical care falls to 51.7. Children under 14 years of age are insured to a slightly greater extent than persons aged 14 and over; 54.3 percent of the children as compared with 50.9 percent of the adolescents and adults were reported as having some type of insurance for medical care.

6. Among the persons in the labor force in the general population, females with some insurance appear in 58.3 percent, males in 55.9 percent. Of those not in the labor force, 46.1 percent of the females were covered in some degree but only 35.1 percent of the males.

7. Wide differences in insurance coverage appear when the persons in the general population are classified by years of schooling completed by the household head. For persons 14 years and over the range is from 41.5 percent for persons in the group with the least-educated heads of households to 65.3 percent in households headed by persons with the most education. For children the same general proportions appear.

8. Among the occupational groups in the labor force of the general population the persons in clerical and sales pursuits showed the highest proportion insured (66.1 percent), followed by proprietors (61.5 percent), professional workers (60.8 percent), craftsmen, etc. (52.9 percent), service occupations other than domestic (48.6 percent), and domestic service (19.4 percent).

9. For the persons in the New York City sample who were hospitalized in 1951, 43.7 percent were reported as having some insurance for hospital care, with 33.9 percent of their hospital days covered. Short stays were covered in higher proportions than longer ones. Only 32.8 percent of the persons and 23.5 percent of the days were covered for the persons who stayed 21 days or longer.

10. For H.I.P. enrollees who were hospitalized in 1951, 502 of 594 (84.5 percent) were reported as covered by insurance. The cases reported as not insured were in large part persons who stayed 21 days or longer. Such instances were about twice as frequent among households headed by a person with less than nine years of schooling as among those with heads having more than 12 years of schooling.

11. In the New York City sample 3,270 medical conditions were reported to have received medical care at some time during the eight weeks preceding the interview. Of these, 77.9 percent were definitely reported as *not* covered by insurance; 7.2 percent were reported as covered. About

the same percentage were reported as treated without cost to the patient, and for a like percentage the insurance status was reported as unknown.

12. Among H.I.P. enrollees the treated medical conditions (2,445) were reported as covered by insurance in 74.7 percent of the cases; 17.1 percent of them were reported as without insurance coverage. A variety of circumstances attend this condition.

13. In both samples marked differences in the proportion of treated conditions covered by insurance appeared among the age and sex groups. But both the levels and the patterns of distribution are different. In both samples, however, the cases of persons aged 65 years and over show low proportions covered by insurance.

14. Although all education classes in the New York City sample show a very small proportion of treated cases as covered by insurance the group with the least education has the lowest proportion—approximately half that of the other two classes.

15. Among H.I.P. enrollees the same tendency appears but with much higher proportions reported for all education classes and a much narrower spread between the classes.

16. Since paid sick leave is in effect a factor in the insurance situation, inquiry was made about its extent among persons in the labor force. In the New York City sample 37.1 percent of these persons were reported as eligible for full pay and 8.9 percent for part pay during illness; 31.2 percent were reported as receiving no pay during absence for illness; the question was inapplicable to 12.9 percent who had their own business or worked without pay in a family business; the sick leave status was reported as unknown in 9.9 percent of the persons. For the persons in H.I.P. households who were not H.I.P. enrollees the pattern of distribution did not differ markedly. For the H.I.P. enrollees the situation was entirely different: 70.2 percent had full pay, 10.4 percent part pay, and only 12.4 percent no pay; for 2.8 percent and 4.2 percent the question was inapplicable or the situation reported as unknown.

17. Among the occupational groups in the New York City sample persons in professional pursuits and those employed as managers and as clerical and sales personnel are most frequently the beneficiaries of paid sick leave; craftsmen, persons in the service occupations, and those in domestic service are less often thus protected. Among the H.I.P. enrollees the occupational group of the person made much less difference, since a high proportion of the enrollees were in public employment, in which there is more uniformity in the application of personnel policies of this kind.

18. The differences among the education groups in the New York City sample are those to be expected from the differences shown in occupational groups. In households headed by persons with the least schooling, the ratio of those with some sick leave pay is 46.1 percent (when the inapplicable cases are omitted from the base population); the corresponding percentage for those in the highest education group is 71.3.

19. In the New York City sample the proportion of persons, both males and females, with sick leave benefits declines as age advances.

CHAPTER V

Physician Contacts, 1951

THE exhortation to "see your doctor" strikes the ear daily from the radio and meets the eye constantly in the articles and advertisements of insurance companies, pharmaceutical houses, and health organizations that appear in popular magazines. Regular medical check-ups are recommended as well as early resort to medical care when symptoms of illness appear or accidents occur. School medical inspectors, industrial health services, and social agencies urge people to see doctors for defects and diseases. People freely counsel one another not to neglect their health or that of their children. Sometimes this advice takes the form of urging that the "family" doctor be seen.

In this survey some questions were asked which were intended to find out the extent to which this flood of advice is taken. Fairly detailed information about physicians seen on the day preceding the interview and during the eight-week period prior to the contact was recorded and will be analyzed and discussed in other sections of this report. In this and succeeding chapters four special phases of this subject will be treated: (1) the proportion of persons who saw a doctor for any reason during 1951, (2) the proportion of families who reported having a family doctor, (3) the extent to which families with young children had special physicians for them, and (4) the extent to which, in the case of the sample of H.I.P. families, outside physicians were being used.

Physician Contacts, by Age and Sex

In the interview with the informant for the household the question was specifically asked about each person, "Did ——— see a doctor for any reason during 1951? If yes, how many times?" The interviewer circled a "yes" or "no" in the appropriate place for the person in question and noted the number of professional contacts if a doctor had been seen.

The status of all members of H.I.P. families was determined as of December 31, 1951, with the exception of covered spouses acquired by H.I.P. subscribers after that date. These were included in the H.I.P. population though they were probably not covered in 1951. The H.I.P. population includes not only these persons, but also those who came on the rolls at some time during 1951 as newly enrolled family members and those who had interrupted coverage during that year. In all of these situations the persons were eligible for H.I.P. service for less than a year in 1951. The number of these enrollees is, however, not very large; it was known that of the persons on the H.I.P. rolls during 1951, 82 percent had been enrolled prior to that year.[1]

In both the H.I.P. and the New York City samples, babies born in the early months of 1952 are included. Since these could not have been seen in 1951, their inclusion in the two populations increases the size of the base and therefore slightly decreases the rates.

Seeing a doctor included all physician contacts irrespective of auspices: private practice, voluntary and public medical and health institutions and agencies, school, college, industrial and insurance examinations, military, Veterans and Workmen's Compensation cases.

Table v–1 shows the percentages of the New York City sample, the H.I.P. enrollees, and the other members of H.I.P. households who were reported as having come under medical observation in the year before the survey.

[1] "The Utilization by H.I.P. Enrollees of the Services of Medical Groups, 1951," H.I.P. Division of Research and Statistics, February 1953.

Table V–1. Percentage of all persons who saw doctor, H.I.P. and New York City samples, 1951

EXPERIENCE IN SEEING A DOCTOR	H.I.P. SAMPLE				NEW YORK CITY SAMPLE	
	H.I.P. enrollees		*Others*			
	Number	Percent	Number	Percent	Number	Percent
Total	*8,040*	100.0	*2,941*	100.0	*13,558*	100.0
Saw a doctor	5,547	69.0	1,569	53.4	7,668	56.6
No doctor's care	2,348	29.2	1,257	42.7	5,460	40.2
Not reported	145	1.8	115	3.9	430	3.2

These returns would seem to indicate that a little over half of the general population and more than two-thirds of the H.I.P. enrollees had contact during the year with at least one physician.

Other sections of this report will give the number of persons in the New York City sample and the H.I.P. enrollees who were so seriously ill or injured during 1951 that they spent at least one night in a hospital or seven days at home in bed. Thus, there will be some measure of the persons who saw physicians for less serious conditions, for preventive care, and for other reasons.

The figures here presented on the H.I.P. enrollees who saw a doctor may be compared with the estimates made by the H.I.P. Division of Research and Statistics in respect of the proportion of the 1951 enrollment that received service from H.I.P. physicians. Of the total persons enrolled in H.I.P. who were "exposed" to service at any time during 1951, it was estimated that 74 percent received service.[2] This relatively small discrepancy in the two percentages—69 and 74—may arise in part from the inflation of the base in the survey data noted above. It may also reflect a failure of memory or a defect in the knowledge of the informants.[3]

It would thus appear that more H.I.P. enrollees, to the extent of 12.4 percentage points, than of the New York City population saw a doctor in 1951. In terms of the difference in rates, almost

[2] "The Utilization by H.I.P. Enrollees of the Services of Medical Groups, 1951," H.I.P. Division of Research and Statistics, February 1953.

[3] Considering that some H.I.P. enrollees saw outside physicians, it might have been expected that the survey would have shown a higher percentage than was reported for contacts between H.I.P. physicians and insured persons.

Table V–2. Percentage of all persons reported for this contact who saw doctor, H.I.P. and New York City samples, 1951, by age and sex

AGE	H.I.P. SAMPLE				NEW YORK CITY SAMPLE	
	H.I.P. enrollees		*Others*			
	Number	Percentage who saw a doctor	Number	Percentage who saw a doctor	Number	Percentage who saw a doctor
		Male				
Total[1]	*4,163*	68.9	*1,117*	50.7	*6,251*	55.3
Under 5	425	86.4	114	83.3	718	77.0
5 to 14	730	72.2	129	62.0	1,081	64.5
15 to 44	1,666	64.8	505	38.6	2,513	46.5
45 to 64	1,191	65.2	191	47.1	1,379	53.4
65 and over	139	82.0	134	65.7	394	61.2
Not reported	12	[2]	44	[3]	166	39.2
		Female				
Total[1]	*3,732*	71.8	*1,709*	58.7	*6,877*	61.2
Under 5	363	88.4	80	85.0	652	77.6
5 to 14	685	68.5	159	61.6	958	58.5
15 to 44	1,777	71.5	752	50.8	3,085	58.4
45 to 64	831	67.7	440	59.5	1,480	61.9
65 and over	52	75.0	212	71.7	464	65.9
Not reported	24	[4]	66	62.1	238	49.4

[1] The persons not reported for doctor contacts numbered 145 H.I.P. enrollees (66 males, 79 females), 115 others in H.I.P. households (50 males, 65 females), 430 in the New York City sample (195 males, 235 females).

[2] Percentage not calculated, base less than 50; 5 reported with doctor contact.

[3] Percentage not calculated, base less than 50; 18 reported with doctor contact.

[4] Percentage not calculated, base less than 50; 17 reported with doctor contact.

22 percent (21.9) more H.I.P. enrollees saw doctors in 1951 than was found for the New York City population. Since differences in the age-sex composition of the three groups of persons may have affected the rates, the details are shown in Table v–2 for each age-sex group in the three populations.

The proportion of H.I.P. enrollees who saw a doctor exceeds that of the New York City population in each age-sex group to the extent shown in Table v–3.

Table V–3. Percentage of excess in rates for contact with physician of H.I.P. enrollees over rates for corresponding age-sex groups in New York City sample, 1951

AGE	PERCENTAGE OF EXCESS IN RATE OF CONTACT	
	Male	*Female*
Total	24.6	17.3
Under 5	12.2	13.9
5 to 14	11.9	17.1
15 to 44	39.3	22.4
45 to 64	22.1	9.4
65 and over	33.9	13.8

The impact of coverage by H.I.P. would seem to have been heaviest on males aged 15 to 44 and those aged 65 and over for whom the H.I.P. rates for seeing a doctor exceed the rates for the New York City sample by 39 and 34 percent, respectively. Among female H.I.P. enrollees in the child-bearing age, the rate was about 22 percent higher than the city rate for women in the same age bracket. At every age the H.I.P. rate was higher by at least 9 percent.

As can be readily seen from Table v–2, the age specific rates of contact for the three samples and for each sex have the same general contour, with higher rates for children and aged, though they are at different levels. Among males not covered by H.I.P. the rates are lowest for those aged 15 to 44—both in the New York City sample and among those without coverage in H.I.P. households—and only a little higher for men of 45 to 64 in these two groups. Since this latter age span marks the time in which chronic conditions begin to appear, it is the period for early discovery of such conditions. These low rates of contact suggest that many opportunities for establishing controls for such conditions are being lost. Among females the differences between the three groups are not so great in respect of this point, since women in these ages often are impelled to see physicians by reason of pregnancy and the menopause. These data show that women of 65 and over in the three samples saw a doctor in 1951 in proportions that do not differ widely from the proportions of men at this age.

Physician Contacts, by Racial Group

The differences in rates for seeing a doctor in 1951 between white and non-white persons[4] in the three population groups (enrollees in H.I.P. households, other persons in such households, and the New York City sample) were inconsequential (see Table v–4). The New York City sample showed a difference of 1.6 percentage points in favor of the white persons in the proportion of

[4] Racial designation was assigned to all persons in a household according to the race of the informant.

Table V–4. Percentage of all persons reported for contact with doctor, H.I.P. and New York City samples, 1951, by racial group

RACE	H.I.P. SAMPLE				NEW YORK CITY SAMPLE	
	H.I.P. enrollees		*Others*			
	Number	Percentage who saw a doctor	Number	Percentage who saw a doctor	Number	Percentage who saw a doctor
Total[1]	*7,895*	70.3	*2,825*	55.5	*13,128*	58.4
White	7,297	70.2	2,559	55.5	11,742	58.6
Non-white	576	71.0	252	56.3	1,317	57.0
Not reported	22	[2]	14	[3]	69	52.2

[1] The persons not reported for doctor contact numbered 145 H.I.P. enrollees, 115 others in H.I.P. households, and 430 in the New York City sample.

[2] Percent not calculated, base less than 50; 18 reported with doctor contact.

[3] Percent not calculated, base less than 50; 8 reported with doctor contact.

those seeing a doctor. In H.I.P. households the white and non-white persons had approximately the same proportion: less than one percentage point difference both for enrollees and for other persons in these households, though again the levels of these two groups differ considerably.

Physician Contacts, by Labor Force Status

Since a person's presence in the labor force may act as a selective factor in respect of both his need for medical care and his ability to acquire it from physicians in private practice as well as through departments of industrial medicine, and since the proportion of people in the labor force differs considerably in the three population groups, an analysis of this factor is pertinent. Table v–5 sets forth such analysis for all persons for whom there was a report on doctor contact.

In the New York City sample fewer persons aged 14 years and over in the labor force saw a doctor than persons of similar age who were outside it—49.2 percent as compared with 64.1. Among H.I.P. enrollees that gap was considerably lessened, 66.3 percent as compared with 72.1 percent. This discrepancy is widest among the members of H.I.P. households who were not covered, but since they were an erratically constituted group in respect of age and sex, they cannot be expected to follow the patterns found in either of the other two populations with more normal age-sex distribution. In the main, however, these persons who were in H.I.P. households but not covered by H.I.P. and not in the labor force have rates similar to those in the corresponding groups in the New York City population. The persons in this group who were at work had the lowest rate of contact with physicians found among all of the labor force classes in the three population groups.

The spread of rates between the New York City sample and H.I.P. enrollees is narrower for persons keeping house and for those going to school than is the spread for persons at work. These conditions probably arise from the facts that among housekeepers the obstetrical conditions for which medical care of some kind must be had are prevalent, while among those attending school there are pressures from educational authorities to have medical care and some services provided by health authorities. Moreover, accidents are more frequent among the youthful

Table V–5. Percentage of all persons reported for contact with doctor, H.I.P. and New York City samples, 1951, by labor force status

LABOR FORCE STATUS	H.I.P. SAMPLE: *H.I.P. enrollees* Number	H.I.P. SAMPLE: *H.I.P. enrollees* Percentage who saw a doctor	H.I.P. SAMPLE: *Others* Number	H.I.P. SAMPLE: *Others* Percentage who saw a doctor	NEW YORK CITY SAMPLE Number	NEW YORK CITY SAMPLE Percentage who saw a doctor
Total[1]	*7,895*	70.3	*2,826*	55.5	*13,128*	58.4
In labor force	*3,728*	66.3	*1,239*	42.1	*5,434*	49.2
Working	3,565	65.8	1,165	41.6	5,095	49.4
Looking for work	49	57.1	57	42.1	233	45.3
Other	114	85.1	17	[2]	106	52.8
Not in labor force	*2,033*	72.1	*1,107*	65.0	*4,333*	64.1
Keeping house	1,496	70.9	720	64.9	3,101	62.3
Going to school	436	66.5	205	56.1	725	56.8
Unable to work	32	[3]	99	75.8	261	76.6
Other	69	78.3	83	57.8	246	66.3
Not reported	*46*	[4]	*23*	[5]	*123*	56.9
Persons less than 14 years of age	*2,088*	77.0	*457*	71.8	*3,238*	68.5

[1] The persons not reported for doctor contact numbered 145 H.I.P. enrollees, 115 others in H.I.P. households, and 430 in the New York City sample.

[2] Percentage not calculated, base less than 50; 12 reported with doctor contact.

[3] Percentage not calculated, base less than 50; 30 reported with doctor contact.

[4] Percentage not calculated, base less than 50; 33 reported with doctor contact.

[5] Percentage not calculated, base less than 50; 15 reported with doctor contact.

Table V–6. Percentage of all persons reported for contact with doctor, H.I.P. and New York City samples, 1951, by religio-cultural group

RELIGIO-CULTURAL GROUP	H.I.P. SAMPLE				NEW YORK CITY SAMPLE	
	H.I.P. enrollees		*Others*			
	Number	Percentage who saw a doctor	Number	Percentage who saw a doctor	Number	Percentage who saw a doctor
Total[1]	*7,895*	70.3	*2,826*	55.5	*13,128*	58.4
Catholic	4,169	63.3	1,487	50.8	6,282	53.6
Protestant	1,316	70.5	497	54.9	2,975	56.1
Jewish	2,236	83.0	739	64.5	3,466	70.3
Other religion	81	84.0	49	[2]	204	52.5
Not reported	93	60.2	54	58.5	201	44.3

[1] The persons not reported for doctor contact numbered 145 H.I.P. enrollees, 115 others in H.I.P. households, and 430 in the New York City sample.

[2] Percentage not calculated, base less than 50; 33 reported with doctor contact.

population and, for a variety of reasons, such conditions usually are medically attended.

Physician Contacts, by Religio-Cultural Group

It was reported in an earlier chapter that in religious composition the H.I.P. enrollment parallels that shown for the New York City sample, and that the data for that sample closely resemble those emanating from prior studies of the subject. In this section the question of differences among these groups in receipt of medical attention has been explored. As was reported earlier, each person in the enumeration was given the religio-cultural designation of the head of the household of which he was a member. The results of this analysis will be found in Table v–6.

From this analysis it becomes evident that in all religio-cultural groups the enrollees of H.I.P. were seen by physicians in greater proportion than were the corresponding groups in the general population, and that the Jewish people in all three samples saw doctors in higher proportions than did Catholics and Protestants. The members of H.I.P. households who were not covered showed distributions in each religious group that resembled those for the general population of the respective religio-cultural group. While the differences between Catholic and Protestant groups in the general population are small, they are a little larger for H.I.P. enrollees.

Physician Contacts, by Education of Household Head

In this study the education—years of schooling completed—of the household head has been adopted as a means of giving a rough indication of the socioeconomic status of the family and its members. All three groups of persons here under consideration (H.I.P. enrollees, others in H.I.P. households, and the New York City sample) show the middle education group with the lowest

Table V–7. Percentage of all persons reported for contact with doctor, H.I.P. and New York City samples, 1951, by education of head of household

YEARS OF SCHOOLING COMPLETED BY HEAD OF HOUSEHOLD	H.I.P. SAMPLE				NEW YORK CITY SAMPLE	
	H.I.P. enrollees		*Others*			
	Number	Percentage who saw a doctor	Number	Percentage who saw a doctor	Number	Percentage who saw a doctor
Total[1]	*7,895*	70.3	*2,826*	55.5	*13,128*	58.4
Less than 9	3,563	70.7	1,309	63.2	6,524	61.9
9 to 12	2,518	66.2	1,014	45.5	4,441	53.0
More than 12	1,496	77.0	360	51.7	1,455	59.2
Not reported	318	65.7	143	66.9	708	57.9

[1] The persons not reported for doctor contact numbered 145 H.I.P. enrollees, 115 others in H.I.P. households, and 430 in the New York City sample.

rates of contact. Among H.I.P. enrollees, however, the rate of contact of the group in families headed by persons with the most years of schooling outranks both of the other classes. Since there is no reason to believe that these persons had greater need for medical care, this higher rate may reflect different attitudes about seeking it when it is available from private physicians on a prepaid basis.

In the New York City sample the group with heads of households with the least schooling had the highest rate of contact, though the difference is small between them and the highest educated class. The difference is probably no greater than would be expected by chance (Table v–7).

The excess of the H.I.P. rate for those in families with heads having the least schooling over the rate for the corresponding class in the New York City sample amounts to 14.2 percent, for the middle groups to 24.9 percent, and for the groups with heads of households with more than 12 years of schooling to 30.1 percent. This widening of the difference in the rates of contact as education increases seems to suggest that it is the people in the highest education class who avail themselves most readily of the benefits of prepaid medical care.

Physician Contacts, by Education and Sex, Persons Aged 25 and Over

Besides examining the data on schooling of the head of the household and on medical contact of the family members, it was thought advisable to look at the fully adult population, i.e., those 25 years of age and over, in terms of the schooling that each person himself had received, and to see what contact such presumably responsible persons had had with physicians in 1951.

Enrollment in H.I.P. brought higher rates of medical contact to all groups of known educational status than the corresponding groups had in the New York City sample. The differences between the H.I.P. enrollees' rates and those of the members of their households who were not covered were even greater for some of the education groups.

As in the preceding analysis of the education of the head of the household, the data for both males and females in the New York City sample would seem to support the assertion that the people at the very lowest and at the very highest economic levels tend to have more medical care than those of intermediate income (Table v–8). The differences, however, are not very great among

Table V–8. Percentage of all persons 25 years of age and over reported for contact with doctor, H.I.P. and New York City samples, 1951, by education and sex

YEARS OF SCHOOLING COMPLETED	H.I.P. SAMPLE				NEW YORK CITY SAMPLE	
	H.I.P. enrollees		*Others*			
	Number	Percentage who saw a doctor	Number	Percentage who saw a doctor	Number	Percentage who saw a doctor
		Male				
Total[1]	*2,748*	65.9	*561*	45.6	*3,663*	50.2
Less than 9	938	62.4	240	54.6	1,441	50.3
9 to 12	1,038	63.7	199	35.7	1,379	47.3
More than 12	703	73.9	93	36.6	648	55.2
Not reported	69	63.8	29	[2]	195	53.3
		Female				
Total[1]	*2,381*	70.0	*1,078*	57.7	*4,139*	60.9
Less than 9	639	63.5	533	63.6	1,754	61.1
9 to 12	1,014	67.6	385	47.0	1,767	57.6
More than 12	691	79.5	100	60.0	464	68.8
Not reported	37	[3]	60	70.0	154	72.1

[1] The persons not reported for doctor contact numbered 104 H.I.P. enrollees (50 males, 54 females), 69 others in H.I.P. households (23 males, 46 females), and 260 in the New York City sample (112 males, 148 females).

[2] Percentage not calculated, base less than 50; 20 reported with doctor contact.

[3] Percentage not calculated, base less than 50; 27 reported with doctor contact.

the males. In the H.I.P. enrollee group this pattern is not found. There the rate of doctor contact in the case of each sex rose directly with education.

Number of Physician Contacts per Patient

To recall for each member of a household whether a doctor had been seen at all during the previous calendar year must have put a strain on the memory of some of the informants. To recall accurately the exact number of times the doctor had been seen must have been more difficult. It would probably not be hard for most people to remember whether there had been a few or many medical contacts, but within those broad limits it would seem that there must have been some estimating, if not downright guessing, on the part of at least some of the informants. Therefore the proportion of schedules on which this item was returned as unknown is strangely small. Some skepticism would seem to be in order as to the complete reliability of the returns. In view of this a priori judgment, the similarity of the percentages shown for each of the three groups under scrutiny is striking (Table v–9).

Table V–9. Percentage of persons who saw doctor, H.I.P. and New York City samples, 1951, by number of times doctor was seen

NUMBER OF TIMES DOCTOR WAS SEEN	H.I.P. SAMPLE		NEW YORK CITY SAMPLE
	H.I.P. enrollees	*Others*	
Total	*100.0*	*100.0*	*100.0*
Not seen	29.2	42.7	40.2
One	19.1	13.1	14.8
Two	13.7	10.2	10.2
Three	7.7	5.7	6.2
Four	5.5	4.1	4.1
Five to nine	9.7	7.9	8.5
Ten to nineteen	7.8	6.6	6.5
Twenty and over	3.9	4.3	4.0
Times seen not reported	1.6	1.5	2.3
Whether seen not reported	1.8	3.9	3.2

These data indicate that the H.I.P. population, considerably more of whom proportionately were seen by physicians, had about the same experience in terms of the number of times the doctor saw them as the general population and the members of their families who were not covered. The question of the extent to which physicians were seen is explored in much greater detail in other sections of this study, particularly in that on the care received during the eight-week period for specified conditions, where the memory factor should have been less of a problem than here.

Summary

1. Of the total persons in each of the three samples, 69.0 percent of the H.I.P. enrollees, 53.4 percent of the other persons in H.I.P. households, and 56.6 percent of the persons in the New York City sample were reported to have seen a physician in 1951. The rate of contact was almost 22 percent higher for H.I.P. enrollees than for persons in the New York City sample.

2. The excess in the rate of contact of H.I.P. enrollees over the rates in the New York City population was comparatively low for children under 15, but high for most of the other age groups, especially for males. For those aged 15 to 44 the excess rose to 39.3 percent; for females of those ages the excess amounted to 22.4 percent.

3. The rates of contact with physicians for white and non-white persons in the two samples, H.I.P. enrollees and the New York City sample, were approximately the same.

4. The rates for persons in the New York City sample who were not in the labor force considerably exceeded those for persons who were employed or seeking work. In the sample of H.I.P. enrollees, the rates of contact were higher in all labor force categories than for those in the New York City sample, but the spread between the labor force categories in the H.I.P. sample was considerably narrowed.

5. Among the religio-cultural groups in the New York City sample, the Jewish people, with 70.3 percent, had a higher rate of contact than did the Protestants (56.1 percent) or the Catholics (53.6 percent).

6. When tested against the criterion of education of the head of the household, all three groups (H.I.P. enrollees, others in H.I.P. households, and the New York City sample) showed a smaller rate for the middle socioeconomic group than for the two ends of the economic scale. For H.I.P. enrollees the rate for those with most education

went somewhat ahead of that for the least educated, a condition that did not obtain in the New York City sample. The widening differential appearing between the rates for H.I.P. enrollees and for the New York City sample as education of the head of the household advanced, strongly suggests the higher degree of responsiveness among the better-educated people in the use of the services offered by H.I.P.

7. For persons 25 years of age and over in the New York City population, those who themselves had the most schooling showed the highest rates of physician contact for both males and females, but the differences among the males in the three education classes were not great. The middle group had rates less than the group with least education, with a considerable spread of rates in the group of females. In this H.I.P. adult population, those with the most schooling had the highest rate of contact with doctors.

8. For persons seeing a doctor in each of the three groups there is a remarkable similarity in the distribution according to the number of times the doctor was seen. About one-fifth to one-seventh saw the doctor once, another one-fifth to one-seventh saw a doctor two or three times, one-seventh to one-eighth saw him four to nine times, and another one-ninth ten times or over.

9. While more H.I.P. enrollees than persons in either of the other two groups came under medical observation in 1951, there was comparatively little difference in the number of times persons in the three groups were seen by physicians after the contact was made.

CHAPTER VI

Persons and Families with Family Physicians

A BASIC tenet of the H.I.P. program has been the encouragement of the use of family physicians, with patients freely referred to the specialists on the staff of the medical group at the discretion of the family physician. The only exceptions to this program of general supervision of the family's health by the family physician have been the routine supervision of pregnant women by obstetricians and of young children by pediatricians and the self-referral of patients to ophthalmologists. It was known, however, that in spite of careful and explicit instructions to H.I.P. enrollees immediately upon enrollment to choose a family doctor from among those affiliated with the medical group that the subscriber had chosen, some enrollees failed to make such a choice. The H.I.P. has no way of knowing the extent to which this failure arises from the family's neglect to have any physician in this relationship, whether it has retained its former family physician and expects to use the H.I.P. physicians only for specialist services, or whether, as reported earlier, the family was simply unaware of its H.I.P. privileges.

In the planning of this survey the inquiry was extended to the questioning of the family as to its having a family doctor and, if so, his name and address and the time at which he had last seen any member of the family. These inquiries were intended to answer the questions cited above about the H.I.P. families as well as to explore the use of family physicians by the non-H.I.P. population.

Enrollment conditions throughout the H.I.P. population made it necessary to distinguish between several groups of enrollees in the interpretation of these data on family physicians. The questions about the family physician on the survey schedule applied to the family as a whole and not to each person within it. When a family had but one member covered by H.I.P. he might or might not have selected an H.I.P. or personal family physician and he might or might not have had a position in the household that would influence the whole family in the selection of one doctor to serve as the family physician. In the analysis, therefore, it was thought advisable to note whether the H.I.P. household had one or more enrollees and, if only one enrollee, whether such person was the head of the family or another member of the family group whose influence in choosing a family doctor could not be assessed. These distinctions are shown in the tables which follow. It was also thought desirable, for the purpose of this discussion, to isolate the instances of H.I.P. enrollees living alone.

Because of the complexity and confusion of this family doctor relationship in households with more than one family and in those composed of unrelated persons, such households were omitted from the tabulations on this question in both samples. These omissions reduced the H.I.P. sample from 8,040 to 6,623 persons and the New York City sample from 13,558 to 10,456.[1] These are persons living either alone or in a single-family household of related persons. When relatives other than spouses and parents and children were present, they were included in the count.

[1] The differential in the loss of population between the two groups of households as such—17.6 percent of the H.I.P. population and 22.9 percent of the New York City population—is not as great as it would appear here. This is because the exclusion of certain categories of households carries a greater loss of non-enrolled than of enrolled members of these households. See Table III–5, Chapter III, for comparison of H.I.P. and New York City households for composition and type.

Table VI–1. H.I.P. enrollees in single-family households, by family enrollment status, claim to having family physician, and time physician was last seen by any member of family

FAMILY ENROLLMENT STATUS	TOTAL	FAMILY DOCTOR CLAIMED: Total: Number	Percent	Last seen by any member: 1952	1951	Percent (4)+(5) of (1)	1950	1949 and earlier and time not reported	FAMILY DOCTOR NOT CLAIMED	NO REPORT ON CLAIM OF FAMILY DOCTOR
	(1)	(2)	(3)	(4)	(5)	(6)	(7)	(8)	(9)	(10)
Total[1]	*6,623*	*5,874*	88.7	*3,734*	*1,461*	78.4	*217*	*462*	*715*	*34*
One-person family	178	113	63.8	61	18	44.9	15	19	63	2
Multi-person family										
One enrollee	*674*	*549*	81.4	*325*	*143*	69.4	*38*	*43*	*123*	*2*
Head	441	359	81.4	213	87	68.0	25	34	80	2
Other member	233	190	81.5	112	56	71.7	13	9	43	—
More than one enrollee	*5,771*	*5,212*	90.3	*3,348*	*1,300*	80.5	*164*	*400*	*529*	*30*

[1] A discrepancy of 58 persons appears when this table is compared with Table III–2; these are in families with more than one enrollee but in which the head of the household is not enrolled because he was in military service; 68.9 percent of these 58 persons had an H.I.P. doctor with whom the family had been in contact after January 1951.

Persons in Households with Family Physicians, H.I.P. Enrollees and New York City Sub-Sample

An over-all comparison of the two population groups shows 88.7 percent of the H.I.P. enrollees in households claiming a family or personal physician, and in the New York City population 77.9 percent in families making such claims (see Tables VI–1 and VI–2). When the families with a physician are limited to those that had seen their physician since January 1, 1951, these percentages fall to 78.4 and 67.4, respectively.[2] It will be recalled that this survey was made in the spring of 1952. The interval between January 1, 1951, and the time of the interview would extend for a period of 14 to 18 months.

[2] Size of family affects the chance that any of its members may have been seen by the family doctor within the specific period. It will be recalled, however, that there were no marked differences in family size in the two samples (see Chapter III).

Table VI–2. Persons in single-family households, New York City sub-sample, by family composition, claim to having family physician, and time physician was last seen by any member of family

COMPOSITION OF FAMILY	TOTAL	FAMILY DOCTOR CLAIMED: Total: Number	Percent	Last seen by any member: 1952	1951	Percent (4)+(5) of (1)	1950	1949 or earlier and time not reported	FAMILY DOCTOR NOT CLAIMED	NO REPORT ON CLAIM OF FAMILY DOCTOR
	(1)	(2)	(3)	(4)	(5)	(6)	(7)	(8)	(9)	(10)
Total	*10,456*	*8,156*	77.9	*4,753*	*2,295*	67.4	*483*	*625*	*2,239*	*61*
One-person family	398	240	60.2	111	70	45.4	28	31	148	10
Multi-person family	*10,058*	*7,916*	78.7	*4,642*	*2,225*	68.3	*455*	*594*	*2,091*	*51*
Husband and wife	1,670	1,238	74.1	628	414	62.4	90	106	424	8
Parents and one or more children under 18 years	6,315	5,092	79.7	3,211	1,340	72.1	212	329	1,195	28
One parent[1] and one or more children under 18 years	510	363	71.2	212	87	58.6	22	42	135	12
Parent or parents and all children over 18 years	1,563	1,223	78.2	591	384	62.4	131	117	337	3

[1] Or parent substitute.

When comparison is made between persons living in H.I.P. households with more than one enrollee and in New York City households with more than one member, the proportion of the former claiming a family doctor rises to 90.3 percent with 80.5 percent in families having had contact after January 1, 1951, and the proportion of the latter rises to 78.7 percent with 68.3 percent in families having had contact in 1951 or 1952. In both samples the persons living alone showed much smaller proportions claiming a personal physician, 63.8 percent in the case of H.I.P. enrollees and 60.2 percent in the general population, with about 45 percent in both instances having seen the doctor in the time since January 1951. It is possible that the question was not well adapted to bring out the best data for this group of persons, since it was cast in terms appropriate to a family group and not to a person living alone.

For the multi-person H.I.P. households with but one enrollee, it could well be that although that enrollee had chosen a personal physician, the family as a whole had no family physician or had some other doctor. In event of these conditions, the enrollee's status has been considered the same as that of the family as a whole.

From this point on the data do not bear upon the comparison of the experience of the H.I.P. population with that of the general population, but rather upon selected details peculiar to each of the two populations. Therefore, all of the data on the New York City population and on the H.I.P. population are discussed below in separate sections.

Households, by Type and Family Physician Status, New York City Sub-Sample

Table VI–2 shows the counts of persons in the various family situations in relation to the family's claim to having a family doctor. A count of the households is shown in Table VI–3 for the New York City sub-sample, but no corresponding table was made of H.I.P. households because of the complications of the partial coverage of the members of households of various types.

As has been pointed out above (Table VI–2), the one-person households contained the smallest proportion of individuals who claimed having a family physician—60.2 percent, with 45.4 percent seen after January 1951. They were followed by the households (Table VI–3) with children under 18 but with only one parent or a parent substitute—66.5 percent having a family doctor, with 53.6 percent having a member or members seen after January 1951. Next came the families composed of adults, either married couples or parents with grown children, 72.9 and 77.5 percent of whom, respectively, had family doctors and 62.8 and 62.1 percent of whom had seen the

Table VI–3. Single-family households, New York City sub-sample, by family composition, claim to having family physician, and time physician was last seen by any member of family

COMPOSITION OF FAMILY	TOTAL	FAMILY DOCTOR CLAIMED					FAMILY DOCTOR NOT CLAIMED		NO REPORT ON CLAIM OF FAMILY DOCTOR	
		Total		*Seen after Jan. 1, 1951*		*Last seen before Jan. 1, 1951, or time not reported*				
		Number	Percent	Number	Percent		Number	Percent	Number	Percent
Total	*3,440*	*2,611*	75.9	*2,222*	64.6	*389*	*803*	23.3	*26*	0.8
One person	398	240	60.2	181	45.4	59	148	37.1	10	2.7
Husband and wife	835	619	72.9	521	62.8	98	212	26.6	4	0.5
Parents and one or more children under 18 years	1,547	1,256	81.3	1,122	72.5	134	282	18.2	9	0.5
Parent[1] and one or more children under 18 years	140	93	66.5	75	53.6	18	45	32.1	2	1.4
Parent or parents, and all children over 18 years	520	403	77.5	323	62.1	80	116	22.3	1	0.2

[1] Or parent substitute.

doctor since January 1, 1951. As is to be expected, the highest proportion was found for the families with children under 18 years. Of these, 81.3 percent claimed a family doctor and 72.5 percent said that some member or members had seen him in 1951 or 1952. The difference between the couples with children under 18 and the broken families with children under that age is arresting; 53.6 percent of the latter had been in fairly recent contact with their family physicians as compared with 72.5 percent of the normally constituted families with children under 18 years within the corresponding period. This may be a reflection of the smaller size of the broken families, as well as of the economic problems and problems of adult supervision over the health of children. Possibly the differing ages of the children also played a part.

Family Physician Status, by Education of Family Head, New York City Sub-Sample

In order to determine whether education of the head of the family conditioned the family's retention of a family physician, the persons in families were tabulated with the results shown in Table VI–4.

From these data it would seem that in the New York City population the differences between the education groups in their claiming or not claiming a family doctor were slight. Moreover, this similarity holds when the distinction is made between the cases in which a family doctor was fairly recently seen and those in which the contact preceded 1951 or the time was unknown.

Family Physician Status, by Composition of Family and Education of Head, New York City Sub-Sample

It has been shown above that whereas there were appreciable differences in the proportions of families of the different types who claimed family doctors, there were very small differences by education of the head of the family. How were these two conditions related to each other?

Among these several types of households the better education of the head of the family had no discernibly consistent effect on the proportion having a family doctor (Table VI–5).

Components of Sub-Sample of H.I.P. Enrollees

In order to minimize the qualifications which must be put upon the answers to the various questions at issue, the H.I.P. population (6,623) in the sub-sample must be broken up into homogeneous groups in respect of the enrollment situation and the fact of claiming a family doctor. These data were shown earlier in Table VI–1. The important base figures in the tables which follow are:

Total persons in sub-sample	*6,623*
Claiming family doctor	5,874
Total persons in multi-person families with two or more enrollees	*5,771*
Claiming family doctor	5,212
Total persons in one-person households	*178*
Claiming family doctor	113

Table VI–4. Persons in New York City sub-sample, by education of head of family and claim to having family physician

YEARS OF SCHOOLING COMPLETED BY HEAD OF FAMILY	TOTAL	FAMILY DOCTOR CLAIMED				NO FAMILY DOCTOR CLAIMED		NO REPORT ON CLAIM OF FAMILY DOCTOR	
		Total		*Seen after Jan. 1, 1951*					
		Number	Percent	Number	Percent	Number	Percent	Number	Percent
Total	*10,456*	*8,156*	77.9	*7,048*	67.4	*2,239*	21.4	*61*	0.6
Less than 9	4,246	3,227	76.0	2,765	65.1	999	23.5	20	0.5
9 to 12	3,959	3,203	80.9	2,803	70.8	747	18.9	9	0.2
More than 12	1,758	1,370	77.9	1,191	67.8	380	21.6	8	0.5
Not reported	493	356	72.3	289	58.7	113	22.9	24	4.7

Table VI–5. Percentage of single-family households, New York City sub-sample, claiming family physician seen since January 1, 1951, by composition of family and education of head

COMPOSITION OF FAMILY	TOTAL	YEARS OF SCHOOLING COMPLETED BY HEAD OF FAMILY							
		Less than 9		*9 to 12*		*More than 12*		*Not reported*	
		Number	Percentage who claimed doctor[1]	Number	Percentage who claimed doctor[1]	Number	Percentage who claimed doctor[1]	Number	Percentage who claimed doctor[1]
Total	*3,440*	*1,412*	62.8	*1,264*	68.4	*601*	64.1	*163*	59.5
One person	398	201	40.8	107	49.5	76	51.3	14	[2]
Husband and wife	835	354	66.4	283	58.0	152	56.6	46	[3]
Parents with one or more children under 18	1,547	484	71.9	690	75.9	319	70.0	54	50.9
Parent[4] with one or more children under 18	140	66	51.5	65	56.9	6	[5]	3	[6]
Parents or parent with all children over 18	520	307	61.1	119	63.9	48	[7]	46	[8]

[1] Family doctor seen after January 1, 1951.
[2] Percentage not calculated, base less than 50; 7 claimed family doctor.
[3] " " " " " " "; 36 " " "
[4] Or parent substitute.
[5] Percentage not calculated, base less than 50; 4 claimed family doctor.
[6] " " " " " " "; none " " "
[7] " " " " " " "; 33 " " "
[8] " " " " " " "; 27 " " "

No special analyses for the characteristics of the family or the head of it have been made for the 674 isolated enrollees among the 6,345 enrollees in multi-person families.

H.I.P. Sub-Sample, by Family Physician Status and Education of Family Head

For the H.I.P. population, not only has the economic barrier between the family and its having a family physician been removed but, as has been said, immediately upon enrollment the family is urged to proceed to choose a family doctor. But as was also pointed out earlier, in the case of the single-person enrollment in a multi-person household, the enrolled person might very well have chosen a personal physician without having the family as a whole considered to have a family physician. Accordingly, only the subscribers with covered dependents (i.e., households with two or more enrollees) were selected for the analysis of the relationship to education of the head of the family. The findings set forth in Table VI–6 refer to the *covered persons* in such households and not to the households themselves. In many of these households there were persons who were not covered (older children, parents and parents-in-law of the subscriber, collateral relatives) and therefore not entitled, under the H.I.P. contract, to the services of the family physician chosen by the subscriber. However, such persons may go under other kinds of arrangements to the same H.I.P. physician chosen by the H.I.P.-covered members of the family, and it is known that some do.

It will be noted that whereas in the New York City population (Table VI–4) the proportion of persons with the highest educational level who had recently seen their family doctors did not rise above the general level of the whole group, the H.I.P. enrollees in this educational status showed an appreciably higher percentage with fairly recent contacts than did the persons in households headed by persons with less education.

From Table VI–6 it is clear that about 90 percent of the H.I.P. enrollees were in families reported by informants as having family physicians. This includes multi-person households of all types within the limitation set up for this analysis. It will be recalled that households composed of more than one family or of unrelated persons were excluded from this analysis.

There is some likelihood that in at least a few of these cases the informant was not fully aware of the benefits available through H.I.P. coverage

Table VI–6. H.I.P. enrollees in families with two or more covered members, by education of head of family, claim to having family physician, and time physician was last seen by any member of family

YEARS OF SCHOOLING COMPLETED BY HEAD OF FAMILY	TOTAL	FAMILY DOCTOR CLAIMED					FAMILY DOCTOR NOT CLAIMED		NO REPORT ON CLAIM OF FAMILY DOCTOR	
		Total		*Seen after Jan. 1, 1951*		*Last seen before Jan. 1, 1951, or time not reported*				
		Number	Percent (2) of (1)	Number	Percent (4) of (1)		Number	Percent (7) of (1)	Number	Percent (9) of (1)
	(1)	(2)	(3)	(4)	(5)	(6)	(7)	(8)	(9)	(10)
Total	*5,771*	*5,212*	90.3	*4,648*	80.5	*564*	*529*	9.2	*30*	0.5
Less than 9	1,585	1,418	89.4	1,240	78.2	178	163	10.3	4	0.3
9 to 12	2,275	2,038	89.6	1,790	80.7	248	231	10.1	6	0.3
More than 12	1,789	1,660	92.8	1,543	86.3	117	119	6.8	10	0.4
Not reported	122	96	78.7	75	61.5	21	16	13.0	10	8.0

or was confused about its existence. Since about 9 percent of the total H.I.P. sample population were in households whose informants did not know that some member or members were covered by H.I.P., it is conceivable that they would not know about the possibility of having an H.I.P. family doctor and might not be aware of a family doctor relationship of any kind.

In the 178 one-person H.I.P. households (not included in Table VI–6) there seemed to be some indication of a relationship between education of the enrollee and family doctor status; the lowest education group showed 37 percent having seen a family doctor recently and the two other groups, respectively, 49.1 and 48.4.

H.I.P. Enrollees with Non-H.I.P. Family Physicians, by Enrollment Status

The gathering of information on the use of non-H.I.P. physicians by H.I.P. enrollees was one of the objectives of this survey. Hitherto, there has been no measurement of its extent or any analysis of the circumstances under which it occurs. The use of an outside physician, as has been said elsewhere, can arise from a variety of causes. The issue of the retention of a family physician is, however, less likely to be affected by extraneous circumstances[3] than would an instance of "having seen a doctor" for any reason, and therefore these figures may have some advantage in revealing the proportion of H.I.P. enrollees who are using their H.I.P. services as the program is set up to be used. In Table VI–7 the persons in the several types of enrollment situations whose families claimed family doctors have been distributed according to the H.I.P. status of the doctors.

About 82 percent of the persons in multi-person families with more than one person covered claimed an H.I.P. doctor as their family physician. For the one-person enrollments in multi-person families about 33 percent reported that their H.I.P. family doctor stood in that relationship to

[3] Such as having seen a physician in connection with accidents in industry and elsewhere, school or college medical inspections, life insurance or pre-employment examinations, etc.

Table VI–7. H.I.P. enrollees in single-family households claiming family physician, by family enrollment status and H.I.P. status of physician

FAMILY ENROLLMENT STATUS	TOTAL	H.I.P. STATUS OF FAMILY DOCTOR					
		H.I.P.		*Non-H.I.P.*		*Not reported*	
		Number	Percent	Number	Percent	Number	Percent
Total	*5,874*	*4,515*	76.9	*1,267*	21.6	*92*	1.5
One-person family	113	70	61.9	35	30.9	8	7.1
Multi-person family							
One enrollee	*549*	*175*	31.9	*356*	64.8	*18*	3.3
Head	359	117	32.6	227	63.2	15	4.2
Other	190	58	30.5	129	67.9	3	1.6
More than one enrollee	*5,212*	*4,270*	81.9	*876*	*16.8*	*66*	1.3

Table VI–8. H.I.P. enrollees in single-person and single-family households claiming family physician, by family enrollment status, H.I.P. status of physician, and recency of contact

FAMILY ENROLLMENT STATUS AND PHYSICIAN'S STATUS IN H.I.P.	TOTAL PERSONS	FAMILY DOCTOR LAST SEEN: *After Jan. 1, 1951*		*Prior to Jan. 1, 1951, or time not reported*	
		Number	Percent	Number	Percent
One-person family					
H.I.P. physician	70	60	85.6	10	14.4
Non-H.I.P. physician[1]	43	19	44.2	24	55.8
Multi-person family					
One enrollee					
Head					
H.I.P. physician	117	100	85.5	17	14.5
Non-H.I.P. physician[1]	242	200	83.0	42	17.0
Other					
H.I.P. physician	58	55	94.7	3	5.3
Non-H.I.P. physician[1]	132	113	85.6	19	14.4
More than one enrollee					
H.I.P. physician	4,270	3,869	90.6	401	9.4
Non-H.I.P. physician[1]	942	779	82.7	163	17.3

[1] Includes persons with family physicians but with H.I.P. status of physicians not reported.

the whole household. In one-person households claiming a family doctor about 62 percent had an H.I.P. physician in that capacity.

Recency of Contact with H.I.P. and Non-H.I.P. Family Physicians

As one measure of the practical reality of the family doctor relationship with both H.I.P. and non-H.I.P. physicians, the recency of the contact was examined. For this purpose all of the persons with family physicians of unknown H.I.P. status are grouped with those of non-H.I.P. status. The results of this analysis appear in Table VI–8.

On the whole, some fairly recent contact with family doctors was reported by more persons in families claiming to have H.I.P. family doctors than in the group reporting non-H.I.P. family doctors. This was especially marked in the case of persons living alone, but it appeared to some extent in all of the enrollment classes.

Use of Non-H.I.P. Physicians, by Education of Family Head

Since H.I.P. enrollees are completely free to use their H.I.P. services as they see fit, the question naturally arises as to how subscribers of different educational levels elect to use them in terms of choice of family physician. As explained above, the equivocal situations of multi-person households with a single enrollee make it advisable in this connection to confine the analysis of the use of H.I.P. versus non-H.I.P. family doctors to the 5,212 persons who lived in multi-person households of related persons with two or more H.I.P. enrollees and with family doctors.

For the 113 one-person households with family doctors, the person's education apparently did not condition the choice of an H.I.P. versus a non-H.I.P. doctor as his personal physician. The percentages of persons with an H.I.P. doctor were 64.7 percent for those with less than nine years of schooling, 60.6 for those with nine to 12 years, and 62.2 for those with more than 12 years.

For the other households, the distribution of each education group of those claiming H.I.P. and non-H.I.P. physicians appears in Table VI–9.

The consistent rise in the use of H.I.P. family physicians with increasing education of the head of the household testifies to the awareness of the better-educated heads of families of the services available to them under the H.I.P. program.

Summary

1. The data on retention of a family physician were examined for 3,440 families with 10,456 members in the New York City sample and for 6,623 persons covered by H.I.P. Multi-family households and households without a nucleus of

Table VI–9. H.I.P. enrollees in families with two or more persons covered and claiming family physician, by education of head of family and H.I.P. status of family physician

YEARS OF SCHOOLING COMPLETED BY HEAD OF FAMILY	TOTAL PERSONS	H.I.P. STATUS OF FAMILY DOCTOR					
		H.I.P		*Non-H.I.P.*		*Not reported*	
		Number	Percent	Number	Percent	Number	Percent
Total	*5,212*	*4,270*	81.9	*876*	16.8	*66*	1.3
Less than 9	1,418	1,077	75.9	329	23.2	12	0.9
9 to 12	2,038	1,697	83.3	310	15.2	31	1.5
More than 12	1,660	1,441	86.9	198	11.9	21	1.2
Not reported	96	55	57.3	39	40.6	2	2.1

spouses or of persons in the parent-child relationship were eliminated from both groups.

2. Among the 10,456 persons in the New York City sample 77.9 percent were in families who claimed to have a family physician; 67.4 percent were in families reporting contact with the family physician in the interval between January 1, 1951, and the time of the interview (March 3, through June 23, 1952).

3. Among the 6,623 H.I.P. enrollees 88.7 percent were in families for which a family doctor was claimed, with 78.4 percent having had contact between January 1, 1951, and the time of the interview.

4. In the New York City sample there was a fairly wide variation in the proportion of households with family doctors, according to composition: 81.3 percent of the households composed of parents and children under 18 years; 77.5 percent of those composed of parents or parent and children over 18; 72.9 percent of those with husband and wife only; 66.5 percent of those with one parent or parent substitute and child or children under 18 years; and 60.2 percent of the one-person households.

5. In the New York City sub-sample the education of the head of the household apparently had little or no effect on the proportion of persons in households claiming to have a family physician.

6. Within households grouped by composition of family (New York City sub-sample), analysis according to education of the head fails to bring out any correlation of the education of the head of the household with having or not having a family doctor except in the case of the one-person household, which showed some inverse relation.

7. In the H.I.P. sample (families with two or more enrollees), 90.3 percent of the enrollees were in families claiming to have a family doctor. Very little difference from this percentage appeared among enrollees grouped by education of the head of the family.

8. Among the enrollees in houscholds claiming to have a family doctor, there were marked differences among those in the several enrollment situations in respect of the choice of an H.I.P. doctor to serve in this capacity. In families with two or more enrollees the proportion of persons with H.I.P. family physicians approximated 82 percent, in single-person households 62 percent, and in the instances of multi-person households with but one enrollee it approached 33 percent of the persons.

9. When recency of contact with the family physician is examined, it is found that slightly higher proportions of persons with H.I.P. physicians had seen them after January 1, 1951, in all enrollment groups and that in the case of single-person households the proportion of those with H.I.P. family doctors with whom they had had recent contact rose to about twice the proportion of those with non-H.I.P. physicians.

10. For the H.I.P. households with two or more enrollees, the proportion of persons in families with an H.I.P. versus a non-H.I.P. family physician rose consistently as the education of the head of the household advanced. In one-person households education seems to have had no effect upon the individual's choice of an H.I.P. versus a non-H.I.P. physician.

CHAPTER VII

Pediatric Services for Families with Small Children

THE discrepancy between the concept of the place of pediatrics as a medical specialty and its exemplification in actual practice in New York City created a good many difficulties in this attempt to compare the experience in receipt of pediatric care of the families with children covered by H.I.P. with the experience of families in the general population. The function of the pediatrician is theoretically conceived as that of a specialist in the care of sick children, in the administration of prophylactic procedures to well children, in the observation of the child's growth and development, and in the management of the correction of remediable deviations from recognized norms in physical and mental attributes. These functions are both clinical and preventive in character. A major issue is the age span over which the child remains a candidate for pediatric care. "Pediatricians," said the American Academy of Pediatrics in 1949, "constitute that branch of the medical profession concerned with the medical care and health supervision of children from birth through adolescence." However, this ideal admittedly finds only partial fulfillment in real life. As the Academy reports, "A large number of children do not receive preventive and curative care compatible with present standards of good pediatric practice: (1) parents are unable to pay for good service; (2) there is unwillingness to use, or lack of knowledge of, available facilities; (3) services are not available where many children live; and (4) there are not enough physicians well trained in the medical care and health supervision of children, especially in the rural areas."[1] In varying degrees all of these factors are present in New York City and have affected not only the medical service of children in the general population but also that of those covered by H.I.P. except for the first condition, i.e., ability to pay. As reported earlier, the H.I.P. contract specifies that the children of subscribers are to have pediatric care but does not define it further. That step was left to the Medical Control Board.

Differences among H.I.P. Medical Groups Regarding Pediatric Policies

Wide differences in the pediatric policies of the H.I.P. medical groups appeared in 1947, at the time at which service was inaugurated, and have continued since that time, though with some modifications in the direction of raising the age during which children are to have routine care by pediatricians as distinguished from a consultative service available through the family physician.[2] Several medical groups have from the beginning provided routine care by pediatricians up to the age of puberty. However, no medical group has carried such care through adolescence, as suggested by the Academy of Pediatrics. Such prolongation of the period of care is probably less necessary in a setting of medical group practice than it would be without such means of closely integrating the services of family physicians and specialists. Late in 1949 the H.I.P. Medical Control Board set up the requirement of routine pediatric care for all children under 1 year of age. By March 1, 1951, 14 of the 30 medical groups, with 50.3 percent of the enrollees under 15 years of age, were providing routine pediatric care through the first year of life; two groups, with 1.2 percent of the children, carried such care through the first 2 years; five medical groups, with 16.6 percent of

[1] The American Academy of Pediatrics, Committee for the Study of Child Health Services, *Child Health Services and Pediatric Education*. New York, The Commonwealth Fund, 1949, pp. xi and xiii.

[2] George Baehr and Neva R. Deardorff, "Pediatric Services Under the Health Insurance Plan of Greater New York," *Pediatrics,* Vol. 8, No. 2, August 1951.

the children, provided such care for the first 5, 6, or 7 years; while nine groups (five in Brooklyn and four in Manhattan), with 31.9 percent of the children, kept them under routine pediatric care to the age of 11 or 12.

It is known that not all H.I.P. subscribers have been anxious to have routine pediatric care for their children. Some have preferred that their children be under the care of their family physicians. These attitudes, together with the choice by subscribers of medical groups providing a minimum of routine pediatric care suggested that the use of a special doctor for the children was not a universally cherished ideal and that, judging by the behavior of the medical groups, the mores of pediatric care probably varied throughout the different communities in the greater city and that the medical groups tended to conform to those mores. This question will be further explored in a later section.

At this point it is well to begin with the broad outlines of the extent of pediatric care in the two population samples. In this connection it should be emphasized that the absence of pediatric care is not to be interpreted as lack of medical care in either sample. It is in effect a distinction between having care by a pediatrician or by a general physician. In all instances in the H.I.P. population the services of the family physician and of the pediatrician as a consultant are guaranteed by the contract.

On the schedule used in the Household Survey the question was asked of the informant in all families with one or more children born after March 1946 (i.e., with a child under the age of six at the time of the survey), "Do you have a special doctor for children?" If the answer to this was "yes," the further questions were asked, "What is his name? What is his address? When is the last time any of the children saw him?" It will be noted that the informant was not asked whether the family had a pediatrician. It was thought that many families would not know whether or not the special physician, if they had one for their children, had been certified by the American Board of Pediatrics. In the text which follows, the term "pediatrician" is used in referring to these special doctors, but there is no assurance that in all cases they were diplomates.

Sub-Samples Used for H.I.P. and New York City Families

In order to simplify the comparison between the H.I.P. families and those in the general population, this analysis for pediatric care is confined to households with children under the age of six years which (*a*) were single-family as distinguished from multi-family units, and (*b*) had only parents, parent, or parent substitute and children as members.[3] In the case of the H.I.P. households, only those with children covered by their parents were included. Since these households contained only relatives, it is proper to refer to them as families rather than as households. Within these limits, 942 families were drawn as a sub-sample from the 4,190 households in the New York City sample —22.6 percent. The corresponding sub-sample from the H.I.P. group contained 622 families, representing 21.6 percent of the 2,874 H.I.P. families with coverage which included the head of the family. In the sub-sample for New York City there was a total of 3,927 persons, 1,377 of them children under six years. In the H.I.P. sub-sample the total persons numbered 2,569, with 845 children under six. The New York City families averaged 4.17 members; the H.I.P. families, 4.13. Something of the other similarities and the differences in the two groups of families can be seen from Table VII–1.

[3] These families were all drawn from the third and fourth types of families (Table III–2, Chapter III). The children here analyzed account for all but 150 of those under six years of age in the H.I.P. sample and an estimated 329 children in the New York City sample.

New York City sample—total children under five = 1,396

4.5)	1,396	(4.5 is divisor for adding increment of one year)
	310	
	1,706	estimated as children under six in the whole sample
	1,377	children under six in sub-sample
	329	children not included in this analysis

H.I.P. enrollees—total children under five = 798

4.5)	798	(4.5 is divisor for adding increment of one year)
	177	
	975	estimated as children under six in the whole sample
	845	children under six in sub-sample
	130	children not included in this analysis

Table VII–1. Single-family households with children under six years, H.I.P. and New York City sub-samples, by number of members and number of children under six years

NUMBER OF MEMBERS	H.I.P. SUB-SAMPLE		NEW YORK CITY SUB-SAMPLE	
	Number	Percent	Number	Percent
Total families	*622*	100.0	*942*	100.0
2 members	2	0.3	14	1.5
3 "	205	33.0	338	35.9
4 "	244	39.2	319	33.9
5 "	104	16.7	154	16.3
6 "	39	6.3	66	7.0
More than 6 members	28	4.5	51	5.4
Total families	*622*	100.0	*942*	100.0
1 child under 6	432	69.4	600	63.7
2 children under 6	159	25.6	268	28.5
3 " " "	30	4.8	56	6.0
4 " " "	1	0.2	17	1.8
5 " " "	—	—	1	[1]

[1] Percentage less than 0.05.

As in the case of the total H.I.P. households, this sub-sample showed extra weight for families with four persons as compared with the corresponding group of New York City families.

In this connection it is well to remember that families with children under the age of six years are not necessarily young families. These children may have been preceded by one or more older children. The size of the family itself gives some clue as to the point it has reached in its life cycle (Table VII–1). It would seem that in these two sub-samples there was a similar range in family size and therefore probably some correspondence in the age of the parents and their prior experience with the care of young children.

Since pediatric care is more likely to be present in a family with a child under one year and to taper off after that age, it is well to see how the two sub-samples compared in respect of the age of the youngest child in the family. The distributions are shown in Table VII–2.

It will be noted that in the H.I.P. group somewhat fewer families had a baby under one year and to that extent were not eligible for routine pediatric care in the medical groups which, at the time of the survey, confined such care to infants of that age.

Table VII–2. Families in H.I.P. and New York City sub-samples, by age of youngest child

AGE OF YOUNGEST CHILD	H.I.P. SUB-SAMPLE		NEW YORK CITY SUB-SAMPLE	
	Number	Percent	Number	Percent
Total	*622*	100.0	*942*	100.0
Under 1 year	117	18.8	237	25.2
1 to 3 years	325	52.3	474	50.3
4 to 6 years	180	28.9	231	24.5

Table VII–3. Families in H.I.P. and New York City sub-samples, by age of youngest child and claim to pediatric care

AGE OF YOUNGEST CHILD AND USE OF PEDIATRIC CARE	H.I.P. SUB-SAMPLE		NEW YORK CITY SUB-SAMPLE	
	Number	Percent	Number	Percent
Total	*622*	100.0	*942*	100.0
With pediatric care	394	63.3	399	42.4
No pediatric care	149	24.0	447	47.4
Not reported	79	12.7	96	10.2
Under 1 year	*117*	100.0	*237*	100.0
With pediatric care	105	89.8	119	50.2
No pediatric care	11	9.4	102	43.0
Not reported	1	0.8	16	6.8
1 to 3 years	*325*	100.0	*474*	100.0
With pediatric care	213	65.5	195	41.1
No pediatric care	85	26.2	238	50.2
Not reported	27	8.3	41	8.7
4 to 6 years	*180*	100.0	*231*	100.0
With pediatric care	76	42.2	85	36.8
No pediatric care	53	29.4	107	46.3
Not reported	51	28.4	39	19.9

Families with Pediatric Care

As was done in the analyses of the claims to having a family doctor, the data on pediatric care have been cast in terms not only of the claim to such care per se, but also the recency of the contact. The data on the claim to having pediatric care, together with an indication of the age of the youngest child in the family, appear in Table VII–3.

Two conditions stand out in any consideration of these figures. First is the wide discrepancy between the proportion of H.I.P. families whose children had pediatric care and that of the families in the general population: 42.4 percent in the New York City families and 63.3 percent in the H.I.P. families, an excess in the rate for the H.I.P. families of about 50 percent over that of the New York City families.[4]

[4] It will also be noted that in the H.I.P. group the number of cases in which the fact of pediatric care is not reported is excessively large in the families whose youngest child is four to six years of age. These could well be instances in which the informant was uncertain as to whether the child could be said to have a special doctor when this doctor is available only for consultations and not for routine care.

The second point to be noted is the declining discrepancy between the rates with the advance in age of the youngest child. For families with a baby under one year the H.I.P. proportion reached almost 90 percent as compared with 50 percent in the New York City sub-sample.

Parenthetically, a question arises as to the proportion of the families in the New York City sample with one, two, and three or more children under six years and their use of pediatric care. In the total of 942 families, the 600 with one child under that age showed 40.8 percent with pediatric care; the 268 with two children had 48.1 percent with such care; but for the 74 with three or more children the percentage fell to 33.8 percent.

Among families who claimed pediatric care there were no great differences between the two samples in the proportions who had been in fairly recent contact with their pediatricians.

Pediatric Care, by Education of Family Head

One immediately wishes to know whether the percentages in these two sub-samples are not affected by differing proportions of families in the several educational and economic classes. It is important to know how families with similar educational attainments in each of the sub-samples compare in their use of pediatricians. For this purpose the analysis is sharpened when families with the youngest child over four years old are omitted, since so large a proportion of the children in H.I.P. families in this situation were not eligible at the time of the survey for routine care by pediatricians (Table VII–4).

For all families with children under four years of age the percentage of children with pediatric care ranged, in the New York City sample, from 41.8 percent of those with heads in the lowest education class to 54.3 for families headed by persons with over 12 years of schooling. In the H.I.P. sample the same ascending scale was found, but was on a much higher level, i.e., from 67.3 percent for families headed by a person with less than nine years of schooling, to 77.6 percent for families with heads having over 12 years of schooling.

The number of families with the youngest child under one year in each education class in the two sub-samples was perhaps too small to be wholly definitive. It is true, however, that these families in the general population sub-sample showed a considerably higher rate for families in the highest education class. As has been said

Table VII–4. Families with youngest child under four years, H.I.P. and New York City sub-samples, by age of youngest child, education of head of family, and pediatric care

YEARS OF SCHOOLING COMPLETED BY HEAD OF FAMILY AND AGE OF YOUNGEST CHILD	H.I.P. SUB-SAMPLE			NEW YORK CITY SUB-SAMPLE		
	Total	*With pediatric care*		*Total*	*With pediatric care*	
		Number	Percent		Number	Percent
Total	*442*	*318*[1]	71.9	*711*	*314*[2]	44.2
Less than 9	55	37	67.3	153	64	41.8
9 to 12	221	152	68.8	367	148	40.3
More than 12	165	128	77.6	175	95	54.3
Not reported	1	1	[3]	16	7	[3]
Youngest child under 1 year	*117*	*105*	89.8	*237*	*119*	50.2
Less than 9	9	8	[3]	53	25	47.2
9 to 12	49	44	[3]	120	56	46.7
More than 12	58	52	89.6	57	34	59.5
Not reported	1	1	[3]	7	4	[3]
Youngest child 1 to 3 years	*325*	*213*	65.5	*474*	*195*	41.1
Less than 9	46	29	[3]	100	39	39.0
9 to 12	172	108	62.8	247	92	37.2
More than 12	107	76	71.0	118	61	51.7
Not reported	—	—	—	9	3	[3]

[1] 96 families reported no pediatric care; 28 others, pediatric care unknown.
[2] 340 families reported no pediatric care; 57 others, pediatric care unknown.
[3] Percentage not calculated, base less than 50.

earlier (Table VII–3), in the general population about 50 percent of these families had pediatric service, while in the H.I.P. the percentage rose to about 90 percent. In the general population there was a differential of about 12 percentage points between the lowest and the highest educational group, in favor of the latter. In the H.I.P. group there was no appreciable difference among the proportions with pediatric care in the three education classes.

For the families with the youngest child from one to three years of age in the New York City sample, a third more families in the highest education group had pediatric care than in the two other education groups, while among the H.I.P. families there was a differential of considerably less magnitude. All education groups in H.I.P. with children aged one to three years outranked the corresponding general population group by 19.3 to 25.6 percentage points.

Borough Differences in Use of Pediatric Care

As has been said, the pediatric policies of the medical groups have from the beginning shown marked differences. These were found to follow borough lines. In the Bronx, Queens, and Richmond the medical groups minimized the use of pediatricians for routine care: 77.0, 96.0, and 100.0 percent, respectively, of their child enrollees on March 1, 1951, did not have routine pediatric care beyond the first year of life. In Brooklyn, 73.8 percent of the children in H.I.P. had such care up to age 11 or 12 years and the rest up to school age. In Manhattan, the medical groups spread over the whole gamut of policy: 36 percent of the child enrollees (i.e., those under 15 years of age) were in medical groups with the maximum age set at 12 months; 41 percent were in groups that set the maximum age at puberty; while the remaining 23 percent were in groups which fixed the maximum age at some point between 24 months and 7 years. Since medical groups were entirely free to advance standards over those set by the Medical Control Board, the central administration of H.I.P. was content to fix the age below which every child should have pediatric services and was pleased to have the medical groups experiment with fixing the age limit at higher levels. It was thought that since medical group policies followed borough lines, they reflected the medical mores within each borough. It was also thought that if the subscribers were anxious to have routine specialist care for their children, they would choose medical groups with policies that they favored, and competition would probably tend toward intraborough uniformity. But this was supposition; there were no data on the proportions in each borough of families with young children, headed by persons of the several different levels of income and education, who were actually using pediatric services. It was hoped that the Household Survey would shed some light on these questions.

At this point it should be made clear that the research design of the Household Survey was not set up specifically to insure reliable borough data from the New York City sample. However, it is also true that in drawing the sample, geographical factors were taken into account along with many other criteria of selection, so that there are some borough data which may be used. The H.I.P. sample was drawn in such a way as to get representative borough samples of the H.I.P. population. Under these circumstances it seemed advisable to look into the possibilities of borough distributions as related to some of the aspects of this matter of pediatric care. The principal question to be asked is whether there is any evidence in the New York City sub-sample of differing mores of pediatric care in the several boroughs among families in the same educational and economic groups, or whether borough differences arise from the differing proportions of families in the several economic levels who live in the several boroughs.

In examining the data from the New York City sub-sample, the first step is to see how characteristic it is for borough distribution itself. Accordingly, the sub-sample's borough distribution has been aligned with related data available from the 1950 United States Census and the New York City Department of Health. The percentage distribution by boroughs of private households and total population in them in 1950 and of 1951

Table VII–5. Percentage distributions of selected demographic data, by borough

SELECTED DEMOGRAPHIC ITEMS	NEW YORK CITY	BRONX	BROOKLYN	MANHATTAN	QUEENS	RICHMOND
Total private households, 1950 (2,359,981)	100.0	18.0	33.7	26.5	19.6	2.2
Total population in private households, 1950 (7,553,980)	100.0	18.8	35.4	23.2	20.2	2.4
Average persons per household, 1950	3.12	3.34	4.14	2.80	3.30	3.52
Live births to residents in 1951	100.0	16.9	36.1	23.4	20.8	2.8
Live births per 100 private households	6.5	6.0	6.9	5.7	6.9	8.1
New York City sub-sample						
Total families	100.0	18.6	41.2	16.7	20.4	3.1
Families with child under 1 year	100.0	18.6	42.2	17.7	20.7	0.8

resident births in New York City are set forth in Table VII–5, together with the distribution of the families in the sub-sample for New York City. Distributions are shown for both families in the sub-sample (all with children under six years) and those with a child or children under one year.

From these figures it would seem that the sub-sample contained approximately the number of families that would be expected for the boroughs of Bronx and Queens. The apparent overweighting of Brooklyn families and the underweighting of Manhattan families grow out of the fact that the type of family here considered (i.e., with small children) constituted a higher proportion of the total households in Brooklyn and a lower proportion in Manhattan than appeared in the general population. This is consonant with the data on the average size of the households in the two boroughs and with the percentage of the households with a birth occurring in 1951. So far, it would seem that the way in which the New York City sample was chosen yielded borough sub-samples of approximately the right size. (The figures for the Borough of Richmond are too small to be used for this purpose.) But this does not tell us that each borough sub-sample was necessarily a fair reflection of the distribution of all the families there for characteristics such as education of the head of the household, a distribution that might be a potent factor in determining the proportion who would secure pediatric care for the young children in the family.[5] The solution of this problem lies in the comparison *within each borough* of the samples of the general population and the H.I.P. population, by education group and by provision of pediatric care for their children. From Tables VII–6 and VII–7 it becomes clear that the education groups in the general population and the H.I.P. population in these samples in each borough showed similar patterns of pediatric care; that is, the Bronx and Queens families at all educational levels in the general population, with the exception of the best-educated group in Queens, showed small minorities of families with pediatric care, as did the H.I.P. families. On the other hand, Brooklyn families in the general population showed pediatric care in a majority of families in the two higher educational levels and in almost half of the lowest education group. In the H.I.P. sample of Brooklyn families likewise a large majority in all three education groups claimed such service. In the general population sample for Manhattan, only the best-educated group showed more than half the families with pediatric care, though the proportion with such care in the least-educated group was higher than it was for similar groups in Bronx and Queens. The wealth of medical charitable resources in Manhattan doubtless accounts in large part for this condition. In the H.I.P. sample all of the education groups showed a preponderance of families claiming pediatric care, but, interestingly enough, the relation between the education groups in Manhattan was different from their relation in the other boroughs.

[5] The only available data on education from the 1950 United States Census that might be used in this connection relate to the education of persons aged 25 and over in the several borough populations and come from the 20 percent sample. Since the older persons with comparatively little formal education are probably not a uniform proportion of the adult population in each borough, this material does not help in judging whether the proportion of the H.I.P. parents of young children in given education groups are patterned in a way characteristic of the general population of their borough of residence.

Table VII–6. Percentage distribution of families in New York City sub-sample, by education of head, pediatric care, and borough

YEARS OF SCHOOLING COMPLETED BY HEAD OF FAMILY AND PEDIATRIC CARE	TOTAL NEW YORK CITY SUB-SAMPLE	BRONX		BROOKLYN		MANHATTAN		QUEENS	
		Number	Percent	Number	Percent	Number	Percent	Number	Percent
Total	*913*[1]	*175*	100.0	*388*	100.0	*158*	100.0	*192*	100.0
With pediatric care	392	49	28.0	196	50.5	77	48.7	70	36.5
No pediatric care or not reported	521	126	72.0	192	49.5	81	51.3	122	63.5
Less than 9	*212*	*42*	[2]	*91*	100.0	*50*	100.0	*29*	[2]
With pediatric care	84	13	[2]	41	45.1	22	44.0	8	[2]
No pediatric care or not reported	128	29	[2]	50	54.9	28	56.0	21	[2]
9 to 12	*470*	*99*	100.0	*204*	100.0	*60*	100.0	*107*	100.0
With pediatric care	188	26	26.3	107	52.5	21	35.0	34	31.8
No pediatric care or not reported	282	73	73.7	97	47.5	39	65.0	73	68.2
More than 12	*210*	*32*	[2]	*81*	100.0	*41*	[2]	*56*	100.0
With pediatric care	112	9	[2]	43	53.1	32	[2]	28	50.0
No pediatric care or not reported	98	23	[2]	38	46.9	9	[2]	28	50.0
Not reported	*21*	*2*	[2]	*12*	[2]	*7*	[2]	—	—
With pediatric care	8	1	[2]	5	[2]	2	[2]	—	—
No pediatric care or not reported	13	1	[2]	7	[2]	5	[2]	—	—

[1] Omits the 29 families in Richmond.
[2] Percentage not calculated, base less than 50.

In Manhattan the patterns for the general population and for H.I.P., though at a different level, were quite similar. These data would seem to indicate fairly conclusively that the H.I.P. medical groups in the several boroughs have adopted pediatric policies that follow parochial customs in the use of family physicians and pediatricians for children's medical care and health supervision.

Use of Non-H.I.P. Children's Doctors by H.I.P. Families

In the face of the varying pediatric policies of the medical groups and of all the circumstances surrounding the retaining of pediatricians by families throughout the greater city, the data on the use of outside pediatricians by H.I.P. subscribers doubtless reflect many conditions; but precisely

Table VII–7. Percentage distribution of families in H.I.P. sub-sample, by education of head, pediatric care, and borough

YEARS OF SCHOOLING COMPLETED BY HEAD OF FAMILY AND PEDIATRIC CARE	TOTAL H.I.P. SUB-SAMPLE	BRONX		BROOKLYN		MANHATTAN		QUEENS	
		Number	Percent	Number	Percent	Number	Percent	Number	Percent
Total	*598*[1]	*119*	100.0	*229*	100.0	*74*	100.0	*176*	100.0
With pediatric care	379	60	50.4	193	84.3	61	82.4	65	36.9
No pediatric care or not reported	219	59	49.6	36	15.7	13	17.6	111	63.1
Less than 9	*99*	*16*	[2]	*41*	[2]	*12*	[2]	*30*	[2]
With pediatric care	55	5	[2]	32	[2]	11	[2]	7	[2]
No pediatric care or not reported	44	11	[2]	9	[2]	1	[2]	23	[2]
9 to 12	*284*	*54*	100.0	*116*	100.0	*34*	[2]	*80*	100.0
With pediatric care	171	25	46.3	99	85.3	24	[2]	23	28.7
No pediatric care or not reported	113	29	53.7	17	14.7	10	[2]	57	71.3
More than 12	*212*	*47*	[2]	*71*	100.0	*28*	[2]	*66*	100.0
With pediatric care	152	29	[2]	62	87.3	26	[2]	35	53.0
No pediatric care or not reported	60	18	[2]	9	12.7	2	[2]	31	47.0
Not reported	*3*	*2*	[2]	*1*	[2]	—	—	—	—
With pediatric care	1	1	[2]	—	—	—	—	—	—
No pediatric care or not reported	2	1	[2]	1	[2]	—	—	—	—

[1] Omits the 24 families in Richmond.
[2] Percentage not calculated; base less than 50.

what they are cannot be deciphered from the survey returns. The bare facts of the H.I.P. sample, as related earlier, show 394 of the 622 families reported as having a special doctor for their children; of the 394 with such care, 63 gave the name of a non-H.I.P. physician and 5 either could not give the name of the physician or gave the name of one who could not be positively identified as a pediatrician on the staff of the H.I.P. medical group. These 68 families approximate 17.3 percent of the families who claimed pediatric care and 11 percent of the total families in the sample.

In examining the families who claimed outside pediatric care it is in order to see how they compared with the families using H.I.P. physicians, in respect of both the age of the youngest child and the recency of contact with the doctor. The figures on these questions are displayed in Tables VII–8 and VII–9.

Table VII–8. Families in H.I.P. sub-sample, by age of youngest child and pediatric care given by H.I.P. and non-H.I.P. physicians

AGE OF YOUNGEST CHILD	TOTAL FAMILIES	FAMILIES WITH PEDIATRIC CARE				
		Total	*H.I.P. pediatrician*		*Non-H.I.P. doctor*	
			Number	Percent	Number	Percent
Total	*622*	*394*	*326*	82.7	*68*	17.3
Under 1 year	117	105	82	78.0	23	22.0
1 to 3 years	325	213	186	87.3	27	12.7
4 to 6 years	180	76	58	76.3	18	23.7

Of the 68 families with outside pediatricians, 23 were families with a baby under a year, 27 with the youngest child one to three years old, and 18 with the youngest child from four to six years old. Of the total families with pediatric care, those with outside doctors constituted 22 percent of those with babies under one year, all of whom were entitled to routine care by H.I.P. pediatricians; 12.7 percent of those with the youngest child one to three years old; and 23.7 percent of those with the youngest child four to six years old. In these latter two age classes some may not have been eligible for H.I.P. pediatric care by reason of the varying age limits set by medical groups. While the survey data throw no further light on the use of outside physicians by these 68 families, it is known that some families have had medical connections and privileges, public and voluntary, which they do not sever when they become subscribers to H.I.P. We have also seen in the chapter on insurance that some families were seemingly unaware of their H.I.P. membership and may, for that reason, have continued to utilize other resources for the care of their children.

Recency of Contact with H.I.P. and Non-H.I.P. Pediatricians

The recency of the contact of H.I.P. families with H.I.P. and non-H.I.P. pediatricians is shown in Table VII–9.

Table VII–9. Families in H.I.P. sub-sample with pediatric care, by use of H.I.P. and non-H.I.P. physicians and recency of contact

DATE OF LAST CONTACT	TOTAL	FAMILIES WITH PEDIATRIC CARE			
		H.I.P. pediatrician		*Non-H.I.P. pediatrician*	
		Number	Percent	Number	Percent
Total	*394*	*326*	100.0	*68*	100.0
1952	296	254	77.9	42	61.8
1951	68	50	15.4	18	26.5
Before 1951	8	5	1.5	3	4.4
Not reported	22	17	5.2	5	7.3

From this it appears that about 78 percent of the families with H.I.P. pediatricians had been in touch with them during 1952, while about 62 percent of those with outside pediatricians had seen them in the same period.

Use of Non-H.I.P. Children's Doctors, by Education of Family Head

A final question arises as to these 68 families: how do they spread over the three education groups? Table VII–10 presents the available data.

While a smaller proportion of families in the lowest education group used non-H.I.P. physicians, the differences were small among the three education groups and the size of the sample precludes the detection of significant differences on this question.

Summary

1. The practice of pediatrics in New York City is in a stage of evolution that considerably

Table VII–10. Families in H.I.P. sub-sample, by education of head, by pediatric care, and use of H.I.P. and non-H.I.P. pediatricians

YEARS OF SCHOOLING COMPLETED BY HEAD OF FAMILY	TOTAL FAMILIES	FAMILIES WITH PEDIATRIC CARE				
		Total	*H.I.P. pediatrician*		*Non-H.I.P. pediatrician*	
			Number	Percent	Number	Percent
Total	*622*	*394*	*326*	82.7	*68*	17.3
Less than 9	102	56	49	87.5	7	12.5
9 to 12	303	184	151	82.1	33	17.9
More than 12	214	153	126	82.3	27	17.7
Not reported	3	1	—	—	1	[1]

[1] Percentage not computed.

complicates comparison of the extent of pediatric care in H.I.P. families and in families of similar circumstances in the general population. These complications arise in large part from the varying attitudes of the physicians and the parents in the different boroughs toward pediatric care and the length of time that a child should receive routine medical care from a pediatrician as distinguished from care by a general physician, and from the reflection of those attitudes in the policies of the H.I.P. medical groups.

2. When the two samples are standardized for family types, the proportion of families with a child or children under the age of six years in receipt of care by a "special doctor" is found to be 42.4 percent of the 942 families in the general population and 63.3 percent of the 622 H.I.P. families.

3. When the comparison is confined to families with the youngest child under one year of age, the rates are found to approximate 50 percent in the general population and 90 percent in the H.I.P. group. Thus the rate for the H.I.P. families was 80 percent higher than is the rate for the general population.

4. In both populations the rates declined as the age of the youngest child in the family advanced. For families whose youngest child was between four and six years, the rate was almost 37 percent for the general population and a little over 42 percent for the H.I.P. families.

5. When the families with children under four years are classified by education of the head of the family, the proportion with pediatric care is seen to ascend as education advances from 41.8 to 54.3 percent in the New York City group, and in the H.I.P. families from 67.3 to 77.6 percent. Among families with a baby under one year in the general population there was a differential of 12.3 percentage points between the education classes, but approximately the rate given above (i.e., 90 percent) obtained for all education groups among the H.I.P. families.

6. Although the subdivision into boroughs of the families in the two samples results in fairly small figures, these give indication of being characteristic of their respective boroughs in several particulars.

7. In the Brooklyn sample for the general population, the use of pediatricians in all education groups outranked the corresponding rates in the other boroughs, with the possible exception of the highest education group in Manhattan; 50.5 percent of all families in Brooklyn, 48.7 percent in Manhattan, 36.5 percent in Queens, and 28.0 percent in the Bronx reported having pediatric care.

8. Of the 394 H.I.P. families with pediatric care, 68, or 17.3 percent, reported the use of outside physicians.

9. The use of outside physicians was as prevalent among families with a baby under a year as for families with the youngest child four to six years of age. The smallest proportion in the use of outside physicians was found among the large group of families with the youngest child aged one to three years.

10. In recency of contact with pediatricians, significantly more families with an H.I.P. pediatrician than with an outside physician had seen him in 1952.

11. While among the H.I.P. families having pediatric care those headed by persons with the least education showed the smallest use of outside physicians for their children, the differences were not sufficient to establish a clear relationship between the use of outside pediatricians and the education of the head of the family.

CHAPTER VIII

Persons with Medical Conditions

THE preceding chapters of this study have been concerned with broad aspects of medical care and have only incidentally referred to the data on medical conditions found among the persons in the two samples. In this section of the study (Chapters VIII–XI), persons with medical conditions, and those conditions themselves, together with the related medical care, including hospitalization, are the foci of interest. General measures of morbidity are presented in this chapter, medical care for these conditions in the next, specific morbid conditions and their medical care in Chapter X, and hospitalization in Chapter XI.

Medical Condition and Frequency Defined

"In the sample covered by this study, one person in four was reported to have had a medical condition on the day preceding the interview." Statements of this sort, describing the level of health in the community, form one of the objectives of this study and are the subject matter of the present chapter. However, if these statements are to convey any meaning, it is necessary to have an understanding of the basic term "medical condition."

"Sickness" is a term that may be, and has been, defined in many ways, differing in characteristics such as severity; that is, along the gradient from perfect health to extreme morbidity and death. Definitions also vary according to the qualifications of the person who is deciding whether sickness is present or not; for example, does the subject believe he is sick, or does a doctor make the decision? Finally, in actual practice, the definition is operationally determined by the manner and diligence with which the information is sought.

In this study the basic concept of sickness is identified by the term "medical condition." For a detailed understanding of this term the reader should consult the glossary (Appendix B), the schedules, particularly items 6, 7, 8, and 9 of Schedule 1 (Appendix A), and the appendices on methodology (particularly Appendices D and H). In general, sickness as defined by medical condition in this survey is (1) broad in its range of severity and diagnosis and includes any condition, except dental conditions, considered as such by the informant; (2) identified by lay informants, the subject or a member of his household; and (3) elicited by a series of cross-checking questions in a single interview situation.

Having identified medical conditions, it is possible to proceed to count and characterize these conditions as they occurred at or during a specified time in the sample population, or it is possible to count and characterize the *people* who had medical conditions within this period. The present chapter is concerned with the latter approach, i.e., with the number and kinds of people who were found to have medical conditions. Detailed data on the number and kinds of medical conditions which these people had are presented in later chapters.

One-Day Prevalence, by Age and Sex

The basic question about the sickness status of each individual in the two samples was whether he had a medical condition on the day preceding the interview. The percentage of persons with a medical condition on that day is an indication of the prevalence of disease in the group at a given point in time. It should be noted that this proportion is based on the number of *persons* with medical conditions, not on the number of medical conditions. We shall refer to this proportion as "the one-day prevalence," or simply "prevalence."

Table VIII–1. Persons with medical conditions on day preceding interview and rate per 100 persons (one-day prevalence), H.I.P. enrollees and New York City sample, by age and sex

AGE	NUMBER OF PERSONS WITH MEDICAL CONDITIONS						RATE PER 100 PERSONS					
	H.I.P.			*N.Y.C.*			*H.I.P.*			*N.Y.C.*		
	Total	Male	Female	Total	Male	Female	Total	Male	Female	Total	Male	Female
All ages	2,086	1,009	1,077	3,631	1,413	2,218	25.9	23.9	28.3	26.8	21.9	31.2
Under 5	125	78	47	234	142	92	15.6	18.0	12.8	16.8	19.4	13.9
5 to 14	224	132	92	349	186	163	15.6	18.0	13.1	16.7	16.8	16.5
15 to 44	869	338	531	1,306	456	850	24.9	20.1	29.4	22.7	17.6	26.8
45 to 64	753	382	371	1,115	388	727	36.2	31.3	43.0	37.6	27.4	47.1
65 and over	104	74	30	517	210	307	53.3	51.7	57.7	57.3	50.7	62.8

The proportion of persons with a medical condition on the day preceding the interview was found to be about 25 percent—26.8 percent in the New York City sample and 25.9 percent in the H.I.P. sample.[1] This prevalence varied greatly according to the age of the individual (see Table VIII–1). Among children under 15 years of age the proportion with a medical condition was around 15 percent, while above that age the prevalence rose rapidly to over 50 percent among people past their sixty-fifth birthday.

This age shift in the one-day prevalence was more marked in females than in males. For example, girls under five years had lower rates than boys, but women over 65 had higher rates than men in the same age group.

In addition, the major increase in prevalence seems to have occurred later in life among males than among females. The first sharp rise in the male rates occurred between the age groups 15 to 44 and 45 to 64, whereas among the females there was a distinct rise between the 5-to-14-year group and the 15-to-44-year group. Thus the most striking difference between male and female prevalence rates occurred in the age group 15 to 44, i.e., in the child-bearing ages for females, where the male rates are about two-thirds of the female rates.

Eight-Week Prevalence, by Age and Sex

In addition to the illness data concerning the day preceding the interview, the schedule also obtained information about the presence of medical conditions during the eight weeks preceding the interview. On the basis of these data it is possible to compute the proportion of persons who had a medical condition at some time during the eight weeks before the interview. This proportion will be referred to as "the eight-week prevalence."

The eight-week prevalence was, of course, larger than the one-day prevalence, being about 40 percent in each sample (38.2 percent in the New York City sample and 41.2 percent in the H.I.P. sample). These rates also varied with age (see Table VIII–2), but did not show the more or less consistent increase with age which was characteristic of the one-day prevalence. Instead the minimum eight-week prevalence rates tended to occur in the age period 15 to 44.

Table VIII–2. Persons with medical conditions during eight-week period, rate per 100 persons (eight-week prevalence), H.I.P. enrollees and New York City sample, by age and sex

AGE	H.I.P. ENROLLEES			NEW YORK CITY SAMPLE		
	Total	Male	Female	Total	Male	Female
All ages	41.2	28.8	43.8	38.2	33.5	42.5
Under 5	48.8	50.9	46.2	41.3	44.7	37.5
5 to 14	40.8	44.1	37.3	39.8	39.8	39.9
15 to 44	36.2	30.1	41.9	31.4	25.2	36.4
45 to 64	45.0	40.6	51.2	43.0	33.1	52.1
65 and over	62.6	62.2	63.5	61.7	55.0	67.3

The sex differences paralleled those noted for the one-day prevalence; that is, the boys had higher rates than girls in early childhood, while in later life the female rates exceeded those for males. Again the largest relative difference between male and female rates was found in the age group 15 to 44 in the H.I.P. sample and in the age group 45 to 64 in the New York City sample.

Turnover Rate

It is not surprising that the eight-week and one-

[1] It will be recalled that this survey was made in March, April, May, and June, with the bulk of the interviews in March and April, when there are seasonal peaks in the prevalence of some conditions.

day prevalence rates show similar findings, since the day before the interview formed a part of the eight weeks before the interview, and the persons with a medical condition on the day before the interview formed about five-eighths of the group reported as having a medical condition at some time during the eight weeks.

Since these two groups overlapped so much, it seemed worth while to examine the difference between them. This difference was made up of those persons who had a medical condition at some time during the eight weeks but did not have a medical condition on the day of the interview. These were a part, but not all, of the individuals in whom a medical condition terminated during the eight weeks. Individuals who terminated one condition but then contracted another which was present on the day before the interview, and those who had multiple conditions one of which terminated while another persisted until the day before the interview, did not contribute to the difference between the eight-week and one-day prevalence. Nevertheless *the magnitude of this difference gives some indication of the frequency with which people pass from the state of having a medical condition to the state of having no medical condition.* We shall therefore examine this difference as an index of the "turnover" of persons with medical conditions.

The turnover rate, i.e., the proportion of persons who had a medical condition during the eight-week period but did not have a medical condition on the day before the interview, was 11.4 percent in the New York City sample and 15.2 percent in the H.I.P. sample. These rates decreased sharply with age, varying from around 25 to 30 percent in children under five to 5 to 10 percent among persons over 65. This age difference is presumably a reflection of the relatively high frequency in childhood of acute short-term illness and the characteristic chronic long-term illness of old age (see Table VIII–3).

Table VIII–3. Persons with medical conditions, turnover rate,[1] H.I.P. enrollees and New York City sample, by age and sex

AGE	H.I.P. ENROLLEES			NEW YORK CITY SAMPLE		
	Total	Male	Female	Total	Male	Female
All ages	15.2	15.0	15.5	11.4	11.6	11.3
Under 5	33.1	33.0	33.3	24.5	25.3	23.5
5 to 14	25.1	26.1	24.1	23.2	23.1	23.3
15 to 44	11.3	10.1	12.5	8.7	7.6	9.6
45 to 64	8.8	9.3	8.1	5.4	5.7	5.1
65 and over	9.2	10.5	5.8	4.4	4.2	4.6

[1] Eight-week prevalence minus one-day prevalence.

The decline in the turnover rates occurred quite abruptly between the age groups 5 to 14 and 15 to 44. There was no striking difference between the sexes in this phenomenon.

The differences in the turnover rates between the two samples for small children and for persons 45 to 64 and males over 65 are fairly marked. This should be borne in mind later when chronic illness indexes are examined.

Index of Chronic Illness, by Age and Sex

If two groups have the same one-day prevalence but differ in their turnover rates, the group with the lower turnover has the higher proportion of chronically ill[2] among those with medical conditions. Similarly, if two groups have the same turnover rates but differ in prevalence, the group with the higher prevalence has the higher proportion of chronically ill persons.

Thus we may construct a rough index of the relative frequency of chronically ill persons by dividing the turnover rate into the one-day prevalence. This "index of chronic illness" is large when prevalence is large and/or turnover is small.

The chronic illness index was found to be relatively small in childhood and to increase continuously after age 15 (Table VIII–4). Girls' indexes were slightly smaller than those for boys, but

Table VIII–4. Persons with medical conditions, index of chronic illness,[1] H.I.P. enrollees and New York City sample, by age and sex

AGE	H.I.P. ENROLLEES			NEW YORK CITY SAMPLE		
	Total	Male	Female	Total	Male	Female
All ages	1.70	1.59	1.82	2.34	1.89	2.77
Under 5	0.47	0.55	0.39	0.69	0.77	0.59
5 to 14	0.62	0.69	0.54	0.72	0.73	0.71
15 to 44	2.20	1.99	2.36	2.61	2.32	2.81
45 to 64	4.12	3.38	5.30	7.01	4.79	9.32
65 and over	5.78	4.93	10.00	12.93	11.97	13.75

[1] One-day prevalence divided by turnover rate.

[2] Note that chronic illness here refers not only to long-term continuing illness but also to illness rapidly recurring in the same individual.

after 15 the female indexes of chronic illness considerably exceeded those for males.

Effect of Possible Underreporting

All of the rates and indexes that we are using may be affected by underreporting of medical conditions. Failure to know of or recognize conditions when they are present will reduce both the one-day and the eight-week prevalence rates. Failure to recall previously known conditions will additionally reduce the eight-week prevalence and the turnover rates.

If there is no recall error, the index of chronic illness will not be affected by the failure to recognize conditions when they are present, since this error reduces both numerator and denominator. The presence of recall error will tend to increase the chronic illness index.

Thus differences between the observed prevalence rates for various groups may represent differences in the occurrence of persons with medical conditions or may represent differences in the recognition of medical conditions when they are present. Differences in observed turnover rates may show differences in the frequency with which persons shift from a status of having a medical condition to a status of having no medical condition or may reflect differences in both recognition and recall of medical conditions. Differences in the index of chronic illness may indicate differences in the frequency of long-term or recurrent disease or may indicate differences in the completeness of recall. It is to be understood that these possible effects of underreporting must be kept in mind in any interpretation of these data.

One-Day Prevalence, Turnover Rate, and Index of Chronic Illness, by Education of Household Head and Age

When the samples were subdivided according to the level of education of the head of the household, the differences among the three education groups were small as compared with the previously noted age and sex differences (see Table VIII–5). There was a general tendency in both the New York City and H.I.P. samples for the turnover rate to increase with increasing education of the household head. Neither the one-day prevalence nor the index of chronic illness showed much consistency in their relationship to education from one sample to another or from age group to age group.

The result of standardizing these data for age are shown in Table VIII–6. In the New York City sample the prevalence rate was stable from one education group to another; the turnover rate in-

Table VIII–5. Persons with medical conditions, one-day prevalence, turnover rate,[1] and index of chronic illness,[2] H.I.P. enrollees and New York City sample, by education of head of household and age

AGE	ONE-DAY PREVALENCE			TURNOVER RATE			INDEX OF CHRONIC ILLNESS		
	Years of schooling completed by head of household			*Years of schooling completed by head of household*			*Years of schooling completed by head of household*		
	Less than 9	9 to 12	More than 12	Less than 9	9 to 12	More than 12	Less than 9	9 to 12	More than 12
					H.I.P. enrollees				
All ages	26.1	23.9	28.6	11.7	16.1	18.6	2.23	1.48	1.54
Under 5	9.7	15.8	18.3	29.8	31.4	37.3	0.32	0.50	0.49
5 to 14	9.6	15.2	21.8	19.8	25.0	31.9	0.49	0.61	0.68
15 to 44	22.6	23.8	28.6	10.1	10.5	13.6	2.24	2.26	2.11
45 to 64	35.3	35.3	39.0	7.8	11.4	8.1	4.55	3.09	4.79
65 and over	51.4	60.9	56.5	9.0	10.9	0.6	5.70	5.60	91.02
					New York City sample				
All ages	28.7	24.8	24.3	9.1	13.1	15.4	3.16	1.90	1.58
Under 5	15.4	17.8	16.4	23.4	23.8	27.3	0.66	0.75	0.60
5 to 14	14.9	17.4	19.1	19.5	25.5	29.1	0.77	0.68	0.66
15 to 44	21.4	23.7	23.3	6.9	9.1	12.3	3.08	2.62	1.90
45 to 64	41.1	33.3	31.6	5.2	5.7	6.1	7.83	5.83	5.17
65 and over	54.8	59.1	63.4	3.4	6.6	5.2	16.05	9.00	12.21

[1] Eight-week prevalence minus one-day prevalence.

[2] One-day prevalence divided by turnover rate.

Table VIII–6. Persons with medical conditions, one-day prevalence, turnover rate,[1] and index of chronic illness,[2] H.I.P. enrollees and New York City sample, by education of head of household, standardized for age

H.I.P. STATUS	ONE-DAY PREVALENCE			TURNOVER RATE			INDEX OF CHRONIC ILLNESS		
	Years of schooling completed by head of household			*Years of schooling completed by head of household*			*Years of schooling completed by head of household*		
	Less than 9	9 to 12	More than 12	Less than 9	9 to 12	More than 12	Less than 9	9 to 12	More than 12
H.I.P. enrollees	23.5	26.1	30.2	13.2	15.4	17.3	1.78	1.69	1.75
New York City sample	26.0	26.0	25.8	10.2	12.5	14.9	2.54	2.08	1.73

[1] Eight-week prevalence minus one-day prevalence.
[2] One-day prevalence divided by turnover rate.

creased with increasing education, and the index of chronic illness decreased with increasing education. In the H.I.P. sample, on the other hand, it was the index of chronic illness that was stable according to education, while both prevalence and turnover increased with education. More light will be thrown on these conditions when the specific illness conditions are examined in a later chapter.

Certain similarities and differences between the findings for the New York City and H.I.P. samples have already been noted. The one-day prevalence rates were quite similar in the two groups, and no consistent differences between the samples were found in the various age, sex, and education groups.

The turnover rate, on the other hand, was quite consistently high in the H.I.P. sample, both for the age and sex groups and for the age and education groups. As a result of this difference and the similarity between the prevalence rates in the two samples, the index of chronic illness was generally lower in the H.I.P. sample than in the New York City sample.

These over-all comparisons between the samples are summarized in Table VIII–7. Whether the data are standardized for age and sex or for education and age, the same basic pattern appears: similarity of the two samples in the proportion of persons with a medical condition on the day preceding the interview, and a higher proportion of the chronically ill in the New York City sample than in the H.I.P. sample.

However, as noted in the preceding section, the relationship of education of the household head to these findings also differed in the two samples. In spite of the over-all similarity of the prevalence rates, the H.I.P. sample showed an increasing prevalence with increasing education, while in the New York City sample education of the household head showed no relationship to prevalence. The index of chronic illness, on the other hand, did not vary greatly with education in the H.I.P. sample but showed a steady decrease as education ascended in the New York City sample. Thus the relatively high index of chronic illness in the New York City sample appears to be mainly a characteristic of the lower education groups.

One-Day Prevalence, by Household Status

The individuals in the study may also be classified according to their status in the household with reference to the household head. The one-day prevalence findings for such a classification are

Table VIII–7. Persons with medical conditions, one-day prevalence, turnover rate,[1] and index of chronic illness,[2] H.I.P. enrollees and New York City sample, standardized rates

CATEGORIES STANDARDIZED	ONE-DAY PREVALENCE		TURNOVER RATE		INDEX OF CHRONIC ILLNESS	
	H.I.P. enrollees	N.Y.C. sample	H.I.P. enrollees	N.Y.C. sample	H.I.P. enrollees	N.Y.C. sample
Standardized for age and sex	26.9	26.2	15.1	11.7	1.78	2.23
Standardized for education of head of household and age	26.0	26.2	15.0	12.2	1.73	2.15

[1] Eight-week prevalence minus one-day prevalence.
[2] One-day prevalence divided by turnover rate.

Table VIII–8. Persons with medical conditions, one-day prevalence, H.I.P. enrollees and New York City sample, by household status and standardized for household status

HOUSEHOLD STATUS	H.I.P. ENROLLEES	NEW YORK CITY SAMPLE
Household head	28.3	31.6
Spouse	36.5	36.0
Child	16.0	16.8
Other	21.9	26.9
Standardized for household status	25.4	27.0

Table VIII–9. Persons with medical conditions, one-day prevalence, H.I.P. enrollees and New York City sample, by labor force status and standardized for labor force status

LABOR FORCE STATUS	H.I.P. ENROLLEES	NEW YORK CITY SAMPLE
In labor force	*27.1*	*23.1*
Working	25.9	22.4
Seeking work	45.1	28.6
Other	56.5	43.1
Not in labor force	*34.6*	*38.7*
Keeping house	36.9	39.9
Going to school	17.3	14.2
Permanently unable to work	90.6	75.8
Other	68.1	54.5
Standardized for labor force status	31.4	29.1

given in Table VIII–8. The differences in the rates for the various categories appear to reflect their age and sex characteristics. Household heads are predominantly adult males. The spouses of household heads are thus, in general, female; and the high rate for spouses is consistent with the high adult female rates noted previously. The children, of course, had the low prevalence rates found in the younger age groups. The comparatively small "other" group, including everything from grandparents to grandchildren of the household head, was too heterogeneous to warrant interpretation.

One-Day Prevalence, by Labor Force Status

The one-day prevalence for groups of individuals classified according to their status in the labor force is given in Table VIII–9. Although this table is restricted to individuals 14 years of age and over, the group identified as going to school was obviously a relatively young group and had low prevalence rates. However, its rates appear to be slightly lower than one might expect on the basis of age alone.

With the exception of the "unable to work" and "other" categories, the highest rates in general were found among the housewives. These rates were of about the same size as those recorded for "spouses" in the preceding section, and were generally consistent with the age and sex characteristics of "housewives."

The lowest prevalence rates, with the exception of those for persons going to school, were found for those classified as working. The rates in this group are in general agreement with the rates for males between the ages of 15 and 65.

Although the differences involved are trivial, it is of some interest to note that for all of the detailed labor force categories except "keeping house," the prevalence rate for the H.I.P. sample exceeded that for New York City. On the other hand, in the household status data presented in the preceding section this picture was reversed. There the New York City rates exceeded those for H.I.P. except for the category of "spouse." This contrast, weak as it is, carries the interesting suggestion that in spite of some superficial similarity in the two sets of categories, role in the household may have implications for illness and medical care quite different from those of role in the labor force.

Persons with Multiple Medical Conditions, Eight-Week Period

Among the individuals for whom at least one medical condition was reported, nearly 30 percent (29.5 percent in the New York City sample and 27.9 percent in the H.I.P. sample) had more than one medical condition during the eight weeks preceding the interview.

With regard to sex and age (see Table VIII–10), this proportion showed a pattern similar to that found for the prevalence of medical conditions on the day preceding the interview: that is, the proportion with multiple conditions increased with age; the age differential was greater in males than in females; boys had higher percentages than girls; and, over 15 years of age, women had higher percentages than men.

Table VIII–10. Percentage of persons with multiple medical conditions, among those with one or more conditions, H.I.P. enrollees and New York City sample, by age and sex

AGE	H.I.P. ENROLLEES			NEW YORK CITY SAMPLE		
	Total	Male	Female	Total	Male	Female
All ages	27.9	24.7	31.2	29.5	23.4	34.0
Under 5	18.5	24.4	10.7	16.5	18.0	14.5
5 to 14	18.8	17.6	20.3	16.9	18.6	15.0
15 to 44	29.2	23.2	33.2	28.3	20.1	33.0
45 to 64	34.6	29.7	40.1	36.7	26.4	42.6
65 and over	35.2	31.5	45.5	50.3	44.5	54.2

There were no consistent differences between the two samples, and when standardized for sex and age the percentages with multiple conditions were practically identical—28.6 for New York City and 28.8 for H.I.P.

The percentage with multiple conditions according to education and age groups is shown in Table VIII–11. There was no association with education that was completely consistent in all age groups. In the H.I.P. sample, however, the general pattern was that of increase in the proportion with multiple conditions as the education of the household head increased. Thus the percentages standardized for age showed no clear trend with education in the New York City data but indicated a consistent rise with education in the H.I.P. sample. The over-all percentages were very similar for the two samples, but the percentage with multiple conditions in the lowest education group

Table VIII–11. Percentage of persons with multiple medical conditions, among those with one or more conditions, H.I.P. enrollees and New York City sample, by education of head of household and age

AGE	H.I.P. ENROLLEES			NEW YORK CITY SAMPLE		
	Years of schooling completed by head of household			*Years of schooling completed by head of household*		
	Less than 9	9 to 12	More than 12	Less than 9	9 to 12	More than 12
All ages	27.8	26.0	30.5	31.5	28.0	25.5
Under 5	12.2	17.8	21.5	17.2	17.6	13.6
5 to 14	18.5	15.9	22.2	13.5	18.8	18.8
15 to 44	22.3	30.1	33.2	26.4	29.9	28.1
45 to 64	36.8	29.3	36.8	37.0	35.4	27.5
65 and over	23.9	48.5	62.5	51.5	49.2	52.1
Standardized for age	24.3	27.4	33.1	27.8	29.5	26.5

was lower in the H.I.P. sample than in the New York City sample, while the figure for H.I.P. exceeded that for New York City in the highest education group.

Degree of Disability, Eight-Week Period, by Age, Sex, and Education of Household Head

Among those with medical conditions during the eight-week period, over one-third were known to have been disabled in bed either at home or in the hospital. Roughly another third were known to have had no disability. However, in about 20 percent of the H.I.P. cases and 25 percent of the New York City cases either the fact of disability or the degree of disability was not reported. Consequently it is difficult to reach firm conclusions about the relative degree of disability in the various age-sex groups and other categories. In most instances, it was the fact of disability that was "not reported."

The proportion of persons with medical conditions for whom the fact of disability was unknown increased from less than 5 percent in children under 15 to about 50 percent in persons over 65 (see Table VIII–12). Among adults over 15 the proportion of unknowns was consistently higher in the New York City sample than in the H.I.P. sample.

If the cases in which the fact of disability is unknown are assumed to be cases of "no disability," the proportion of disabling medical conditions is high in children (about 75 percent) and decreases to 30 or 40 percent in the adult age groups.

If, on the other hand, the cases in which the fact of disability is unknown are assumed to contain the same proportion of disabled as the "known" cases, the proportion of disabling medical conditions is lowest (about 50 percent) in the middle age group (15 to 44 years) and rises to about 60 percent in the oldest age group and to over 75 percent in the youngest age group.

Or, if it is assumed that at least the fact of hospitalization is unlikely to be unknown, and consequently the observed proportion of hospitalized individuals is correct, we may say that the pro-

Table VIII–12. Percentage of persons with medical conditions, H.I.P. enrollees and New York City sample, eight-week period, by degree of disability, age, and sex

AGE AND SEX	H.I.P. ENROLLEES Degree of disability[1] 1	2	3	4	5	6	NEW YORK CITY SAMPLE Degree of disability[1] 1	2	3	4	5	6
All ages	3.3	33.3	9.3	2.6	33.8	17.7	4.1	31.3	7.5	2.1	31.2	23.8
Male	3.2	33.9	9.9	2.3	34.0	16.7	3.4	33.3	8.8	1.5	30.8	22.2
Female	3.5	32.6	8.7	2.9	33.6	18.7	4.6	29.8	6.6	2.5	31.5	25.0
Under 5	2.6	48.7	21.3	2.1	22.1	3.3	4.7	52.7	18.1	1.4	19.5	3.7
Male	4.1	49.3	22.2	3.2	17.2	4.1	3.1	54.4	19.9	1.2	17.7	3.7
Female	0.6	47.9	20.1	0.6	28.4	2.4	6.9	50.4	15.7	1.6	21.8	3.6
5 to 14	1.3	59.1	8.7	4.1	21.7	5.0	2.7	61.0	10.0	1.8	19.9	4.6
Male	1.2	57.6	8.7	3.1	25.1	4.3	2.9	57.0	11.6	1.6	21.0	5.8
Female	1.5	60.9	8.8	5.4	17.6	5.7	2.5	65.4	8.1	2.0	18.6	3.3
15 to 44	3.6	25.1	8.6	2.2	45.0	15.4	5.5	24.4	6.5	1.5	43.3	18.7
Male	2.0	27.6	8.7	1.0	47.6	13.2	3.5	24.0	6.4	—	46.2	19.9
Female	4.8	23.5	8.6	3.0	43.2	16.9	6.7	24.6	6.6	2.4	41.6	18.0
45 to 64	4.2	23.7	5.9	1.8	32.8	31.6	3.0	18.1	4.2	2.0	31.7	41.0
Male	4.9	21.5	6.9	1.8	34.8	30.2	3.2	17.1	5.1	1.9	32.6	40.1
Female	3.4	26.3	4.8	1.8	30.6	33.1	2.9	18.8	3.6	2.0	31.2	41.5
65 and over	4.9	16.4	7.4	6.6	22.1	42.6	3.8	19.6	4.1	4.5	18.5	49.6
Male	5.6	16.9	9.0	6.7	25.8	36.0	5.7	20.2	3.1	4.4	18.0	48.7
Female	3.0	15.2	3.0	6.1	12.1	60.6	2.4	19.1	4.9	4.6	18.8	50.2

[1] Degree of disability: 1—Hospitalized; 2—Disabled in bed, no hospital; 3—Disabled, no bed or hospital; 4—Disabled, degree unknown; 5—Not disabled; 6—Unknown if disabled

Table VIII–13. Percentage of persons with medical conditions, H.I.P. enrollees and New York City sample, eight-week period, by degree of disability, education of head of household, and age

AGE AND YEARS OF SCHOOLING COMPLETED BY HEAD OF HOUSEHOLD	H.I.P. ENROLLEES Degree of disability[1] 1	2	3	4	5	6	NEW YORK CITY SAMPLE Degree of disability[1] 1	2	3	4	5	6
All ages												
Less than 9	3.2	28.8	8.2	2.2	31.7	25.9	3.5	28.4	6.0	2.6	29.9	29.5
9 to 12	3.8	34.2	10.9	2.8	33.0	15.3	4.1	34.5	9.2	1.4	31.2	19.6
More than 12	2.8	37.0	8.9	2.3	36.3	12.6	5.6	34.3	6.8	1.1	34.5	17.8
Under 5												
Less than 9	—	44.9	16.3	—	30.6	8.2	4.0	59.6	12.6	4.0	17.9	2.0
9 to 12	1.6	44.5	23.0	3.7	23.6	3.7	4.0	50.7	19.8	0.4	21.6	3.6
More than 12	4.7	55.0	20.8	0.7	17.4	1.3	4.8	53.6	16.8	0.8	18.4	5.6
5 to 14												
Less than 9	0.8	57.1	6.7	4.2	22.7	8.4	2.3	58.1	10.3	2.3	23.3	3.7
9 to 12	1.8	61.2	8.8	4.8	19.4	4.0	2.1	62.4	10.1	1.1	18.0	6.3
More than 12	1.3	58.5	9.8	3.4	22.6	4.3	3.5	64.6	7.6	2.8	18.8	2.8
15 to 44												
Less than 9	3.4	23.6	8.9	3.1	39.0	21.9	5.7	24.8	5.8	3.1	40.6	20.1
9 to 12	4.0	24.8	11.0	1.0	43.3	15.8	5.8	23.5	7.9	0.9	42.4	19.6
More than 12	3.3	26.4	6.2	2.7	50.4	10.9	5.3	26.8	4.7	0.6	49.1	13.5
45 to 64												
Less than 9	4.1	24.8	6.7	1.7	30.3	32.5	1.9	18.4	4.0	2.0	31.0	42.6
9 to 12	6.4	22.3	4.9	2.3	34.3	29.8	3.8	19.4	4.5	2.2	33.8	36.3
More than 12	2.3	25.0	5.9	0.9	35.9	30.0	6.3	13.4	3.5	0.7	32.4	43.7
65 and over												
Less than 9	3.0	13.4	11.9	—	23.9	47.8	4.0	17.0	4.0	3.1	16.4	55.6
9 to 12	3.0	27.2	3.0	15.2	18.2	33.3	1.5	22.3	5.4	6.2	18.5	46.2
More than 12	—	6.7	—	13.3	33.3	46.7	10.2	20.4	2.0	2.0	24.5	40.8

[1] Degree of disability: 1—Hospitalized; 2—Disabled in bed, no hospital; 3—Disabled, no bed or hospital; 4—Disabled, degree unknown; 5—Not disabled; 6—Unknown if disabled

portion of hospitalization among those with medical conditions is lowest in childhood (around 2 or 3 percent) and rises to 4 or 5 percent among adults.

The proportion with unknown disability tended to vary inversely with the years of education of the household head (see Table VIII–13). This tendency was more marked in the H.I.P. data than in the New York City data.

Assuming that unknown disability means no disability, there was a very slight tendency toward a lower proportion with disability in the higher education groups. This tendency would be reduced or removed if one assumed that the unknown were distributed in the same way as the reported cases.

Taking at face value the observed proportions of those who were hospitalized, the H.I.P. sample had lower proportions than the New York City sample in each education and age group up to age 45, after which the lower education groups in the H.I.P. tended to exceed those in the New York City sample.

Summary

In this chapter we have examined the proportion of individuals for whom medical conditions were reported and some of their characteristics. With regard to age and sex, three conceptually independent and basic measures produced similar patterns. These measures were: (1) the proportion of persons with a medical condition on the day preceding the interview—the one-day prevalence; (2) the index of chronic illness—the one-day prevalence divided by the difference between the eight-week prevalence and the one-day prevalence; and (3) the proportion of persons with multiple conditions among those with one or more medical conditions.

For all three of these measures the rates increased with increasing age, the age differential was greater for females than for males, and boys' rates exceeded girls' rates, while women's rates exceeded men's rates.

Beyond these basic and perhaps not very startling relationships with age and sex, the findings are not so clear cut. Although the age and sex relationships were essentially the same in both the New York City and H.I.P. samples, the findings with regard to educational status were in general not the same in the two samples.

In terms of the three basic measures identified above (one-day prevalence, index of chronic illness, and proportion with multiple conditions), the H.I.P. sample was differentiated from the New York City sample by a relative tendency for the measures to increase with increasing education in the H.I.P. sample. The one-day prevalence was stationary with respect to education in the New York City sample, while it increased with education in the H.I.P. sample. The index of chronic illness decreased with education in the New York City sample while remaining stationary in the H.I.P. sample. The proportion with multiple conditions was relatively stationary with respect to education in the New York City sample, but increased with education in the H.I.P. sample.

Thus in H.I.P., as compared with New York City, increasing education appeared to be associated with higher prevalence, more chronic illness, and more multiple conditions. The interpretation of this finding is by no means obvious.

One plausible suggestion is that the participants in H.I.P. have a better opportunity to learn to recognize medical conditions when they are present and that the groups with higher education are better able to take advantage of this opportunity. A similar explanation involves the concept of selection rather than learning, and suggests that persons who enter H.I.P. tend to perceive medical conditions more readily and that this selection operates more strongly in the higher education groups.

Any attempt to proceed beyond mere speculation concerning such hypotheses would require more detailed study of the processes by which individuals enter H.I.P. and of the perception of medical conditions by the various groups after they are enrolled.

Some further light is thrown on these measures of illness in the H.I.P. and New York City samples in a later chapter which describes the kinds of illnesses found in them.

CHAPTER IX

Medical Care for Medical Conditions

Utilization of Medical Care, Eight-Week Period

In addition to information concerning the prevalence of medical conditions, the survey collected data on the type and amount of medical care obtained in connection with conditions reported during the eight-week period.[1] In this chapter we shall focus upon three measures of the medical care used by the various groups in the study: (1) the proportion of those individuals with a medical condition during the eight weeks who were seen by a doctor, (2) the proportion of those seen by a doctor who saw the doctor more than once, and (3) the proportion of those seen by a doctor who received all of their service from private practitioners outside of a hospital. In addition we shall examine the frequency with which H.I.P. enrollees made use of doctors who were not members of H.I.P.

About 60 percent of those individuals who had a medical condition during the eight weeks were also reported to have been seen by a physician (57.1 percent in the New York City sample and 67.4 percent in the H.I.P. sample). An additional 2 to 3 percent had made contact with a doctor by phone only, but nearly 40 percent reported no contact with a doctor.

Among those who had seen a doctor, about 60 percent had seen him for more than one visit (62.4 percent in the New York City sample and 56.5 in the H.I.P. sample). Thus approximately 35 percent of those with a medical condition during the eight weeks not only saw a doctor but also received medical care to the extent of two or more doctor visits.

A high proportion of this medical care was obtained from private practitioners without hospitalization of the patient (see Table IX–1).

Table IX–1. Source of medical care, eight-week period, H.I.P. enrollees and New York City sample

SOURCE OF CARE	PERCENTAGE OF THOSE WHO SAW A DOCTOR	
	H.I.P. enrollees	*New York City sample*
Total who saw a doctor	100.0	100.0
Hospitalized and private physician care established (office and/or home visits in addition)	4.3	5.4
Hospitalized but no private physician care established (no known office and/or home visits)	1.2	2.5
No known hospitalization; private physician care only (no out-patient department care)	87.5	77.6
No known hospitalization; private physician care plus other (out-patient department care plus office and/or home visits)	1.6	2.3
No known hospitalization; no private physician care (out-patient department care only)	2.7	9.8
No known hospitalization; type of physician care unknown	2.8	2.4

Utilization of Medical Care, by Age and Sex

Tables IX–2, IX–3, and IX–4 show the three basic measures of medical care for age and sex groups of the H.I.P. and New York City samples. In general there were no consistent or striking differentials between the sexes in these measures of medical care. However, age differences appeared throughout the data.

The proportion who saw a doctor, among those with a medical condition during the eight weeks, declined with age for both sexes in both the H.I.P. and New York City samples. Children under five years of age were seen most frequently by a physician (76.3 percent in the New York City sample and 84.0 percent in the H.I.P. sample). In the

[1] See Chapter VIII, p. 73 for definition of "medical condition."

Table IX–2. Percentage of persons with medical conditions who saw doctor, eight-week period, H.I.P. enrollees and New York City sample, by age and sex[1]

AGE	H.I.P. ENROLLEES			NEW YORK CITY SAMPLE		
	Total	*Male*	*Female*	*Total*	*Male*	*Female*
All ages	67.4	67.5	67.2	57.1	59.1	55.8
Under 5	84.0	83.8	84.3	76.3	74.5	78.7
5 to 14	74.6	76.4	71.9	67.1	68.8	65.1
15 to 44	64.2	60.8	66.4	54.9	57.5	53.4
45 to 64	61.3	62.3	60.3	49.3	49.1	49.4
65 and over	58.2	62.9	45.4	46.5	46.3	46.6

[1] See Table v–9 for 1951 experience of all persons in the samples.

Table IX–4. Percentage of physician-attended persons who used private physicians, office and/or home visits only, eight-week period, H.I.P. enrollees and New York City sample, by age and sex

AGE	H.I.P. ENROLLEES			NEW YORK CITY SAMPLE		
	Total	*Male*	*Female*	*Total*	*Male*	*Female*
All ages	87.5	86.6	88.4	77.6	78.8	76.7
Under 5	93.9	90.3	98.5	81.7	85.5	77.0
5 to 14	92.9	91.9	94.2	82.7	82.1	83.3
15 to 44	85.2	85.7	84.9	74.9	76.9	73.7
45 to 64	84.7	82.2	87.6	78.2	75.1	80.1
65 and over	81.7	82.1	80.0	73.0	74.3	72.2

young adult group, age 15 to 44, these rates dropped about 20 percentage points to 54.9 percent in New York City and 64.2 percent in H.I.P. After that age the decline was slight. Thus, although the H.I.P. proportions were consistently higher than those for New York City, it appears that in both populations children with medical conditions were decidedly more likely to be seen by a physician than were adults.

Once a person was seen by a physician, it appears that the number of doctor visits varied only slightly with age. The proportion who had more than one doctor visit rose in the older age groups. This increase may well reflect the increase in chronic illness that occurs with advancing age.

However, the rates also suggest that the youngest group of children, those under five, received more doctor visits than the older children. This may reflect the same basic tendency to provide medical care for the very young that was noted in the table above.

The proportion who received their medical care from private physicians without hospitalization showed a fairly consistent tendency to decline slightly with age. Much of this decline was probably associated with the increased hospitalization of older people and thus reflected the difference in the characteristic illnesses of old age and youth. It may also have been associated with the use of out-patient services by older persons with reduced incomes.

Table IX–3. Percentage of physician-attended persons who saw doctor more than once, eight-week period, H.I.P. enrollees and New York City sample, by age and sex[1]

AGE	H.I.P. ENROLLEES			NEW YORK CITY SAMPLE		
	Total	*Male*	*Female*	*Total*	*Male*	*Female*
All ages	56.5	56.2	56.7	62.4	60.0	64.2
Under 5	54.3	58.5	49.2	55.1	52.0	58.9
5 to 14	48.6	46.2	51.8	53.4	54.6	51.9
15 to 44	57.1	56.4	57.5	64.8	62.7	66.2
45 to 64	62.2	61.7	62.9	66.0	61.3	68.8
65 and over	54.5	57.7	42.8	73.5	75.2	72.2

[1] See Table v–9 for 1951 experience of all persons in the samples.

Utilization of Medical Care, by Education of Household Head and Age

The relationship of educational level of the household head to the utilization of medical care is not very striking in these data. Nevertheless, the rates, standardized for age, in Table IX–5 suggest that in households at the lower educational levels there is a smaller probability that a person with

Table IX–5. Percentage of persons with medical conditions who saw doctor, eight-week period, H.I.P. enrollees and New York City sample, by education of head of household and age

AGE	H.I.P. ENROLLEES: *Years of schooling completed by head of household*			NEW YORK CITY SAMPLE: *Years of schooling completed by head of household*		
	Less than 9	9 to 12	More than 12	Less than 9	9 to 12	More than 12
All ages	63.2	69.6	69.1	53.1	59.3	63.4
Under 5	85.7	83.1	84.6	73.6	76.8	77.6
5 to 14	74.8	75.4	74.0	60.5	69.3	74.8
15 to 44	58.8	64.7	67.2	53.9	53.0	61.0
45 to 64	61.7	65.5	58.0	50.1	49.2	44.7
65 and over	53.7	63.6	56.2	41.8	50.8	64.6
Standardized for age	65.1	68.8	67.2	55.4	57.4	61.3

a medical condition will be seen by a physician. This difference between education groups seems to have been greater in the New York City sample than in the group of H.I.P. enrollees.

The association between educational level and the probability of consulting a physician when a medical condition appeared was not found in each specific age group. For both the H.I.P. and New York City samples the young adults, age 15 to 44, showed increasing use of physician with increasing education.

Among children, however, this relationship was found only in the New York City sample. The H.I.P. enrollees appeared to call on a physician for their sick children with equal frequency regardless of their educational level.

For people over age 45, educational level of the household head did not seem to bear a clear relationship to the consulting of a physician, with the possible exception of those over 65 in the New York City sample. Among this group, those in households in which the head had completed less than nine years of schooling showed the lowest rate of physician contact of any of the groups examined—only about 40 percent of those with medical conditions saw a physician during the eight weeks.

Table IX–6 shows the relative frequency of multiple physician contact among those who saw a physician, according to educational level. As seen in the figures standardized for age, multiple

Table IX–6. Percentage of physician-attended persons who saw doctor more than once, eight-week period, H.I.P. enrollees and New York City sample, by education of head of household and age

AGE	H.I.P. ENROLLEES *Years of schooling completed by head of household*			NEW YORK CITY SAMPLE *Years of schooling completed by head of household*		
	Less than 9	9 to 12	More than 12	Less than 9	9 to 12	More than 12
All ages	57.8	54.2	57.8	60.0	63.2	62.1
Under 5	47.6	48.5	63.6	45.1	40.1	58.4
5 to 14	36.8	44.3	58.8	51.9	52.1	58.0
15 to 44	62.6	59.7	51.8	61.6	68.1	60.0
45 to 64	63.2	59.2	63.2	62.5	71.0	62.5
65 and over	52.8	50.0	66.7	70.3	72.3	82.8
Standardized for age	54.9	54.3	58.6	58.0	64.8	61.8

physician contacts also seemed to increase with increasing level of education. However, this relationship was not as great as that observed in connection with the basic question of whether a physician was seen or not.

The variation in the proportion of individuals whose contact was with a private physician apart from hospitalization is shown in Table IX–7. Among the H.I.P. enrollees, educational level did not seem to affect the frequency with which private doctors were called upon. In the New York City sample, however, the lowest educational group showed a consistently lower utilization of private physician's services.

Table IX–7. Percentage of physician-attended persons who used private physicians, office and/or home visits only, eight-week period, H.I.P. enrollees and New York City sample, by education of head of household and age

AGE	H.I.P. ENROLLEES *Years of schooling completed by head of household*			NEW YORK CITY SAMPLE *Years of schooling completed by head of household*		
	Less than 9	9 to 12	More than 12	Less than 9	9 to 12	More than 12
All ages	86.0	87.5	89.3	72.8	80.9	81.7
Under 5	95.2	95.6	91.2	74.0	83.5	88.9
5 to 14	92.5	93.8	92.0	73.2	87.4	90.2
15 to 44	84.1	82.0	89.4	68.6	76.1	80.3
45 to 64	84.2	84.6	85.7	76.9	83.0	73.3
65 and over	83.3	95.2	87.5	69.9	81.8	71.0
Standardized for age	87.3	87.8	89.2	72.3	81.4	81.2

Thus, in general, the data suggest that increasing level of education is associated with an increased probability of calling upon a physician when illness occurs, an increased probability of making repeated visits once a physician is seen, and an increased probability of utilizing the services of a private physician. However, these differences were not found consistently in all age groups, and differences were noted between the H.I.P. and New York City samples. These differences will be discussed in the next section.

Standardized Rates of Utilization

The major features of the difference between H.I.P. enrollees and the New York City sample

Table IX–8. Percentages standardized for age and sex, and for education of head of household and age, H.I.P. enrollees and New York City sample, eight-week period

CATEGORIES STANDARDIZED	PERCENTAGE WHO SAW A PHYSICIAN		PERCENTAGE WITH MORE THAN ONE PHYSICIAN VISIT		PERCENTAGE UTILIZING PRIVATE PHYSICIAN[1]	
	H.I.P. enrollees	*N.Y.C. sample*	*H.I.P. enrollees*	*N.Y.C. sample*	*H.I.P. enrollees*	*N.Y.C. sample*
Standardized for age and sex	66.6	57.3	55.8	61.9	87.7	78.0
Standardized for education of head of household and age	67.0	57.7	55.8	61.7	89.2	81.2

[1] In home or office only.

in their utilization of medical care have been mentioned earlier and are summarized in Table IX–8. If an H.I.P. enrollee had a medical condition during the eight weeks, his probability of seeing a physician exceeded that of a member of the general New York City sample by about 10 percentage points, an excess in rate of contact of 18.4 percent.

Once the H.I.P. enrollee had made contact with a physician, however, he was slightly less likely to make use of more than one physician visit. Thus the members of the New York City sample may have tended to seek the services of a physician only when serious conditions requiring extended treatment were present.

In obtaining his doctor's services the H.I.P. member showed a distinctly higher probability of relying upon office calls or home visits of a private physician. Although this form of service was also the one most frequently encountered in the New York City sample, it fell 10 percentage points below the proportion in the H.I.P. sample and to that extent was replaced by hospital in-patient and out-patient clinic services.

In both the H.I.P. and New York City samples there were some indications that the educational level of the household head bore some relationship to the utilization of medical services. In general those with higher educational status showed an increased tendency to utilize physician services, to utilize them repeatedly, and to call chiefly upon private physicians rather than hospital or clinic services.

The educational differential seemed to be slightly greater in the New York City sample than among H.I.P. enrollees. Moreover, the differences between education groups were not large enough to obscure the fundamental differences between the utilization of medical services in the two samples. Thus the lowest education group of H.I.P. enrollees made contact with a physician as frequently as the highest education group of the New York City sample (see Table IX–5). Furthermore, when they obtained the services of a physician, the lowest education group of H.I.P. enrollees were more likely than the New York City sample members to use a private physician in his office or on home call.

Utilization of H.I.P. Physicians by H.I.P. Enrollees

In the case of the H.I.P. enrollees it is also of interest to determine whether the physician from whom they received service was on the staff of an H.I.P. medical group or not. Among the H.I.P. enrollees who had seen a physician for a medical condition during the eight-week period, approximately 80 percent had obtained their medical

Table IX–9. Percentage of H.I.P. enrollees who saw H.I.P. physicians only, eight-week period, by education of head of household and age

AGE	YEARS OF SCHOOLING COMPLETED BY HEAD OF HOUSEHOLD			
	Total	Less than 9	9 to 12	More than 12
All ages	79.4	73.3	79.3	85.7
Under 5	85.8	85.0	84.3	87.9
5 to 14	87.1	90.9	85.8	87.0
15 to 44	78.8	63.0	77.9	87.4
45 to 64	72.1	69.4	74.2	79.1
65 and over	67.2	71.9	57.1[1]	71.4[1]
Standardized for age	79.4	73.9	78.8	84.7

[1] Based on less than 25 cases.

services exclusively from H.I.P. physicians. Practically all of the remainder had dealt exclusively with non-H.I.P. physicians, since only 1.3 percent had seen both H.I.P. and non-H.I.P. physicians.

Table IX–9 shows the variation in the use of H.I.P. physicians by H.I.P. enrollees according to education of the household head and age. Inspection of the rates standardized for age indicates that in general the higher the educational level, the larger the proportion of enrollees who use H.I.P. physicians exclusively.

When age-specific groups are studied, two additional points of interest may be observed. In the first place, the proportion of enrollees who used H.I.P. doctors exclusively decreased with advancing age of the enrollee. Secondly, the educational status differential in exclusive use of H.I.P. physicians was most apparent among adults.

These facts suggest that the older an individual is, the more likely he is to have established patterns of medical service before enrolling in H.I.P. and the less likely he is to use H.I.P. doctors exclusively. However, it also appears that such patterns may be modified and that the shift to exclusive use of H.I.P. physicians is made more rapidly by groups with higher educational levels.

Summary

The utilization of medical services by individuals who had a medical condition during the eight-week period has been examined in terms of the proportion who saw a physician and, among those, the frequency of contact and type of physician seen.

In terms of these measures it appears that, in general, medical services were used by children more than by adults, by higher education groups more than by lower education groups, and by H.I.P. enrollees more than by the persons in the New York City sample.

CHAPTER X

Morbidity, Disability, and Medical Care Related to Specific Illness Conditions

THE broad picture of the number of illnesses experienced by individuals in the New York City and H.I.P. samples and the amount of medical care received for these illnesses has been presented in preceding chapters. In this chapter an account is given of the specific kinds of illness conditions that were reported, with especial reference to their acute or chronic character.

The determination of the frequency of various kinds of illness conditions was approached with the thought that the findings would be of value from the following points of view:

1. They would supply a description of specific health problems of the New York City population, at least insofar as the sample may be considered representative of the city at large. Such knowledge is essential to the study of the health needs of New York City's population.

2. They would permit an examination of the effect, if any, exerted by a comprehensive prepaid medical care plan such as H.I.P. on the pattern of medical care of the population.

The data from each of these viewpoints are examined in this chapter. As in any such study, a number of decisions had to be made concerning the units to be counted and the methods of coding diagnoses. The detailed description of these decisions and the procedures followed may be found in Chapter II and Appendices C and D. In this chapter the emphasis will be on illness conditions found rather than on persons who were ill. All illness conditions were counted that were present during the eight-week period, whether their onset occurred within the period or prior to the beginning of the period. Also, individuals reporting multiple conditions during the period were counted once under each condition so that the total number of conditions exceeds the number of persons who suffered from them.

Frequency of Specific Illness Conditions

The specific conditions contributing to morbidity in the two samples during the eight-week period are shown in Figure X–1 and Table X–1. As in most other surveys, the respiratory conditions accounted for the greatest proportion of cases. The graph also shows the importance of the diseases of the bones and organs of movement, especially arthritis and rheumatism, and back conditions. Other diagnoses occurring with relatively high frequencies were minor digestive conditions, such as functional disorder of the stomach, circulatory conditions, and accidents. The contrast between these figures on morbidity and those relating to mortality, which show heart disease and cancer as the predominant causes of death, is striking. If the public health movement is concerned with the prevention of ill health as well as the postponement of death, a profile of morbidity data such as that presented here is essential.

A tabular summary (page 88) of the similarities and differences between the H.I.P. and New York City samples reveals some interesting patterns.

The majority of conditions were reported with essentially the same frequency in both samples. This suggests the possibility of being able to estimate the frequency of such conditions in the New York City population from data arising through the operation of the Health Insurance Plan. But the prospect, though tempting, is likely to contain hidden pitfalls. Some of these may be uncovered in more detailed examination of the data, but others are not likely to be revealed in a one-time

Tabular comparison of gross illness rates for specific conditions, H.I.P. and New York City samples

H.I.P. and New York City rates essentially the same	*H.I.P. rate greater than New York City rate*[1]	*New York City rate greater than H.I.P. rate*[1]
Infective and parasitic diseases	Allergies other than asthma	Heart disease
Neoplasms	Hemorrhoids	Hypertension
Asthma	Acute upper respiratory infection	Arteriosclerosis and peripheral vascular disease
Diabetes	Influenza and grippe	Arthritis and rheumatism
Obesity		
Diseases of blood and blood-forming organs		
Mental, psychoneurotic, and personality disorders		
Diseases of nervous system and sense organs		
Varicose veins and phlebitis		
Bronchitis		
Chronic and other upper respiratory infection		
Ulcer of stomach and ulcerative colitis		
Functional disorder of stomach and intestines		
Disorder of genito-urinary tract		
Deliveries		
Diseases of skin and cellular tissue		
Disorders of back and symptoms referable to limbs or back		
Accidental injuries		

[1] These differences are greater than would be expected purely by chance.

survey. It must be remembered in interpreting both the similarities and differences between the two samples that at the time of the survey H.I.P. had been in operation for only four years, a very short time in which to expect any really profound effects on the enrollees' health *per se*. One might hypothesize that an effect, however it might manifest itself, would increase with time. On the other hand, if the similarities revealed in Figure X–1 and Table X–1 continued to be present in subsequent surveys of an H.I.P. population covered for longer periods, and if the data derived from operating records were to be found to be highly correlated with survey materials, one would feel less quixotic about generalizing the H.I.P. experience to New York City's population.

Turning to the differences between the two samples in the gross frequency rates of certain conditions, a quite evident pattern is brought out in the tabular summary. Those conditions for which the New York City rate was higher than the H.I.P. rate were more dramatic and more likely to be incapacitating for long periods of time than those in which the H.I.P. rate was greater than the New York City rate. Since by its very nature the H.I.P. population contained a higher proportion of employed persons, more detailed examination by labor force status is clearly in order. However, we shall first examine the variation in the specific illness rates with sex and age, since these are the usual demographic variables to be considered in presenting a morbidity profile of a population group. Most of the tables and the following text are cast in terms of rates. Tables X–33—X–42 at the end of the chapter give the actual numbers of cases.

Sex

Illness rates by sex are shown in Table X–1. With the exception of a few conditions, the rates in both samples were higher among females than among males, a finding in accord with most reports in the literature. Among the conditions with higher rates in the female were obesity, diseases of the blood, hypertension, circulatory conditions other than heart disease, respiratory conditions, minor digestive disorders, arthritis and rheumatism. Males, on the other hand, showed a higher

Figure X–1. Frequency of certain broad classes and of specific conditions, H.I.P. enrollees and New York City sample, eight-week period

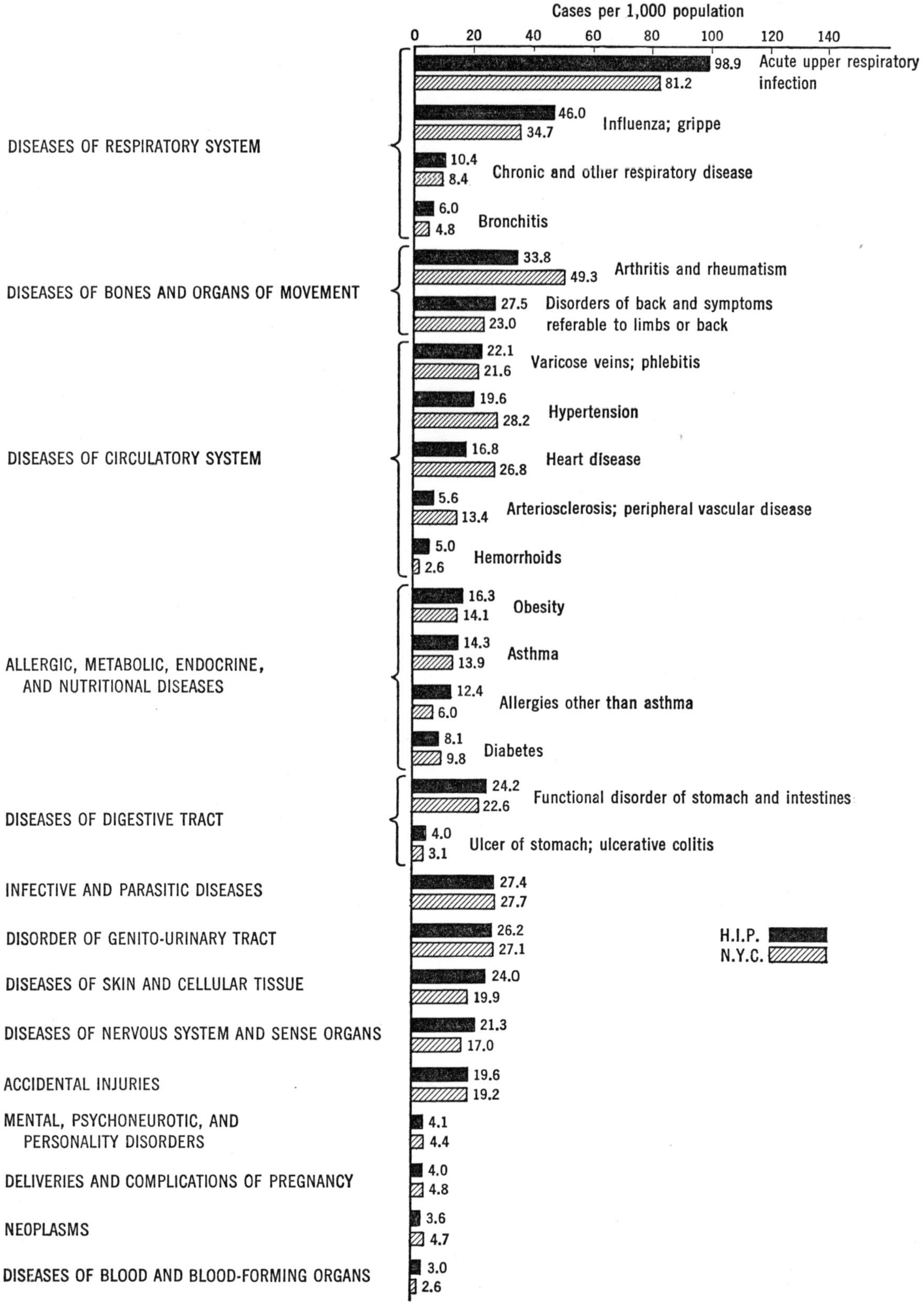

Table X–1. Medical conditions reported (rates per 1,000 persons), H.I.P. enrollees and New York City sample, eight-week period, by diagnosis and sex

DIAGNOSTIC GROUP	H.I.P. ENROLLEES				NEW YORK CITY SAMPLE			
	TOTAL PERSONS WITH CONDITION	Rate per 1,000 persons			TOTAL PERSONS WITH CONDITION	Rate per 1,000 persons		
		Both sexes	Male	Female		Both sexes	Male	Female
Infective and parasitic diseases	*221*	*27.4*	*26.5*	*28.6*	*375*	*27.7*	*31.2*	*24.5*
Tuberculosis	10	1.2	1.4	1.0	28	2.1	2.3	1.8
Other	211	26.2	25.1	27.6	347	25.6	28.8	22.6
Neoplasms	*29*	*3.6*	*3.5*	*3.7*	*64*	*4.7*	*3.2*	*6.0*
Allergic, metabolic, endocrine, and nutritional diseases	*431*	*53.5*	*46.6*	*61.4*	*623*	*45.9*	*36.9*	*54.1*
Asthma	115	14.3	16.3	12.1	189	13.9	16.1	12.0
Other allergies	100	12.4	12.1	12.8	81	6.0	5.9	6.0
Diabetes	65	8.1	7.6	8.6	133	9.8	7.9	11.5
Obesity	131	16.3	9.5	23.9	191	14.1	6.0	21.4
Other	20	2.4	1.2	3.9	29	2.1	0.9	3.2
Diseases of blood and blood-forming organs	*24*	*3.0*	*0.5*	*5.8*	*36*	*2.6*	*0.8*	*4.4*
Mental, psychoneurotic, and personality disorders	*33*	*4.1*	*3.1*	*5.2*	*60*	*4.4*	*4.0*	*4.8*
Diseases of nervous system and sense organs	*172*	*21.3*	*23.4*	*19.1*	*232*	*17.0*	*14.7*	*19.3*
Vascular lesions and inflammatory disorder of C.N.S.	41	5.1	5.4	4.7	88	6.5	5.6	7.3
Diseases of ear	68	8.4	11.6	5.0	79	5.8	5.1	6.5
Diseases of eye	63	7.8	6.4	9.4	65	4.7	4.0	5.4
Diseases of circulatory system	*573*	*71.1*	*61.7*	*81.9*	*1,282*	*94.4*	*67.5*	*119.0*
Heart disease	135	16.8	18.4	15.0	364	26.8	28.8	25.0
Hypertension	158	19.6	17.5	22.0	382	28.2	11.8	43.0
Other	280	34.7	25.8	44.9	536	39.4	26.8	51.0
Diseases of respiratory system	*1,311*	*164.0*	*159.1*	*169.5*	*1,799*	*132.6*	*127.0*	*137.8*
Acute upper respiratory infection	795	98.9	96.0	102.1	1,101	81.2	81.0	81.4
Other	516	65.1	63.1	67.4	698	51.4	46.1	56.4
Diseases of digestive tract	*351*	*41.0*	*40.4*	*45.1*	*506*	*35.7*	*29.0*	*44.8*
Ulcer of stomach and ulcerative colitis	40	4.0	4.2	3.7	42	3.1	4.3	2.0
Gastroenteritis	21	2.6	1.9	3.4	13	1.0	1.1	0.8
Functional disorder of stomach and intestines[1]	194	24.2	21.3	27.3	307	22.6	15.0	29.5
Other	96	10.2	13.0	10.8	144	9.0	8.5	12.5
Disorder of genito-urinary tract	*211*	*26.2*	*4.5*	*50.4*	*367*	*27.1*	*3.2*	*48.6*
Disorder of menstruation and menopause	155	19.2	—	40.7	287	21.2	—	40.4
Other	56	7.0	4.5	9.7	80	5.9	3.2	8.3
Deliveries and complications of pregnancy	*33*	*4.0*	—	*8.6*	*64*	*4.8*	—	*8.9*
Delivery without complication	18	2.2	—	4.7	46	3.4	—	6.5
Other	15	1.8	—	3.9	18	1.4	—	2.4
Diseases of skin and cellular tissue	*193*	*24.0*	*22.9*	*25.2*	*270*	*19.9*	*16.6*	*22.9*
Diseases of bones and organs of movement	*684*	*84.9*	*82.3*	*88.2*	*1,232*	*90.8*	*65.9*	*113.5*
Arthritis and rheumatism	272	33.8	24.6	44.1	669	49.3	29.2	67.6
Disorders of back and symptoms referable to limbs or back	221	27.5	27.9	27.0	312	23.0	15.5	29.8
Other	191	23.8	29.8	17.1	251	18.5	21.3	16.0
Accidental injuries	*158*	*19.6*	*23.9*	*15.0*	*260*	*19.2*	*24.0*	*14.8*
All other	*224*	*27.8*	*20.8*	*35.7*	*316*	*23.3*	*18.3*	*27.8*

[1] Includes gastritis and symptoms referable to gastrointestinal tract.

rate than females for ulcers of the stomach and ulcerative colitis, heart disease, and accidents. Since most of the reported heart disease was not differentiated further, it was not possible to determine whether the higher rate for males applied to all categories of heart disease or—as seems more likely, judging by other data in the literature—was confined to coronary artery disease.

It is probable that for some of the conditions the higher illness rates among females reflected the fact that the informant was usually the housewife. However, other studies[1] have shown that females who were not respondents still had higher sickness rates than males. The extent to which these differences in illness patterns in the two sexes persist when severity of illness is taken into account is examined in the next section.

While in general the relationship of the frequency rates for the various illness conditions in

[1] Edgar Sydenstricker, "Illness Rate Among Males and Females," *Public Health Reports*, U.S. Public Health Service, Vol. 42, No. 30, pp. 1939–1957, July 29, 1927.

the two samples remains unchanged when examined separately for each sex, this is not true for all conditions. For example, the rate for diseases of the ear was not very different in the two samples when taken as a whole. However, when broken down by sex, males were found to have a rate quite a bit higher in the H.I.P. sample (11.6) than in the New York City sample (5.1), whereas the rate for females was practically the same in the two samples.

The most striking change in the relationship of the two samples to each other when the rates are examined by sex is seen in respect of hypertension. Taken as a whole the rate was higher in the New York City sample than in the H.I.P. sample (28.2 as compared with 19.6), but a close look seems to show this higher New York City rate to have obtained only among females. Among males the reported frequency of hypertension for the eight-week period was 17.5 per 1,000 in the H.I.P. sample, but only 11.8 per 1,000 in the New York City sample, while the female rate in the New York City sample was about twice that of the H.I.P. female rate. We shall leave speculation as to the possible reasons for this difference in the patterns of hypertension until later.

Functional disorder of the stomach, with rates essentially the same for both sexes combined, showed a higher rate for males in the H.I.P. sample (21.3) than in the New York City sample (15.0), while the rates for females did not differ greatly. A similar pattern is revealed for disorders of the back when the sexes are considered separately, males in the H.I.P. sample showing a rate of 27.9 per 1,000 as contrasted with 15.5 per 1,000 in the New York City sample.

Although the frequency of gastroenteritis was low in both samples, it seems to have been higher among females of the H.I.P. sample (3.4 per 1,000) than among females of the New York City sample (0.8 per 1,000).

It will be noted that the effect of the differences between male and female rates for the conditions just discussed is to remove these conditions from the "same" column of the tabular arrangement on page 88 and to place them in the column showing conditions with higher rates in H.I.P. for one or the other of the sexes. However, the H.I.P. column is still characterized by relatively less dramatic and disabling conditions than that showing higher rates in the New York City sample. The one exception to this generalization is hypertension in males.

Age and Sex

The variation with age in the illness rates for specific conditions is shown in Table x–2, and the rates for the more frequent conditions are graphed by age and sex in Figure x–2. Three general patterns in the age-specific rates may be distinguished:

1. Conditions which had high rates in childhood and declined with age. Among these were acute respiratory conditions, other diseases of the respiratory system, allergies other than asthma, and diseases of the ear.

2. Conditions which increased in frequency with age. This group included heart disease, hypertension, asthma, functional disorder of the stomach, arthritis and rheumatism, and diseases of the eye.

3. Conditions in which the trend with age was not consistent. Only diseases of the skin fell in this category. While in both samples the rates for skin disease in males declined with age after reaching a peak in childhood, those for females showed little tendency to rise or fall with age. It is quite possible that the disparity in trend of male and female rates was due to the broadness of this diagnostic category. If it were possible to examine the special skin conditions included in this broad group for each of the sexes, the apparent inconsistency might disappear.

The differences between the two samples in the rates for the two sexes remain essentially unaltered when age is also considered, except for heart disease and for functional disorder of the stomach. In the case of heart disease, which appeared to have a generally higher rate in the New York City sample, it is found that while this continued to hold at each age for males, the differences being small but consistent, the age-specific rates for females did not show consistent differences. Here

Table X–2. Medical conditions reported (rates per 1,000 persons), H.I.P. enrollees and New York City sample, eight-week period, by diagnosis and age

DIAGNOSTIC GROUP	H.I.P. ENROLLEES							NEW YORK CITY SAMPLE						
	All ages	Under 5	5 to 14	15 to 44	45 to 64	65 and over	Not reported	All ages	Under 5	5 to 14	15 to 44	45 to 64	65 and over	Not reported
Infective and parasitic diseases	*27.4*	*90.2*	*80.8*	*6.0*	*5.3*	*5.1*	—	*27.7*	*100.6*	*77.3*	*9.4*	*3.1*	*5.5*	*11.1*
Tuberculosis	1.2	—	0.7	1.1	2.4	—	—	2.1	0.7	1.9	3.0	1.7	—	2.2
Other	26.2	90.2	80.1	4.9	2.9	5.1	—	25.6	99.9	75.4	6.4	1.4	5.5	8.9
Neoplasms	*3.6*	*2.5*	*0.7*	*4.0*	*4.8*	*5.1*	*24.4*	*4.7*	*2.9*	*0.5*	*6.2*	*5.7*	*4.4*	*4.4*
Allergic, metabolic, endocrine, and nutritional diseases	*53.5*	*37.6*	*48.8*	*46.4*	*73.5*	*76.8*	*24.4*	*45.7*	*19.3*	*32.5*	*37.7*	*67.8*	*105.1*	*33.3*
Asthma	14.3	11.3	23.0	10.0	15.4	25.6	24.4	13.9	10.0	16.7	10.1	13.2	42.1	11.1
Other allergies	12.4	21.3	16.7	11.2	9.1	5.1	—	6.0	7.9	8.6	6.4	3.7	3.3	2.2
Diabetes	8.1	—	3.5	2.0	22.1	35.9	—	9.8	—	1.0	1.6	23.6	52.0	11.1
Obesity	16.3	—	4.9	20.9	23.5	10.2	—	14.1	0.7	5.2	16.3	25.3	6.6	8.9
Other	2.4	5.0	0.7	2.3	3.4	—	—	2.1	0.7	1.0	3.3	2.0	1.1	—
Diseases of blood and blood-forming organs	*3.0*	—	*2.1*	*4.3*	*2.4*	*5.1*	—	*2.6*	*1.4*	*0.5*	*2.4*	*2.7*	*10.0*	*4.4*
Mental, psychoneurotic, and personality disorders	*4.1*	—	*2.8*	*6.6*	*2.9*	—	—	*4.4*	*0.7*	*3.3*	*6.4*	*4.4*	*2.2*	—
Diseases of nervous system and sense organs	*21.3*	*26.3*	*16.6*	*20.9*	*22.1*	*41.0*	*24.4*	*17.0*	*14.4*	*18.6*	*12.2*	*15.8*	*53.1*	*17.7*
Vascular lesions and inflammatory disorder of C.N.S.	5.1	2.5	1.4	3.7	9.6	20.5	—	6.5	—	4.3	4.0	8.4	28.8	11.1
Diseases of ear	8.4	21.3	7.7	8.0	4.3	10.2	24.4	5.8	12.9	11.5	4.2	2.7	3.3	4.4
Diseases of eye	7.7	2.5	7.0	9.2	8.1	10.3	—	4.7	1.5	2.8	4.0	4.7	21.0	2.2
Diseases of circulatory system	*71.1*	*1.2*	*9.1*	*55.4*	*147.4*	*287.1*	*73.2*	*94.4*	*0.7*	*10.1*	*48.8*	*182.3*	*438.5*	*95.6*
Heart disease	16.8	1.2	7.0	8.9	36.0	92.3	—	26.8	0.7	9.1	14.6	48.3	114.1	31.1
Hypertension	19.6	—	0.7	11.5	48.5	82.0	—	28.2	—	—	9.7	67.5	121.8	35.6
Other	34.7	—	1.4	35.0	62.9	112.8	73.2	39.4	—	1.0	24.5	66.5	202.6	28.9
Diseases of respiratory system	*164.0*	*309.5*	*230.6*	*127.5*	*125.3*	*148.7*	*146.4*	*132.6*	*251.4*	*240.5*	*99.5*	*84.1*	*104.1*	*64.4*
Acute upper respiratory infection	98.9	201.7	151.2	75.1	64.8	87.2	73.2	81.2	181.0	157.5	52.4	51.3	56.5	31.1
Other	65.1	107.8	79.4	52.4	60.4	61.5	73.2	51.4	70.4	83.0	47.1	32.8	47.6	33.3
Diseases of digestive tract	*41.0*	*35.1*	*20.2*	*46.4*	*55.2*	*41.0*	*24.4*	*35.7*	*23.7*	*13.9*	*35.6*	*55.0*	*74.2*	*19.9*
Ulcer of stomach and ulcerative colitis	4.0	—	—	4.3	7.7	—	24.4	3.1	—	0.5	2.4	8.1	1.1	4.4
Gastroenteritis	2.6	13.8	—	1.7	1.9	—	—	1.0	3.6	—	0.9	1.0	—	—
Functional disorder of stomach and intestines[1]	24.2	15.0	18.1	28.9	24.0	25.6	—	22.6	11.5	8.6	21.7	31.7	53.2	13.3
Other	10.2	6.3	2.2	11.5	21.6	15.4	—	9.0	8.6	4.8	10.6	14.2	19.9	2.2
Disorder of genito-urinary tract	*26.2*	*1.2*	*2.1*	*38.1*	*34.1*	*10.2*	*24.4*	*27.1*	—	*2.9*	*35.3*	*46.3*	*14.4*	*17.7*
Disorder of menstruation and menopause	19.2	—	1.4	30.7	21.6	—	24.4	21.2	—	1.9	27.8	39.5	—	13.3
Other	7.0	1.2	0.7	7.4	12.5	10.2	—	5.9	—	1.0	7.5	6.8	14.4	4.4
Deliveries and complications of pregnancy	*4.0*	—	—	*9.5*	—	—	—	*4.8*	—	—	*11.1*	—	—	—
Delivery without complication	2.2	—	—	5.2	—	—	—	3.4	—	—	8.0	—	—	—
Other	1.8	—	—	4.3	—	—	—	1.4	—	—	3.1	—	—	—
Diseases of skin and cellular tissue	*24.0*	*23.8*	*24.4*	*26.6*	*20.2*	*10.2*	*48.8*	*19.9*	*14.4*	*20.5*	*24.5*	*15.2*	*17.7*	*11.1*
Diseases of bones and organs of movement	*84.9*	*20.0*	*14.6*	*82.5*	*148.4*	*251.3*	*122.0*	*90.8*	*11.5*	*20.5*	*73.2*	*156.0*	*280.2*	*82.2*
Arthritis and rheumatism	33.8	—	0.7	23.5	78.8	128.2	97.6	49.3	—	—	28.0	98.6	218.2	42.2
Disorders of back and symptoms referable to limbs or back	27.4	1.2	0.7	34.1	41.8	66.7	—	23.0	—	2.9	27.6	33.1	39.9	28.9
Other	23.7	18.8	13.2	24.9	27.8	56.4	24.4	18.5	11.5	17.6	17.6	24.3	22.1	11.1
Accidental injuries	*19.6*	*22.5*	*27.2*	*17.8*	*15.8*	*15.4*	*72.2*	*19.2*	*19.4*	*19.6*	*18.9*	*18.2*	*21.0*	*22.2*
All other	*27.8*	*35.1*	*22.3*	*26.1*	*30.2*	*46.2*	*24.4*	*23.3*	*30.2*	*14.8*	*18.8*	*25.3*	*43.2*	*46.7*

[1] Includes gastritis and symptoms referable to gastrointestinal tract.

Figure X–2. Frequency of specific conditions, H.I.P. enrollees and New York City sample, eight-week period, by age and sex

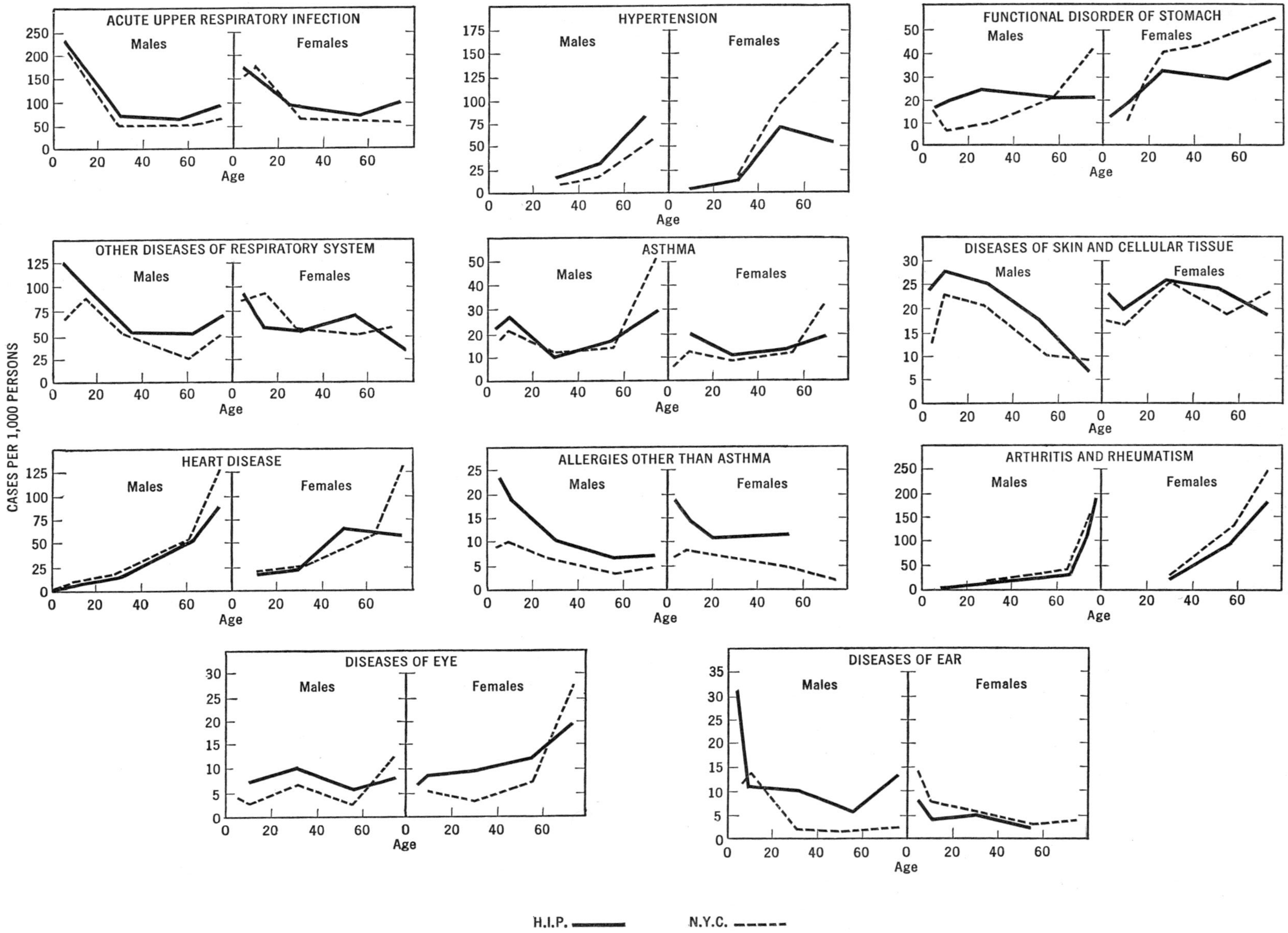

again, as in diseases of the skin, diseases of the heart are a broad category and this apparent difference in the pattern for males and females might disappear if it were possible to make a more detailed examination of this group of diagnostic conditions.

The age-specific rates for functional disorder of the stomach and intestines indicated a higher rate for males in the H.I.P. sample throughout most of the life span, but a higher rate for females in the New York City sample during most of the age span. Again, one may question the relative vagueness of the diagnosis.

Before going on to consider the influence of education and labor force status on the frequency of illness, the impression gained from the foregoing of the relative frequency of various conditions in the two samples is that for a majority of the conditions there was little difference in frequency. Where there were differences, the H.I.P. sample tended to have higher rates for relatively less dramatic and disabling conditions than the New York sample. On the other hand, the New York City sample tended to have somewhat higher rates for the more serious chronic conditions. Exceptions to this general statement have been noted, and this summary will be reviewed again in the light of additional data to be presented.

Education of Household Head

The variation in frequency of the several disease conditions with education of the head of the household is shown in Table x–3 and Figure x–3. Three groups of conditions may be distinguished:

Group 1. Conditions in which the greatest frequency appeared in the highest education class. Among these were acute upper respiratory infections, other respiratory infections, allergies other than asthma, diseases of the skin.

Group 2. Conditions having the highest rate in the lowest education class. These included heart disease, hypertension, asthma, arthritis and rheumatism.

Group 3. Conditions in which the trend with education was not consistent. Functional disorder of the stomach and intestines and diseases of the eye, for example, showed opposite trends in the two samples. In the H.I.P. sample these two conditions increased with education of the head of the household, but in the New York City sample the highest rate for these conditions was found in the lowest education class. By contrast, diseases of the ear, while showing a similar pattern in the two samples, did not show a consistent trend with education.

What is the significance of these patterns? Turning to the first group of conditions, did the better educated really have a greater frequency of these conditions? This is a possibility, but it seems more likely that higher rates among the better educated may have reflected a different conception of illness from that held by those with less schooling, the better-educated groups being inclined to consider as illnesses conditions which either passed unnoticed or were not considered sufficiently noteworthy to be reported by those with relatively little education.[2] It is to be noted that conditions in Group 1 are usually considered by the layman to be less serious than those in Group 2, that these conditions were found to have higher over-all rates in H.I.P. than in New York City, and that, as can be seen in Figure x–3, the greatest difference between the two samples occurred in the most highly educated group.

The second group of conditions, those with the higher rates in the lowest education class, are generally considered by the public as more serious than those in Group 1. Since these are relatively serious conditions, the variation with education seems less likely to be due to differences in recognition of the presence of the condition than is the case for the diseases in Group 1. It may be that there was actually a greater frequency of these conditions in the less-educated class of the population. If so, one would want to examine the influence of other variables such as environmental factors likely to be closely correlated with education.

Or another hypothesis which suggests itself, again concerned with conceptions of illness, is that

[2] E. L. Koos in his study, *The Health of Regionville* (New York, Columbia University Press, 1954), also suggests that conceptual differences with regard to illness exist in different classes of the population.

Table X–3. Medical conditions reported (rates per 1,000 persons), H.I.P. enrollees and New York City sample, eight-week period, by education of head of household

DIAGNOSTIC GROUP	YEARS OF SCHOOLING COMPLETED BY HEAD OF HOUSEHOLD — *H.I.P. enrollees*				*New York City sample*			
	Less than 9	9 to 12	More than 12	Not reported	Less than 9	9 to 12	More than 12	Not reported
Infective and parasitic diseases	*20.8*	*35.7*	*37.3*	*19.2*	*27.7*	*32.2*	*50.2*	*19.4*
Tuberculosis	3.2	0.3	0.4	—	2.4	2.0	1.4	1.4
Other	14.8	32.8	31.6	9.6	20.4	26.6	42.0	12.5
Neoplasms	*2.8*	*2.6*	*5.3*	*9.6*	*4.9*	*3.6*	*6.8*	*5.5*
Allergic, metabolic, endocrine, and nutritional diseases	*56.7*	*43.8*	*62.2*	*62.2*	*52.1*	*39.6*	*37.2*	*66.5*
Asthma	18.8	14.1	11.0	—	16.1	13.6	7.2	18.0
Other allergies	6.4	6.5	28.0	—	4.2	6.5	11.1	1.4
Diabetes	10.4	6.2	6.1	28.7	13.2	6.1	3.4	27.7
Obesity	21.1	13.1	14.0	28.7	17.6	11.0	12.6	12.5
Other	—	3.9	3.1	4.8	1.0	2.4	2.9	6.9
Diseases of blood and blood-forming organs	*2.8*	*3.0*	*3.5*	—	*2.6*	*3.2*	*1.4*	*2.8*
Mental, psychoneurotic, and personality disorders	*3.6*	*5.2*	*3.1*	*4.8*	*5.4*	*3.4*	*3.9*	*5.5*
Diseases of nervous system and sense organs	*21.6*	*21.6*	*21.7*	*14.4*	*17.4*	*17.7*	*14.6*	*18.1*
Vascular lesions and inflammatory disorder of C.N.S.	8.4	3.9	3.6	—	7.5	5.6	4.9	9.7
Diseases of ear	8.4	11.1	5.2	4.8	3.5	8.7	5.8	4.2
Diseases of eye	4.8	6.6	12.9	9.6	6.4	3.4	3.9	4.2
Diseases of circulatory system	*93.7*	*63.0*	*58.3*	*62.2*	*122.9*	*69.6*	*62.3*	*137.3*
Heart disease	24.3	13.8	14.0	—	36.5	18.5	16.9	37.4
Hypertension	25.1	17.1	14.9	43.1	40.5	18.3	17.4	30.5
Other	44.3	32.1	29.4	19.1	45.9	32.8	28.0	69.4
Diseases of respiratory system	*123.7*	*157.4*	*222.5*	*105.2*	*105.0*	*151.9*	*170.3*	*106.9*
Acute upper respiratory infection	74.6	94.8	135.6	47.8	68.4	89.2	105.7	55.5
Other	49.1	62.6	86.9	57.4	36.6	62.7	64.6	51.4
Diseases of digestive tract	*39.6*	*46.5*	*42.2*	*28.8*	*39.5*	*34.8*	*30.9*	*48.6*
Ulcer of stomach and ulcerative colitis	3.2	4.2	4.4	4.8	3.1	3.0	2.4	5.5
Gastroenteritis	1.2	3.0	4.0	—	0.9	0.4	2.4	1.4
Functional disorder of stomach and intestines[1]	20.8	27.2	25.0	9.6	25.1	20.9	15.9	34.7
Other	14.4	12.1	8.8	14.4	10.4	10.5	10.2	7.0
Disorder of genito-urinary tract	*26.0*	*24.0*	*30.2*	*19.2*	*26.5*	*25.7*	*24.5*	*48.5*
Disorder of menstruation and menopause	18.8	15.8	25.0	14.4	22.3	19.9	18.3	29.1
Other	7.2	8.2	5.2	4.8	4.2	5.8	6.2	19.4
Deliveries and complications of pregnancy	*2.0*	*3.9*	*6.7*	*4.8*	*3.3*	*5.5*	*7.7*	*2.8*
Delivery without complication	0.4	3.0	3.1	4.8	1.8	4.7	4.8	2.8
Other	1.6	0.9	3.6	—	1.5	0.8	2.9	—
Diseases of skin and cellular tissue	*16.8*	*21.3*	*35.1*	*28.7*	*17.7*	*21.5*	*23.7*	*15.3*
Diseases of bones and organs of movement	*86.5*	*72.8*	*97.8*	*105.3*	*105.8*	*79.3*	*66.1*	*126.3*
Arthritis and rheumatism	45.8	25.3	28.9	67.0	64.4	37.3	32.4	68.8
Disorders of back and symptoms referable to limbs or back	24.7	27.2	32.5	9.6	23.3	23.1	17.4	36.1
Other	16.0	20.3	36.4	28.7	17.9	18.9	16.4	26.4
Accidental injuries	*21.5*	*21.0*	*17.1*	*4.8*	*14.9*	*23.9*	*17.4*	*25.0*
All other	*20.4*	*32.1*	*31.7*	*14.4*	*22.2*	*22.8*	*25.1*	*30.5*

[1] Includes gastritis and symptoms referable to gastrointestinal tract.

the higher the education the more likely it is that the reported diagnosis will be specific for the disease entity. Thus, it may be that "heart disease" when reported by persons with little education is a far more general term, encompassing a variety of conditions, than when the same term is used by a person with more schooling. Since the term is more embracing in the less-educated groups, the apparent frequency would be found to be higher in that class. Such a hypothesis, of course, cannot be tested with data obtained by household interviewers.

It is also noted that the conditions in Group 2, with the exception of asthma, generally had higher rates among persons in the New York City sample than among H.I.P. enrollees. The question arises whether these differences were simply a reflection of differences in the age and sex composition of

Figure X-3. Frequency of specific conditions, H.I.P. enrollees and New York City sample, eight-week period, by education of head of household

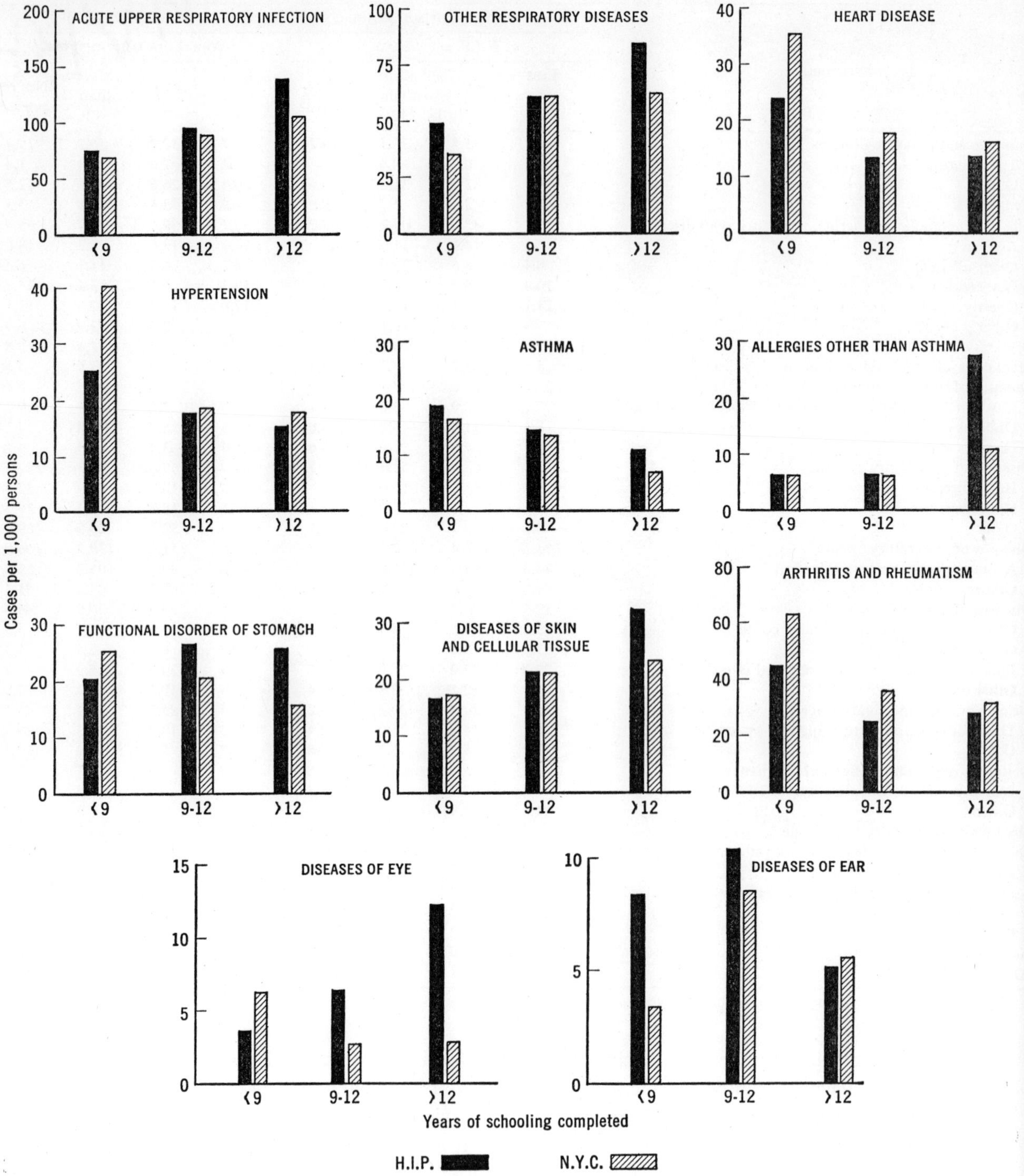

the two samples. It will be recalled that the New York City sample had a higher proportion of older people and a slightly higher proportion of females than the H.I.P. sample. When the influence of age is eliminated by standardizing to the age distribution of the total for the two samples combined, there is no change in the relationship of the education-specific rates for the H.I.P. and New York City samples *in the lowest education group* (education of household head less than nine years) for this group of diseases. Age standardization does, however, eliminate or reduce both the difference between the H.I.P. and New York City samples in the crude rates for heart disease and hypertension in the two higher education groups, and the difference in the crude rates for arthritis and rheumatism in the highest education group. The age-adjusted rate for asthma in the highest education group remains higher in the H.I.P. sample, while that for arthritis and rheumatism in the intermediate education group remains higher in the New York City sample. It seems clear that whatever the reasons for the differences in the rates between the two samples for persons in households whose head completed less than nine years of schooling, these differences are not attributable to differences in age composition. It is these differences *in the group with lowest education of household head* that in effect produced the higher rates in the New York City sample for heart disease, hypertension, and arthritis and rheumatism (Table x–4 and page 88).

Table X–4. Age-adjusted rates per 1,000 persons for conditions in Group 2, by education of head of household

DISEASE CONDITIONS WITH GREATEST FREQUENCY IN LOWEST EDUCATION GROUP	YEARS OF SCHOOLING COMPLETED BY HEAD OF HOUSEHOLD					
	Less than 9		*9 to 12*		*More than 12*	
	H.I.P.	N.Y.C.	H.I.P.	N.Y.C.	H.I.P.	N.Y.C.
Asthma	19.2	16.0	13.8	13.4	10.6	6.5
Heart disease	24.6	36.6	15.4	17.8	15.8	15.1
Hypertension	25.3	40.2	18.0	17.4	15.8	15.4
Arthritis and rheumatism	45.0	65.0	26.2	34.9	29.8	30.0

If there is anything to the hypothesis advanced in the paragraph immediately preceding the last, the persistently higher rate in the New York City sample in the lowest education group[3] may mean that among the H.I.P. enrollees the disease categories tend to be more specific, with the result that the total frequency appears less. While this cannot be determined directly, such a hypothesis would be consistent with a higher rate of medical care for these conditions in the H.I.P. sample, a point which will be examined in the third part of this chapter.

Finally, it will be recalled that the New York City sample had a higher proportion of persons *not* in the labor force than did the H.I.P. sample and that the conditions in Group 2 often result in removal from the labor force, especially in occupations in which education is not a major qualifying factor. The labor force status of persons with the specified conditions will be examined in the next section.

Little can be said about the conditions in Group 3. The dissimilar trends by education groups in the two samples for functional disorder of the stomach and intestines and diseases of the eye, and the lack of any clear trend for diseases of the ear may reflect the relatively non-specific character of these broad classes of diagnoses. More detailed examination of specific conditions within these classes would be required to study the problem of the relation of frequency to educational background.

Labor Force Status

Since it is known that of the persons 14 years of age and over those in the labor force tend to have less illness than those not in the labor force, a comparison of illness rates for persons in the two samples should take cognizance of this difference in the two population groups.

Two kinds of data were examined for this purpose: (1) the prevalence of specific conditions on the day preceding the survey, and (2) the fre-

[3] Standardization of the crude rates for the conditions under discussion for both *age and sex* leaves the rates for heart disease, hypertension, and arthritis and rheumatism higher in the New York City sample, although the size of the difference is in each case decreased. It is not likely, therefore, that the slightly higher proportion of males in the H.I.P. sample could account for the differences remaining in the lowest education group.

quency of diagnostic conditions during the eight-week period.

Prevalence of illness conditions, day preceding interview. These data, presented in Table x–5, refer to persons 14 years of age and over. When this age restriction is placed upon the data, arthritis and rheumatism, circulatory diseases other than heart disease and hypertension, and disorders and symptoms referable to the limbs or back emerge as the conditions with greatest prevalence both for persons in the labor force and those not in the labor force. In the former group these conditions accounted for about 28 percent of all conditions and in the latter about 33 percent. These percentages were about the same in the H.I.P. and New York City samples. Other conditions falling among the first ten in both labor force status groups are hypertension, heart disease, obesity, diseases of the skin, acute upper respiratory infections, and other diseases of the bones and organs of movement.

The rank order comparison tends to minimize

Table X–5. Medical conditions reported (rates per 1,000 persons 14 years of age and over), H.I.P. enrollees and New York City sample, day preceding interview, by labor force status

DIAGNOSTIC GROUP	H.I.P. ENROLLEES			NEW YORK CITY SAMPLE		
	In labor force	*Not in labor force*	*Not reported*	*In labor force*	*Not in labor force*	*Not reported*
Infective and parasitic diseases	*2.4*	*1.4*	*20.0*	*2.3*	*4.3*	—
Tuberculosis	1.6	1.4	—	1.4	3.0	—
Other	0.8	—	—	0.9	1.3	—
Neoplasms	*3.2*	*1.9*	*20.0*	*2.1*	*4.8*	*7.2*
Allergic, metabolic, endocrine, and nutritional diseases	*47.6*	*69.6*	*80.0*	*32.5*	*69.9*	*50.4*
Asthma	10.5	11.3	20.0	9.4	18.4	7.2
Other allergies	8.9	9.4	40.0	4.1	4.8	7.2
Diabetes	9.5	11.3	—	7.3	19.1	14.4
Obesity	16.6	28.3	20.0	10.5	23.6	21.6
Other	2.1	3.3	—	1.2	3.7	—
Diseases of blood and blood-forming organs	*1.3*	*6.1*	—	*1.6*	*4.8*	—
Mental, psychoneurotic, and personality disorders	*5.2*	*3.3*	—	*3.9*	*6.1*	—
Diseases of nervous system and sense organs	*13.1*	*16.5*	*40.0*	*3.7*	*23.0*	*7.2*
Vascular lesions and inflammatory disorder of C.N.S.	3.9	6.6	40.0	1.2	13.7	—
Diseases of ear	4.2	4.2	—	1.0	3.5	7.2
Diseases of eye	5.0	5.7	—	1.5	5.8	—
Diseases of circulatory system	*78.0*	*121.3*	*60.0*	*71.3*	*181.8*	*79.2*
Heart disease	16.3	28.3	20.0	21.6	48.1	—
Hypertension	24.4	29.3	20.0	20.4	55.9	57.6
Other	37.3	63.7	20.0	29.3	77.8	21.6
Diseases of respiratory system	*37.6*	*27.8*	*20.0*	*26.8*	*30.6*	*28.8*
Acute upper respiratory infection	20.5	17.0	20.0	13.5	16.3	7.2
Other	17.1	10.8	—	13.3	14.3	21.6
Diseases of digestive tract	*32.8*	*41.5*	*20.0*	*27.6*	*42.9*	*14.4*
Ulcer of stomach and ulcerative colitis	6.6	6.6	—	4.3	2.8	—
Gastroenteritis	1.3	1.4	—	0.2	0.4	—
Functional disorder of stomach and intestines[1]	16.0	18.4	20.0	16.7	27.8	—
Other	8.9	15.1	—	6.4	11.9	14.4
Disorder of genito-urinary tract	*16.3*	*47.2*	—	*19.2*	*44.4*	*43.2*
Disorder of menstruation and menopause	12.9	38.2	—	16.5	37.1	28.8
Other	3.4	9.0	—	2.7	7.3	14.4
Deliveries and complications of pregnancy	*0.5*	*3.8*	—	*0.2*	*3.1*	—
Delivery without complication	—	—	—	—	1.1	—
Other	0.5	3.8	—	0.2	2.0	—
Diseases of skin and cellular tissue	*18.9*	*20.3*	—	*16.0*	*20.4*	*14.4*
Diseases of bones and organs of movement	*92.2*	*113.3*	*40.0*	*74.6*	*149.1*	*79.2*
Arthritis and rheumatism	38.4	56.2	—	37.3	96.0	43.2
Disorders of back and symptoms referable to limbs or back	28.6	36.8	20.0	20.6	31.6	28.8
Other	25.2	20.3	20.0	16.7	21.5	7.2
Accidental injuries	*10.0*	*7.1*	—	*14.9*	*11.3*	*7.2*
All other	*15.5*	*21.2*	—	*12.6*	*23.8*	*7.2*

[1] Includes gastritis and symptoms referable to gastrointestinal tract.

the diagnostic differences between the two labor force status groups. For example, in the New York City sample the prevalence of arthritis and rheumatism among persons *not* in the labor force (96 per 1,000 persons) was considerably greater than for those *in* the labor force (37.3 per 1,000 persons). A similar picture may be observed for most of the other chronic conditions among the first ten in prevalence. Acute upper respiratory infections, on the other hand, showed relatively little variation with labor force status. These facts serve to emphasize once again the importance of the chronic diseases in the economic and social fabric of the community.

In order to examine the differences between the H.I.P. and New York City samples, the data in Table x–5 are portrayed in slightly different form in Figure x–4. Here the horizontal scale represents the ratio of the New York City prevalence to the H.I.P. prevalence. Bars to the right of the center line indicate a higher rate in the New York City sample than in the H.I.P. sample; those to the left represent the converse situation.

For the first nine conditions shown, the prevalence was quite a bit higher in the New York City sample than in the H.I.P. sample for those *not* in the labor force (black bars). Most of these conditions may be classed as chronic. However, with two exceptions, for those *in* the labor force the rates for this group of conditions were nearly the same in the two samples (i.e., had a ratio of nearly 1.0). The two exceptions were "heart disease" and the category called "other allergic and metabolic diseases." The first of these showed rates which were higher in the New York City sample both in and out of the labor force. "Other allergic and metabolic diseases," on the other hand, showed a much lower rate in the New York City sample than in the H.I.P. sample for persons in the labor force.

The rest of the conditions shown in Figure x–4 all tended to have a higher prevalence in the H.I.P.

Figure X–4. Frequency of specific conditions, H.I.P. enrollees and New York City sample, day preceding interview, by labor force status

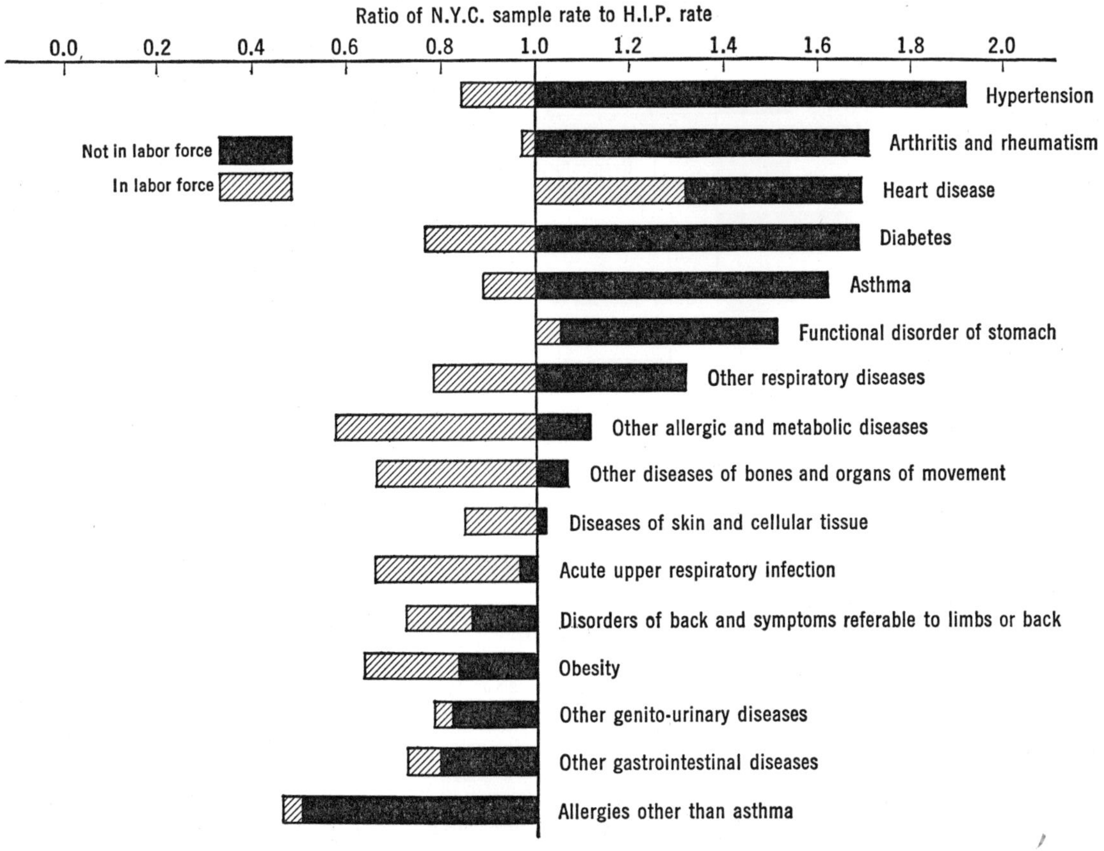

sample than in the New York City sample, irrespective of labor force status.

When labor force status and sex are both considered (Figures x–5 and x–6) it is seen that the shaded or black bars generally appear to the left of the equal rate line (that is, the line at which the ratio of the prevalence in the two samples is equal to unity) and the unshaded bars to the right. Speaking generally, *the prevalence of most of the conditions shown was higher in H.I.P. for persons in the labor force but higher in New York City for persons not in the labor force.*[4]

Before speculating on the possible significance of these variations with labor force status in the prevalence of illness conditions, we shall examine the picture for the eight-week period.

Prevalence of illness conditions, eight-week period. The several diagnostic conditions reported for the eight-week period have been grouped in Table x–6 into acute and chronic conditions, and

[4] The circulatory diseases as a group were an exception to this general rule (see Figures x–5 and x–6), as were disorders of the back, allergies other than asthma, and gastrointestinal diseases other than functional disorder of the stomach and intestines.

Figure X–5. Frequency of specific conditions, H.I.P. enrollees and New York City sample, day preceding interview, by labor force status and sex (males)

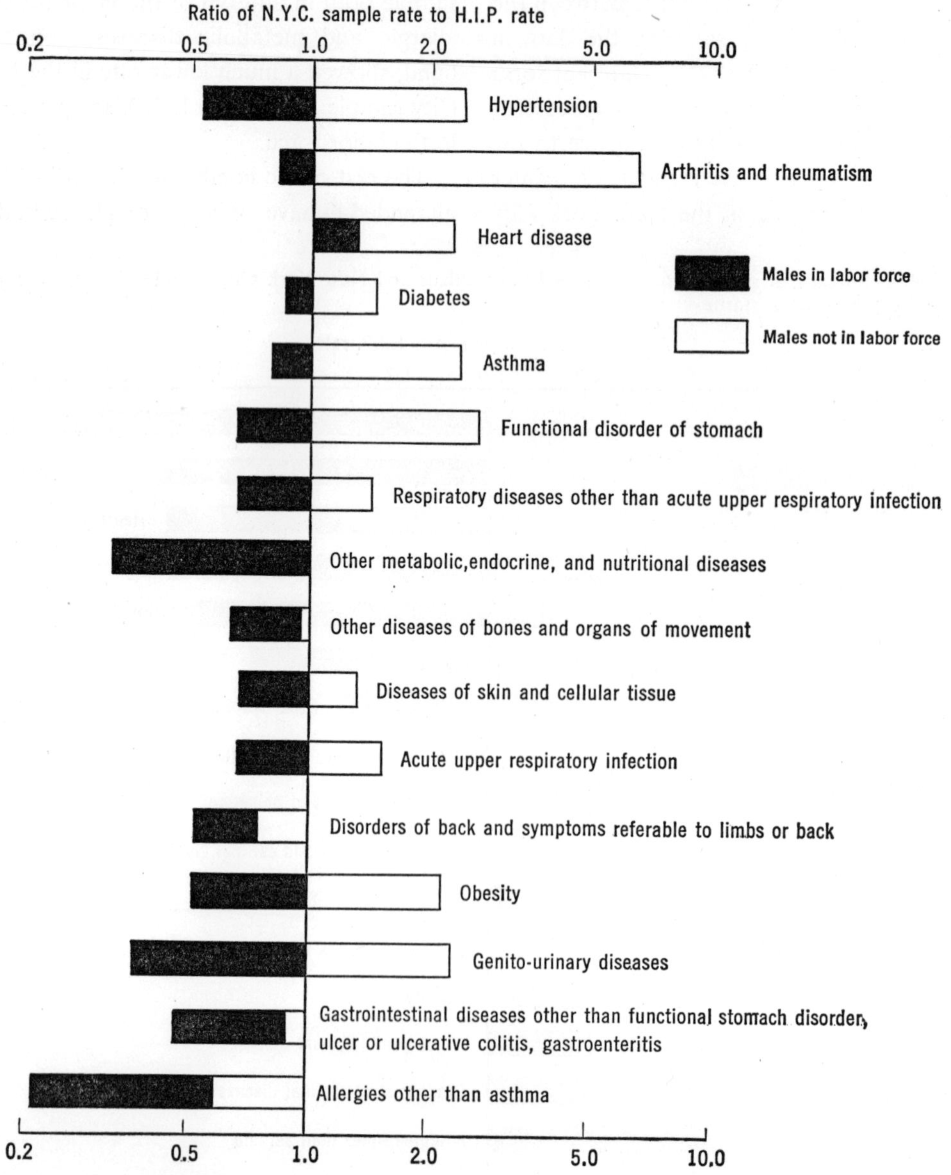

rates specific for sex, labor force status, and education of the head of the household computed. These rates, in turn, have been standardized as shown in Table x–7. The tabular summary on page 102 shows the pertinent comparisons available from these two tables.

The reader who wishes to go beyond the general patterns set forth in the tabular comparison will find the frequency of the specific conditions reported in the eight-week period set forth in Table x–8. For the comparison by labor force status, the rates have been standardized by sex and education of the head of the household.[5] In general, the picture presented in the tabular comparison is supported by the data for the specific diagnostic categories.

Prevalence of acute and chronic conditions, by labor force status. Now, what may be said about the meaning of these observations in respect of

[5] It should be recognized that since standardization is an averaging process, some detail is inevitably lost. The interested reader is referred to Table x–33 for data cross-tabulated in further detail and to Tables x–34 and x–35 for cross-tabulations of labor force status and education of head of household for nine selected conditions.

Figure X–6. Frequency of specific conditions, H.I.P. enrollees and New York City sample, day preceding interview, by labor force status and sex (females)

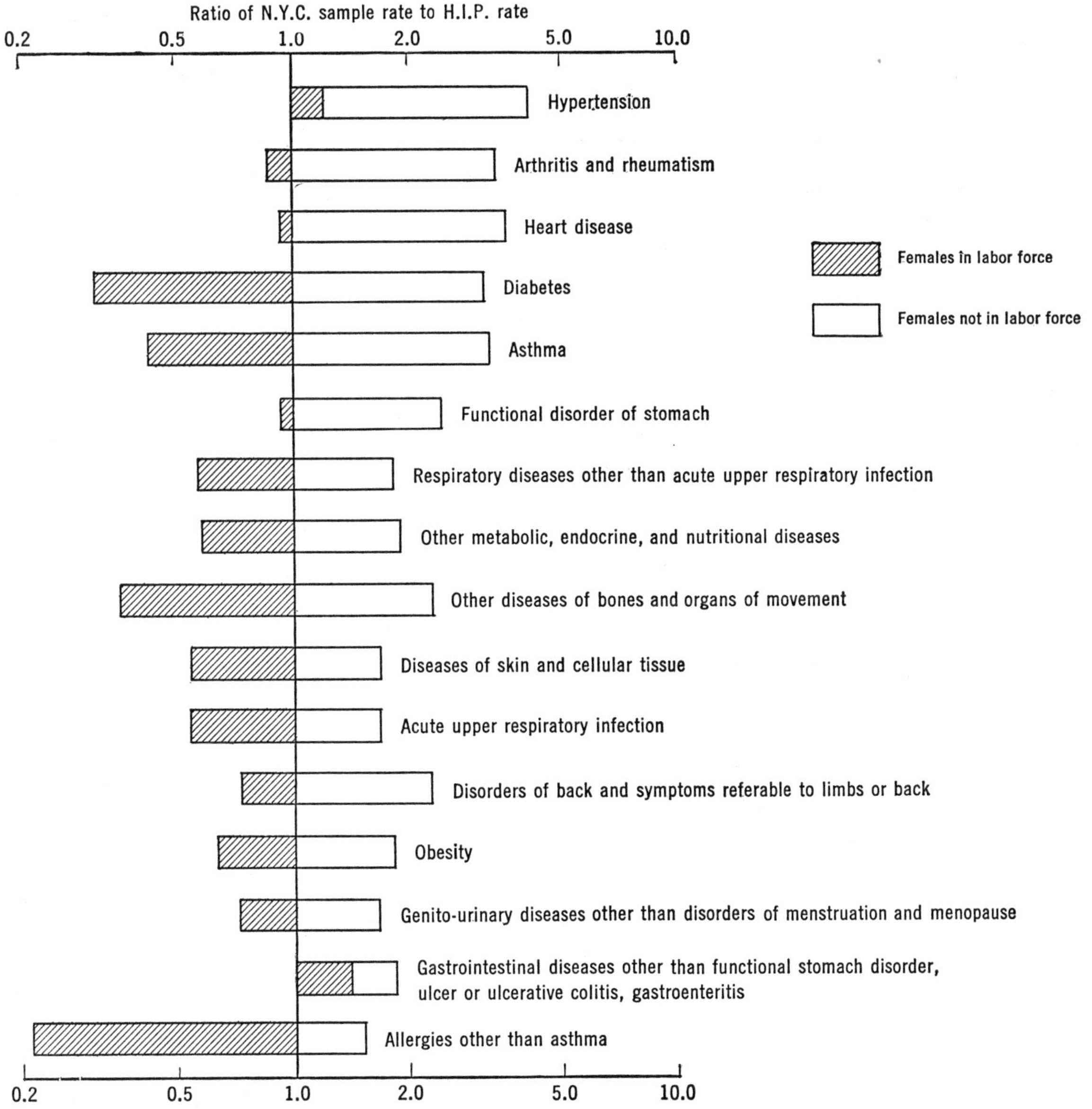

Tabular comparison of frequency of acute and chronic conditions reported for eight-week period

COMPARISON	TYPE OF CONDITION	
	Acute	*Chronic*
By labor force status	About the same for persons in the labor force as for persons not in the labor force.	Much greater for persons not in the labor force, with differences between those in the labor force and those not in the labor force greater in New York City than in H.I.P.
By education of head of household	Education-specific rates increased in both samples irrespective of labor force status.	Rates in New York City sample were highest in the lowest education group. There was relatively little variation with education in the H.I.P. sample.
By sex	In the labor force, males had a lower rate than females. Not in the labor force, females had a lower rate than males.	Males had a lower rate than females irrespective of labor force status.
H.I.P. vs. New York City	H.I.P. rate higher than New York City rate irrespective of labor force status.	In the labor force, H.I.P. rate higher than New York City rate. Not in the labor force, New York City rate higher than H.I.P. rate.

illness and labor force status? The very great importance, both of chronic diseases as a group and of specific conditions within the group, in the economic and social fabric of the community is once again underscored by the much higher rates observed for these conditions among persons not in the labor force. This, in turn, emphasizes not only the need to know more about the natural history of these diseases in order to provide a firm base for treatment, for alleviation of disability in the individual, and for community health programs, but also the need for more knowledge about the dynamics of these diseases in relation to the economic and social standing of the family. What is the sequence of events when chronic illness strikes various members of the family? If

Table X–6. Acute and chronic conditions (rates per 1,000 persons 14 years of age and over), H.I.P. enrollees and New York City sample, eight-week period, by labor force status and education of head of household

LABOR FORCE STATUS AND SEX	ACUTE — *Years of schooling completed by head of household*					CHRONIC — *Years of schooling completed by head of household*				
	Total	Less than 9	9–12	More than 12	Not reported	Total	Less than 9	9–12	More than 12	Not reported
					H.I.P. enrollees					
In labor force	157.2	137.4	143.1	200.6	137.6	352.5	364.5	332.1	368.5	302.8
Male	134.1	135.2	124.9	148.3	117.6	317.2	339.6	295.0	314.0	341.2
Female	221.8	145.4	202.6	294.3	208.3	451.5	453.9	453.4	466.1	166.7
Not in labor force	160.0	132.2	159.8	210.8	72.5	486.2	494.5	470.3	495.2	507.2
Male	201.3	170.0	275.0	203.1	125.0	373.8	333.3	475.0	328.1	437.5
Female	153.2	122.2	146.2	211.9	56.6	506.8	537.5	469.7	518.8	528.3
Labor force status not reported	407.2	309.6	409.4	485.9	76.9	118.1	77.4	102.3	170.4	76.9
Male	446.2	361.6	456.0	493.2	—	135.9	71.4	116.0	202.7	142.8
Female	365.3	263.8	356.2	477.4	105.3	96.9	82.7	86.8	132.2	52.6
					New York City sample					
In labor force	117.9	102.3	126.2	144.0	112.7	284.0	293.2	255.8	266.1	364.2
Male	105.4	91.6	115.4	129.4	77.6	241.4	254.9	228.7	217.2	288.9
Female	145.0	123.9	150.8	181.8	184.2	377.3	370.5	354.1	392.6	517.9
Not in labor force	127.8	103.0	139.7	193.0	98.4	605.0	609.5	516.1	429.0	870.1
Male	150.4	120.5	184.8	247.5	78.1	514.5	539.8	426.5	326.7	937.5
Female	123.0	98.5	132.4	182.5	105.3	624.5	729.6	530.4	448.7	847.4
Labor force status not reported	376.6	332.5	394.4	431.4	321.1	94.2	79.0	108.3	93.2	64.2
Male	386.6	354.3	408.8	419.4	222.2	107.4	88.6	121.2	112.9	74.1
Female	365.4	309.7	377.9	446.7	418.2	79.5	69.0	93.4	69.7	54.5

the breadwinner is removed from the labor force, as is suggested by the data, what is the economic and social course of the family over a period of time? To what extent are the community resources called upon to help the family? We are beginning to get cross-sectional snapshots of these problems, but very little is known about the evolutionary processes which result in these cross-sectional pictures. A better understanding of this evolutionary process would be of great help in the development of community programs aimed at the chronic disease problems. To cite but one example to illustrate the point: there is a mounting body of evidence indicating that the health problems of the aged can only be understood in relation to the health history of the individual in his earlier years. The significance of this for pension programs of industry and labor and for community-sponsored welfare programs is not difficult to see.

It is not immediately clear what the full meaning is of the observations that the reported frequency of acute conditions tended to be higher in the H.I.P. sample than in the New York City sample, irrespective of labor force status; that among persons in the labor force, chronic diseases were reported more frequently in the H.I.P. sample than in the New York City sample; and that among persons not in the labor force, the New York City sample reported a higher frequency of chronic conditions. Considering the acute conditions first, it is difficult to credit the hypothesis that there was actually more acute illness in the H.I.P. sample than in the New York City sample. Rather, it would seem more likely that the H.I.P. enrollees, who were free to seek medical care for such conditions under a prepayment plan, might have had (1) more awareness of the existence of these conditions, whether they chose to consult the doctor or not, and (2) a better recollection of the occurrence of illnesses because medical care was in fact more often sought.

In respect of chronic conditions, the observations are consistent with several hypotheses, such as the following: (1) Persons enrolled in H.I.P. see a doctor more readily than persons not enrolled; hence the condition is more likely to be diagnosed. Because of this the condition is more likely to be seen at an earlier stage than is the case among persons in the New York City sample; hence it can be more readily controlled, and the individual is more likely to remain in the labor force. (2) A large proportion of persons in the New York City sample are employees of the City of New York, which has a liberal sick-leave program, and many other H.I.P. enrollees are members of organized groups of workers likely to come under sick-leave programs; these sick-leave programs make it possible for such H.I.P. enrollees as contract a chronic disease to remain in the labor force. Neither of these two hypotheses can be proved or disproved from the available

Table X–7. Acute and chronic conditions (rates per 1,000 persons 14 years of age and over), H.I.P. enrollees and New York City sample, eight-week period, standardized for labor force status, education of head of household, and sex

CLASSIFICATION OF PERSONS	ACUTE CONDITIONS		CHRONIC CONDITIONS	
	H.I.P. enrollees	*New York City sample*	*H.I.P. enrollees*	*New York City sample*
By labor force status (standarized for sex and education of head of household)				
In the labor force	153.6	119.7	358.1	276.0
Not in the labor force	157.6	132.6	485.7	579.4
Labor force status inapplicable	397.4	383.8	110.5	95.7
By education of head of household (standardized for sex and labor force status)				
Less than 9 years	170.9	148.0	355.9	384.8
9 to 12 years	230.5	210.5	304.6	288.4
More than 12 years	282.3	239.7	342.3	264.1
By sex (standardized for education of head of household and labor force status)				
Male	224.3	192.2	269.9	226.0
Female	211.3	191.5	394.8	415.5

Table X–8. Specified medical conditions (rates per 1,000 persons 14 years of age and over), H.I.P. enrollees and New York City sample, eight-week period, standardized for education of head of household, sex, and labor force status[1]

DIAGNOSTIC CATEGORY	ALL PERSONS[2]		MALES[3]		FEMALES[3]		IN LABOR FORCE[4]		NOT IN LABOR FORCE[4]	
	H.I.P. enrollees	*New York City sample*	*H.I.P. enrollees*	*New York City sample*	*H.I.P. enrollees*	*New York City sample*	*H.I.P enrollees*	*New York City sample*	*H.I.P. enrollees*	*New York City sample*
Infective and parasitic diseases	6.5	7.6	8.0	8.2	5.0	7.0	4.5	7.0	9.3	8.4
Neoplasms	3.7	5.7	3.6	3.7	3.8	7.6	3.6	4.7	3.9	7.1
Asthma	14.1	12.6	15.0	14.1	13.3	11.2	14.9	9.4	13.0	17.2
Allergies other than asthma	9.8	5.4	8.8	5.0	10.8	5.8	9.8	5.0	9.8	6.0
Diabetes	10.3	10.9	10.0	9.3	10.6	12.3	10.1	7.2	10.6	16.2
Obesity	22.2	17.0	11.3	7.6	32.5	25.8	16.6	11.3	30.2	25.1
Diseases of blood and blood-forming organs	4.2	3.0	0.3	0.9	7.8	5.0	1.4	1.6	8.1	5.0
Mental, psychoneurotic, and personality disorders	5.2	5.0	3.0	4.0	7.3	6.0	6.7	4.3	3.1	6.0
Diseases of nervous system and sense organs	21.7	16.2	22.4	12.3	21.0	19.8	17.9	7.9	27.2	28.1
Heart disease	23.0	31.8	26.8	33.6	19.4	30.2	16.8	21.6	32.1	46.6
Hypertension	26.7	34.6	23.9	14.9	29.4	53.1	24.7	18.8	29.6	57.3
Arteriosclerosis; peripheral vascular disease	8.2	15.7	11.9	14.2	4.8	17.1	8.2	7.7	8.3	27.2
Varicose veins; phlebitis	33.1	27.3	15.6	15.5	49.6	38.4	22.4	16.3	48.7	43.1
Hemorrhoids	6.8	3.3	6.5	2.4	7.2	4.1	7.1	2.9	6.4	3.8
Acute upper respiratory infection	68.9	54.7	59.7	47.8	77.6	61.2	73.2	53.4	62.6	56.6
Influenza, grippe	36.9	28.3	28.9	23.3	44.5	33.0	35.7	25.5	38.8	32.4
Bronchitis	4.4	3.5	6.6	2.5	2.4	4.4	5.0	3.0	3.6	4.2
Chronic and other respiratory disease	8.4	7.8	6.7	7.4	10.0	8.2	10.3	9.4	5.7	5.5
Ulcer of stomach and ulcerative colitis	5.8	3.9	6.8	5.8	4.8	2.1	5.6	4.6	6.1	2.9
Functional disorder of stomach and intestines[5]	26.4	25.4	21.3	15.5	31.1	34.7	25.8	20.9	27.2	31.9
Disorder of genito-urinary tract	38.4	32.2	6.6	2.8	68.3	60.0	24.4	19.1	58.5	51.2
Deliveries and complications of pregnancy	5.7	6.4	—	—	11.0	12.4	0.6	1.3	13.0	13.8
Diseases of skin and cellular tissue	21.8	20.9	20.8	16.4	22.8	25.1	21.8	19.1	21.9	23.4
Arthritis and rheumatism	47.4	61.7	31.9	36.4	62.1	85.6	39.1	37.8	59.4	96.3
Disorders of back and symptoms referable to limbs or back	29.7	24.8	29.5	18.0	29.9	31.2	27.3	19.7	33.0	32.2
Accidental injuries	19.0	19.3	22.4	22.5	15.8	16.3	20.0	20.1	17.5	18.2

[1] Rates have been standardized to the distribution of the population of the two samples combined.
[2] Standardized for sex, education of head of household, and labor force status.
[3] Standardized for education of head of household and labor force status.
[4] Standardized for sex and education of head of household.
[5] Includes gastritis and symptoms referable to gastrointestinal tract.

data, and other hypotheses will undoubtedly occur to the reader. The value of such hypotheses, however, is that they suggest other ways of assessing the impact of medical care plans on population groups. For example, information on the stage at which particular conditions are seen in the H.I.P. enrollees as compared with the general population would be of considerable interest to all concerned with medical care. The seeking of such hypotheses and of methods of testing them should be a constant endeavor of such plans as H.I.P.

Leaving the question of labor force status and its relation to illness rates, we return, by way of summary, to the question of the over-all differences between the H.I.P. and New York City samples after all the variables which have been considered in this section are taken into account. It will be recalled that at the beginning of this chapter a tabular summary was made of the frequency of diagnostic conditions in the two samples as revealed by the gross rates for the various conditions. A similar summary appears on this page, based on the data in the first two columns of Table x–8, in which the rates for the specific conditions are standardized for sex, education of the head of the household, and labor force status. While it was not possible to standardize for age at the same time, age is controlled to some extent by confining the table to persons 14 years of age and over.[6]

By and large, the picture presented in the initial tabular summary remains unchanged. Most of the conditions showed about the same frequency in the two samples, but the kinds of conditions for which the H.I.P. rate was higher can generally be classified as acute, while the New York City rate tended to be higher for chronic conditions. Whether these similarities and differences continue in the same pattern in respect of disability as well as frequency is considered in the next section.

Disability Resulting from Acute and Chronic Illness

The previous section of this chapter examined the frequency with which various illness conditions contributed to the total morbidity picture

[6] As noted in the footnote on page 101, it is inevitable that some of the differences between the two samples will be obscured in the process of standardization. Nevertheless, the process does provide a means of summarizing the large mass of detail present in the basic tables.

Tabular comparison of standardized illness rates for specific conditions, H.I.P. and New York City samples

H.I.P. and New York City rates essentially the same	*H.I.P. rate greater than New York City rate*	*New York City rate greater than H.I.P. rate*
Infective and parasitic diseases	Allergies other than asthma	Heart disease
Neoplasms	Hemorrhoids	Hypertension
Asthma	Acute upper respiratory infection	Arteriosclerosis; peripheral vascular disease
Diabetes	Influenza and grippe	Arthritis and rheumatism
Obesity		
Diseases of blood and blood-forming organs		
Mental, psychoneurotic, and personality disorders		
Diseases of nervous system and sense organs		
Varicose veins and phlebitis		
Bronchitis		
Chronic and other respiratory disease		
Ulcer of stomach and ulcerative colitis		
Functional disorder of stomach and intestines		
Disorder of genito-urinary tract		
Deliveries		
Diseases of skin and cellular tissue		
Disorders of back and symptoms referable to limbs or back		
Accidental injuries		

among the groups surveyed. Often, however, it is not the frequency with which illness occurs but the amount of disability resulting from it which is of immediate practical import to the individual, his family, and society in general. The ulcer which keeps a man from his usual activities for several weeks looms as a far more important problem in his mind than the two or three colds he has every year.

Disability resulting from illness may be examined in several ways. Following the many excellent reports of Collins,[7] we shall employ two general measures of disability:[8] (1) the frequency of disabling cases and (2) the days of disability resulting from illness. Both measures are expressed as rates per 1,000 persons surveyed. Each may be further subdivided to consider cases and days of bed-disability and of hospitalization. The

[7] Selwyn D. Collins, Katharine S. Trantham, and Josephine L. Lehmann, *Sickness Experience in Selected Areas of the United States*, Public Health Monograph No. 25 (Public Health Service Publication No. 390). Washington, D.C., U.S. Government Printing Office, 1955.

[8] In this study, as in Collins', a disabling case is defined as one "causing inability of the patient to be about his or her usual activities for one day or longer. Usual activities include work away from home for wages or salary, cooking or housekeeping or other work at home, attending school or going about other usual activities, whatever they may be." (See Collins et al., *ibid.*, p. 28.)

Table X–9. Medical conditions (rates per 1,000 persons), H.I.P. enrollees and New York City sample, eight-week period, by age, sex, and degree of disability[1]

TYPE OF CONDITION, AGE, AND SEX	H.I.P. ENROLLEES			NEW YORK CITY SAMPLE		
	Disabling	*Bed-disabling*	*Non-disabling*	*Disabling*	*Bed-disabling*	*Non-disabling*
ACUTE[2]						
All ages						
Male	160.8	124.9	60.1	135.0	106.0	53.5
Female	166.1	129.6	61.9	136.4	107.8	43.7
Under 5						
Male	416.7	256.9	97.2	352.1	253.4	78.1
Female	344.2	243.2	73.8	315.7	232.6	52.9
5 to 14						
Male	314.3	270.7	66.7	300.3	248.9	49.6
Female	280.0	231.4	45.7	311.4	273.8	30.4
15 to 44						
Male	89.7	74.2	56.4	66.1	52.9	53.7
Female	107.5	80.3	69.2	88.4	66.0	43.9
45 to 64						
Male	82.8	66.4	47.5	49.4	36.7	40.9
Female	120.6	100.9	54.5	68.7	54.4	48.6
65 and over						
Male	111.9	76.9	69.9	70.2	58.1	55.7
Female	115.4	96.2	38.5	98.0	67.4	53.1
CHRONIC[2]						
All ages						
Male	49.9	32.9	224.2	43.1	32.1	196.2
Female	60.1	38.3	321.4	65.2	47.8	373.8
Under 5						
Male	34.7	30.1	106.5	37.0	27.4	57.5
Female	27.3	10.9	60.1	15.1	12.1	33.2
5 to 14						
Male	36.7	21.8	95.2	28.9	21.6	82.1
Female	35.7	24.3	75.7	30.4	22.3	73.0
15 to 44						
Male	35.6	20.8	190.6	29.4	24.0	155.3
Female	67.0	38.8	336.8	59.7	44.8	298.3
45 to 64						
Male	69.7	50.0	349.2	52.2	37.4	299.2
Female	78.9	61.5	575.4	94.6	73.2	661.9
65 and over						
Male	167.8	97.9	532.4	145.3	101.7	673.1
Female	57.7	19.2	769.2	144.9	91.9	1,038.8

[1] See Table X–36 for actual numbers of cases.

[2] See Appendix H for lists of diseases classified as acute and chronic.

data on hospitalization are considered separately in Chapter XI.

Although the data reported here refer to an eight-week period and are based upon a single-visit survey, the material exhibits certain general patterns in relation to age, sex, and education of the head of the household which are similar to those reported by Collins on an annual basis resulting from periodic visits to surveyed households. In the summary of these trends which follows, disabled cases include the bed-disabled group.

Cases per 1,000 Persons Surveyed (Case Rate)

1. The frequency of acute conditions in all three severity groups—disabling, bed-disabling, and

Figure X–7. Specific case rates for three severities of acute and chronic conditions, H.I.P. enrollees and New York City sample, eight-week period, by age and sex

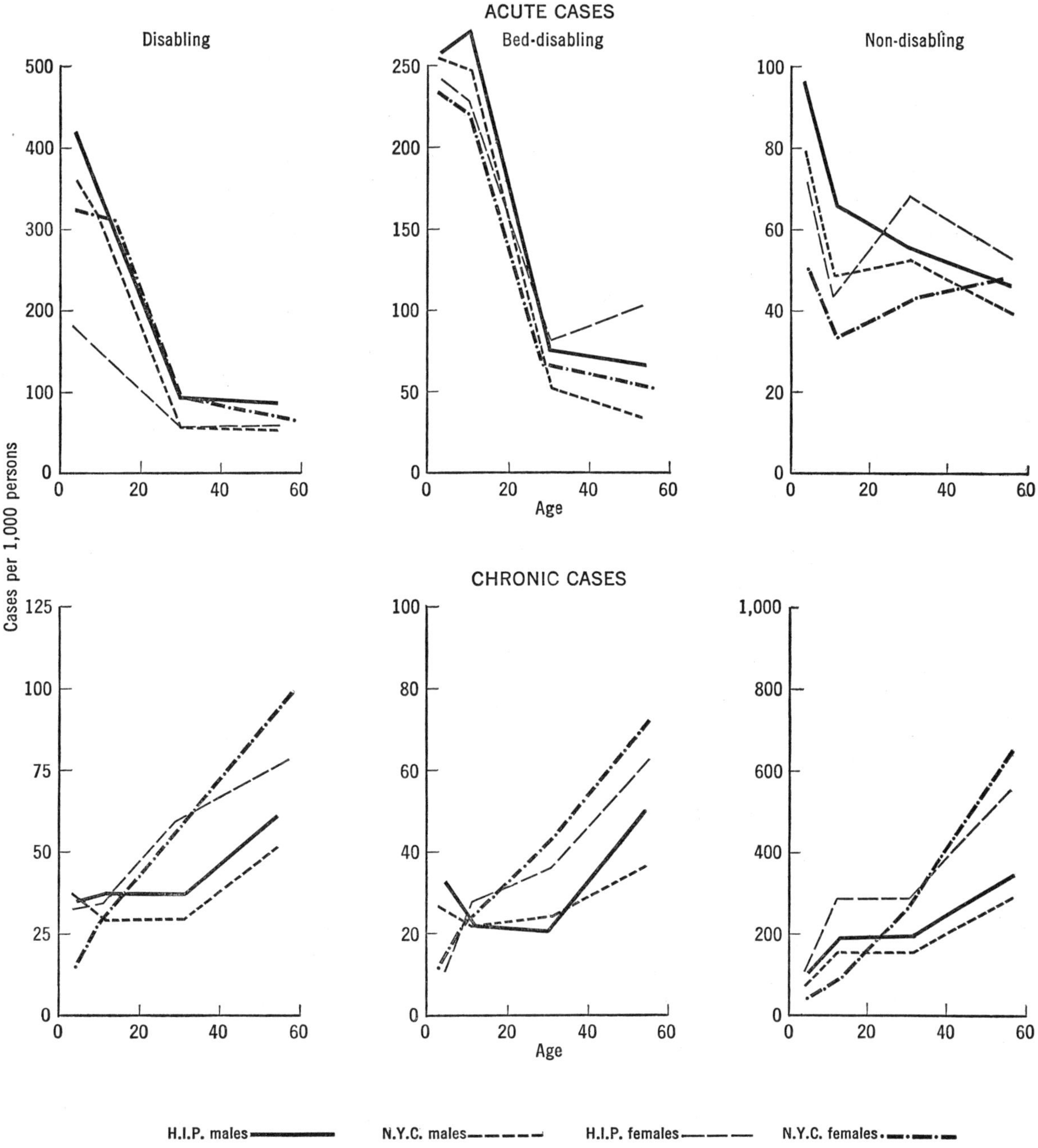

non-disabling—was high at early ages, dropped to a low in early adulthood, and remained low or rose slightly at later ages. The lowest case rate occurred at a somewhat earlier age for the non-disabling cases than for the disabling group. (Table x–9, Figure x–7.)

2. The case rate for chronic conditions rose sharply with age in all severity groups.

Table X–10. Medical conditions (rates per 1,000 persons), H.I.P. enrollees and New York City sample, eight-week period, by age, education of head of household, and degree of disability[1]

TYPE OF CONDITION, AGE, AND YEARS OF SCHOOLING COMPLETED BY HEAD OF HOUSEHOLD	H.I.P. ENROLLEES			NEW YORK CITY SAMPLE		
	Disabling	*Bed-disabling*	*Non-disabling*	*Disabling*	*Bed-disabling*	*Non-disabling*
ACUTE						
All ages						
Less than 9	118.9	94.2	45.1	110.4	88.8	35.3
9 to 12	170.0	128.6	54.2	157.7	122.5	46.8
More than 12	212.0	167.3	73.3	167.1	136.6	62.3
Under 5						
Less than 9	250.0	169.4	96.8	357.3	275.1	54.0
9 to 12	376.2	230.2	59.4	321.3	228.2	55.6
More than 12	458.6	319.5	78.9	339.2	258.7	62.9
5 to 14						
Less than 9	207.4	175.3	39.5	244.5	213.2	34.8
9 to 12	311.0	252.6	49.5	342.5	288.8	37.7
More than 12	379.0	333.3	57.1	384.6	331.1	36.8
15 to 44						
Less than 9	89.5	73.8	34.7	68.0	52.8	29.9
9 to 12	86.8	66.9	61.3	83.3	61.3	47.8
More than 12	126.9	96.8	80.8	99.0	80.2	70.8
45 to 64						
Less than 9	95.3	74.6	46.6	57.5	44.2	37.9
9 to 12	96.7	87.9	38.7	65.8	52.2	42.2
More than 12	111.3	87.8	70.7	50.5	42.6	55.9
65 and over						
Less than 9	90.0	45.0	81.1	66.4	48.5	39.5
9 to 12	195.7	195.7	43.5	101.0	70.7	70.7
More than 12	87.0	43.5	—	171.4	142.9	71.4
CHRONIC						
All ages						
Less than 9	57.9	39.1	146.8	58.3	41.8	161.8
9 to 12	55.8	34.1	147.7	49.7	37.7	138.5
More than 12	49.2	32.5	205.9	40.6	33.3	130.9
Under 5						
Less than 9	8.1	8.1	56.4	10.3	5.1	23.1
9 to 12	34.6	19.8	54.4	30.0	22.5	51.1
More than 12	37.6	30.1	105.3	28.0	21.0	28.0
5 to 14						
Less than 9	29.6	27.2	19.8	30.1	19.7	42.9
9 to 12	26.5	21.2	44.2	28.5	22.8	53.7
More than 12	57.1	22.8	107.3	33.4	30.1	73.6
15 to 44						
Less than 9	50.3	24.6	147.6	49.2	34.9	139.2
9 to 12	56.5	31.0	184.7	48.2	38.5	167.4
More than 12	45.1	31.0	234.0	33.3	29.2	171.9
45 to 64						
Less than 9	78.8	59.1	204.1	77.1	57.5	256.5
9 to 12	84.4	59.8	221.4	69.6	52.2	196.2
More than 12	57.8	49.3	278.4	55.9	42.6	154.2
65 and over						
Less than 9	99.1	63.1	189.2	123.9	88.0	262.0
9 to 12	217.4	87.0	195.7	166.7	106.0	222.2
More than 12	43.5	—	608.7	100.0	85.7	242.9

[1] See Table x–37 for actual numbers of cases.

Figure X–8. Specific case rates for three severities of acute conditions, H.I.P. enrollees and New York City sample, eight-week period, by education of head of household and age

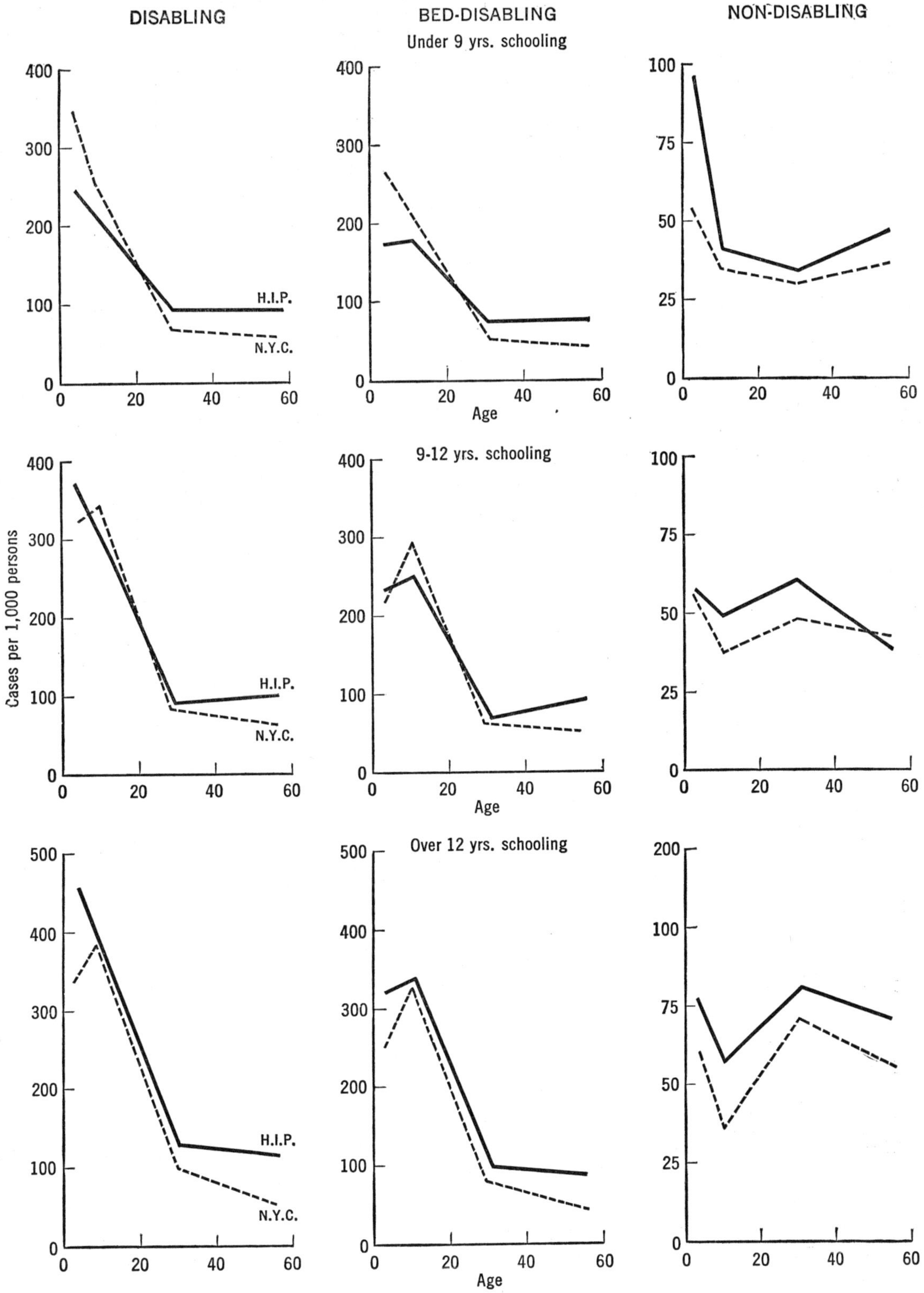

Figure X–9. Specific case rates for three severities of chronic conditions, H.I.P. enrollees and New York City sample, eight-week period, by education of head of household and age

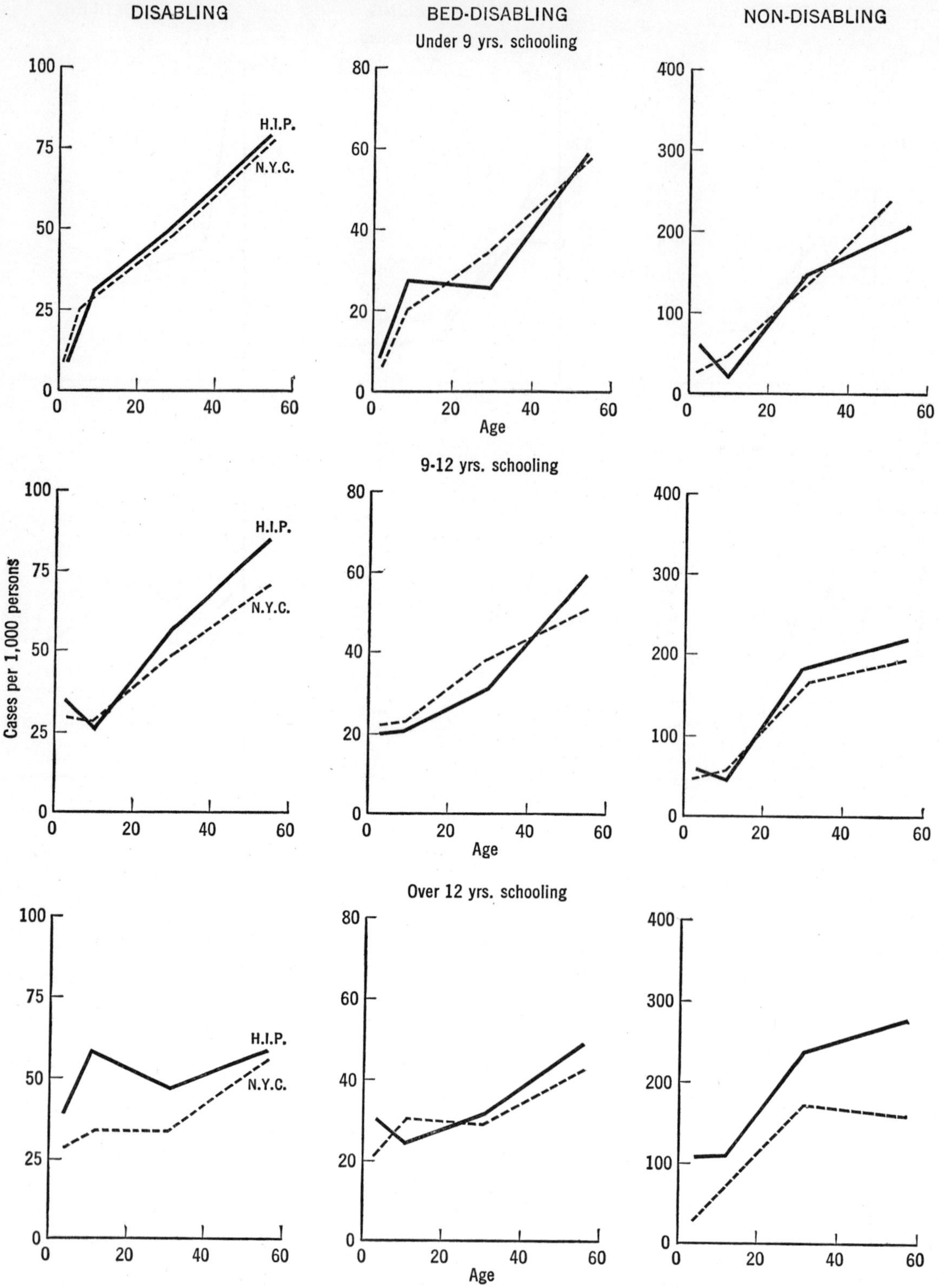

Table X–11. Acute and chronic cases producing specified degree of disability (rates per 1,000 persons standardized for age, education of head of household, and labor force status)

TYPE OF STANDARDIZED RATE	ACUTE						CHRONIC					
	Disabling		*Bed-disabling*		*Non-disabling*		*Disabling*		*Bed-disabling*		*Non-disabling*	
	H.I.P. enrol-lees	N.Y.C. sample	H.I.P. enrol-lees	N.Y.C. sample	H.I.P. enrol-lees	N.Y.C. sample	H.I.P. enrol-lees	N.Y.C. sample	H.I.P. enrol-lees	N.Y.C. sample	H.I.P. enrol-lees	N.Y.C. sample
All persons (standardized for age and education of head of household)	159.1	142.8	122.7	113.5	55.3	45.2	55.8	50.9	35.4	38.4	159.6	147.4
Years of schooling completed by head of household (standardized for age)												
Less than 9	120.1	110.7	93.7	89.1	47.0	35.5	57.4	58.7	38.0	42.1	143.0	163.9
9 to 12	171.5	159.9	130.2	123.8	54.4	46.8	57.9	49.5	34.4	37.9	148.3	137.8
More than 12	209.7	171.7	163.8	140.8	72.7	60.9	48.7	38.6	32.4	32.2	212.3	134.2
All persons 14 years of age and over (standardized for education of head of household and labor force status)	98.7	76.3	78.9	60.1	56.0	49.1	63.2	57.9	40.4	43.5	344.5	342.9
In labor force (standardized for education of head of household)	97.2	69.4	78.9	55.4	56.0	50.7	50.8	36.2	31.3	30.2	302.5	241.4
Not in labor force (standardized for education of head of household)	100.8	86.2	78.9	66.9	56.1	46.8	81.0	89.3	53.5	62.6	405.1	489.6

3. Females had a higher case rate than males in all severity groups for both acute and chronic diseases. The one exception to this statement occurred among the case rates for acute non-disabling illnesses in the New York City sample, in which the rates for males were higher than those for females throughout most of the age scale.

4. Children showed an increasing rate of disabling, as well as bed-disabling, acute illness with increasing education of the head of the household. On the other hand, adults showed an increasing rate of non-disabling illness with increasing education (Table x–10, Figures x–8 and x–9). In order to show the trends with education a little more clearly, the rates in each severity class have been standardized for age (Table x–11). The frequency of acute illness in all three severity classes increased with education of the head of the household.

5. The frequency of disabling and bed-disabling chronic conditions was highest in the lowest education group, when the rates were standardized for age. This was also true of non-disabling chronic conditions in the New York City sample, but the trend was reversed in the H.I.P. sample, where the rates rose with education (Table x–11).

6. As would be expected, persons not in the labor force had a much higher frequency of chronic illness of all degrees of severity than persons in the labor force (Table x–12). Acute illness showed relatively little variation with labor force status, although persons in the New York City sample not in the labor force showed a greater frequency of acute disabling and bed-disabling illness than appeared for those in the labor force.

7. For persons not in the labor force the amount of chronic disabling illness, including bed-disability, was greater among those with least education (Table x–12). On the other hand, the frequency of acute illness was generally higher in the highest education group irrespective of degree of severity or labor force status.

Days Lost per 1,000 Persons Surveyed

1. On the average the amount of time lost during eight weeks because of disability was about two days per person in each sample. The time lost decreased with age for acute conditions and increased for chronic conditions (Figure x–10).

Table X–12. Acute and chronic medical conditions (rates per 1,000 persons 14 years of age and over), H.I.P. enrollees and New York City sample, eight-week period, by labor force status, education of head of household, and degree of disability[1]

TYPE OF CONDITION, LABOR FORCE STATUS, AND YEARS OF SCHOOLING COMPLETED BY HEAD OF HOUSEHOLD	H.I.P. ENROLLEES			NEW YORK CITY SAMPLE		
	Disabling	*Bed-disabling*	*Non-disabling*[2]	*Disabling*	*Bed-disabling*	*Non-disabling*[2]
ACUTE[3]						
In labor force	99.9	81.8	57.3	67.8	53.3	50.1
Less than 9	86.5	66.4	51.0	62.1	50.1	40.2
9 to 12	91.9	76.8	51.2	71.8	53.4	54.4
More than 12	126.9	106.3	73.7	79.5	69.1	64.5
Not in labor force	100.0	77.3	59.9	83.2	64.4	44.7
Less than 9	99.2	82.6	33.1	68.7	52.7	34.3
9 to 12	91.1	71.3	68.7	92.5	70.8	47.2
More than 12	123.8	85.1	87.0	116.4	94.1	76.6
CHRONIC[3]						
In labor force	50.0	31.3	302.6	37.5	30.4	246.5
Less than 9	52.5	32.4	312.0	35.2	26.1	258.0
9 to 12	58.0	33.1	274.1	38.9	34.4	227.9
More than 12	35.4	26.1	333.1	33.4	31.1	232.7
Not in labor force	80.2	53.2	406.0	96.6	65.7	508.5
Less than 9	85.4	56.5	409.1	104.9	74.5	586.6
9 to 12	79.3	51.5	392.0	84.6	57.1	431.5
More than 12	73.5	50.3	421.6	60.6	44.7	368.4

[1] See Table x–38 for actual numbers of cases.
[2] Includes conditions with fact of disability not reported.
[3] Includes conditions in persons with education of head of household not reported.

Figure X–10. Days of disability and days in bed for acute and chronic conditions (rates per 1,000 persons), H.I.P. enrollees and New York City sample, eight-week period, by age and sex

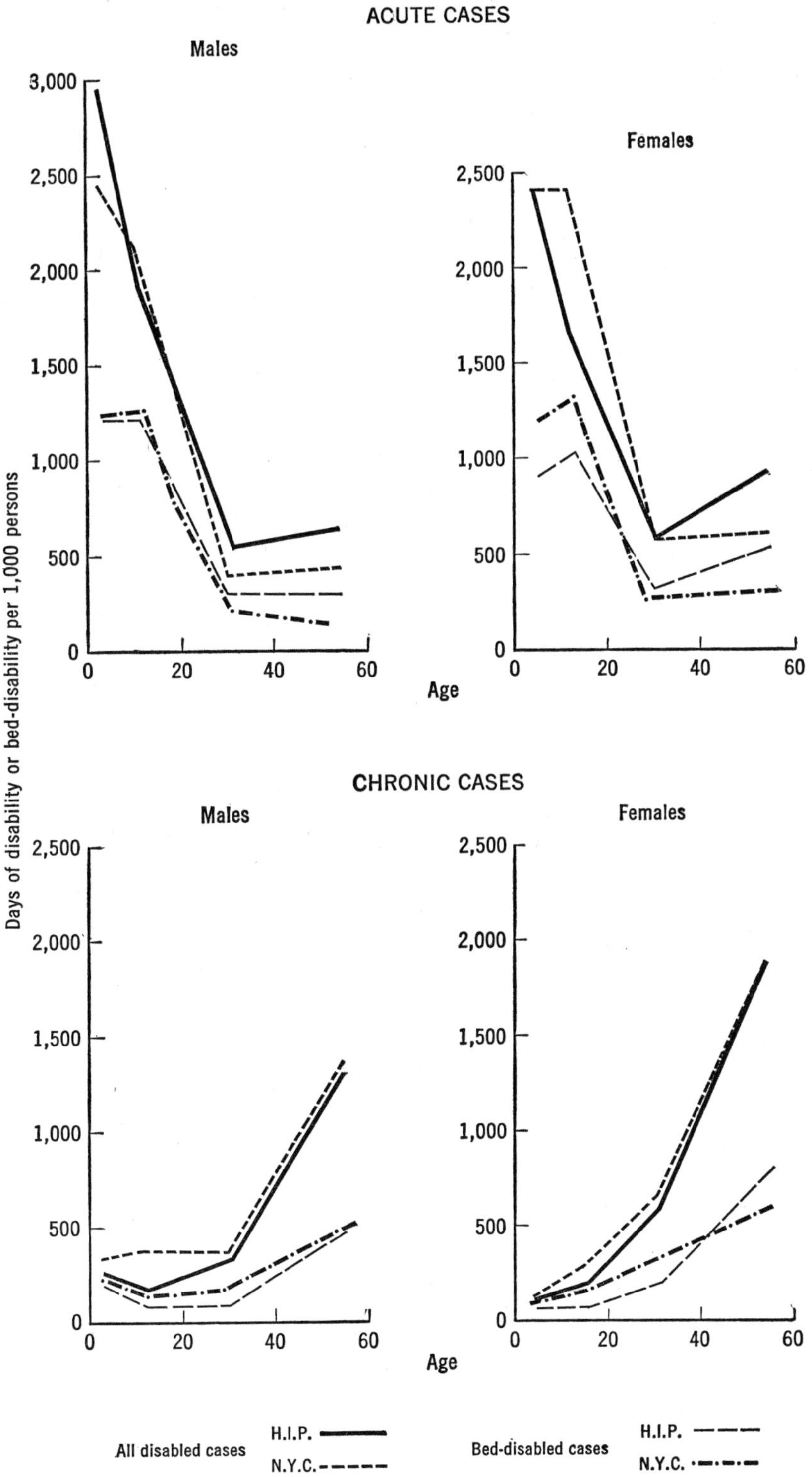

2. The days lost because of disability tended to be greater for females than males in the middle ranges of the age scale, but males at the extremes of the age scale lost more time from their usual activities than females of the same age (Table x–13).

3. Days lost from disabling acute illness increased with education of the head of the household, but chronic illness resulted in more lost time in the least-educated group than in the most-

Table X–13. Days of disability and days in bed for acute and chronic conditions (rates per 1,000 persons), H.I.P. enrollees and New York City sample, eight-week period, by age and sex[1]

TYPE OF CONDITION, AGE, AND SEX	DAYS OF DISABILITY		DAYS IN BED	
	H.I.P. enrollees	*N.Y.C. sample*	*H.I.P. enrollees*	*N.Y.C. sample*
ACUTE				
All ages[2]				
Male	1092.9	951.1	567.7	500.3
Female	1055.6	1070.8	565.7	550.7
Under 5				
Male	2993.0	2465.7	1208.3	1216.4
Female	2423.5	2435.0	918.0	1207.0
5 to 14				
Male	1960.5	2147.0	1240.8	1248.9
Female	1730.0	2406.7	1025.7	1327.6
15 to 44				
Male	532.1	401.7	333.1	212.8
Female	565.1	566.3	310.8	272.4
45 to 64				
Male	609.8	446.7	304.1	144.7
Female	924.6	617.9	545.2	312.2
65 and over				
Male	1643.3	598.1	223.8	414.0
Female	846.2	1061.2	500.0	461.2
CHRONIC				
All ages[2]				
Male	669.2	836.9	286.4	379.8
Female	777.2	1089.2	295.7	486.5
Under 5				
Male	243.0	337.0	196.8	163.0
Female	101.1	116.3	79.2	43.8
5 to 14				
Male	146.9	377.8	92.5	147.9
Female	170.0	276.9	74.3	184.6
15 to 44				
Male	323.0	376.2	94.4	170.7
Female	579.5	643.6	177.8	347.9
45 to 64				
Male	1293.4	1181.4	462.3	507.4
Female	1952.4	1777.2	801.6	919.7
65 and over				
Male	3461.5	4578.7	2342.6	1615.0
Female	1076.9	4536.7	403.8	1406.1

[1] See Table x–39 for actual numbers of days of disability and days in bed.
[2] Includes persons whose age was not reported.

Table X–14. Days of disability and days in bed for acute and chronic conditions (rates per 1,000 persons), H.I.P. enrollees and New York City sample, eight-week period, by age and education of head of household[1]

TYPE OF CONDITION, AGE, AND YEARS OF SCHOOLING COMPLETED BY HEAD OF HOUSEHOLD	DAYS OF DISABILITY		DAYS IN BED	
	H.I.P. enrollees	*N.Y.C. sample*	*H.I.P. enrollees*	*N.Y.C. sample*
ACUTE				
All ages[2]				
Less than 9	907.7	773.8	409.0	426.5
9 to 12	1074.5	1238.2	570.1	609.4
More than 12	1323.6	1193.0	764.3	690.4
Under 5				
Less than 9	1903.2	2236.5	556.4	1380.5
9 to 12	2556.9	2527.0	930.7	1079.6
More than 12	3387.2	2688.8	1541.4	1391.6
5 to 14				
Less than 9	1200.0	1682.6	659.2	953.7
9 to 12	1837.5	2642.8	1123.7	1475.0
More than 12	2568.5	3030.1	1657.5	1822.8
15 to 44				
Less than 9	545.9	422.3	300.9	242.2
9 to 12	543.8	573.8	325.3	246.9
More than 12	578.9	499.0	337.4	290.6
45 to 64				
Less than 9	847.7	490.2	389.6	209.7
9 to 12	638.0	572.7	397.2	290.7
More than 12	713.1	375.0	466.8	159.6
65 and over				
Less than 9	1973.0	675.0	207.2	359.1
9 to 12	1065.2	974.8	387.0	474.7
More than 12	173.9	1271.5	173.9	1000.0
CHRONIC				
All ages[2]				
Less than 9	805.2	1186.9	271.3	510.4
9 to 12	756.5	707.7	310.5	293.6
More than 12	519.3	509.8	234.0	317.7
Under 5				
Less than 9	56.4	46.3	40.3	30.8
9 to 12	198.0	261.3	168.3	76.6
More than 12	206.8	297.2	154.1	199.3
5 to 14				
Less than 9	76.5	417.2	42.0	112.4
9 to 12	183.7	213.5	111.3	139.3
More than 12	210.0	481.6	91.3	424.8
15 to 44				
Less than 9	332.2	651.7	73.8	393.4
9 to 12	583.1	544.2	154.4	213.1
More than 12	322.4	226.1	169.2	138.6
45 to 64				
Less than 9	1623.9	1672.8	562.7	691.1
9 to 12	1852.4	1176.4	773.3	662.1
More than 12	1353.3	744.7	582.4	446.8
65 and over				
Less than 9	1045.0	4087.9	441.4	1452.4
9 to 12	4456.5	4979.8	3000.0	1388.9
More than 12	2434.8	2885.8	—	2357.2

[1] See Table x–40 for actual numbers of days of disability and days in bed.
[2] Includes persons whose age was not reported.

Figure X–11. Days of disability and days in bed for acute and chronic conditions (rates per 1,000 persons), H.I.P. enrollees and New York City sample, eight-week period, by education of head of household and age

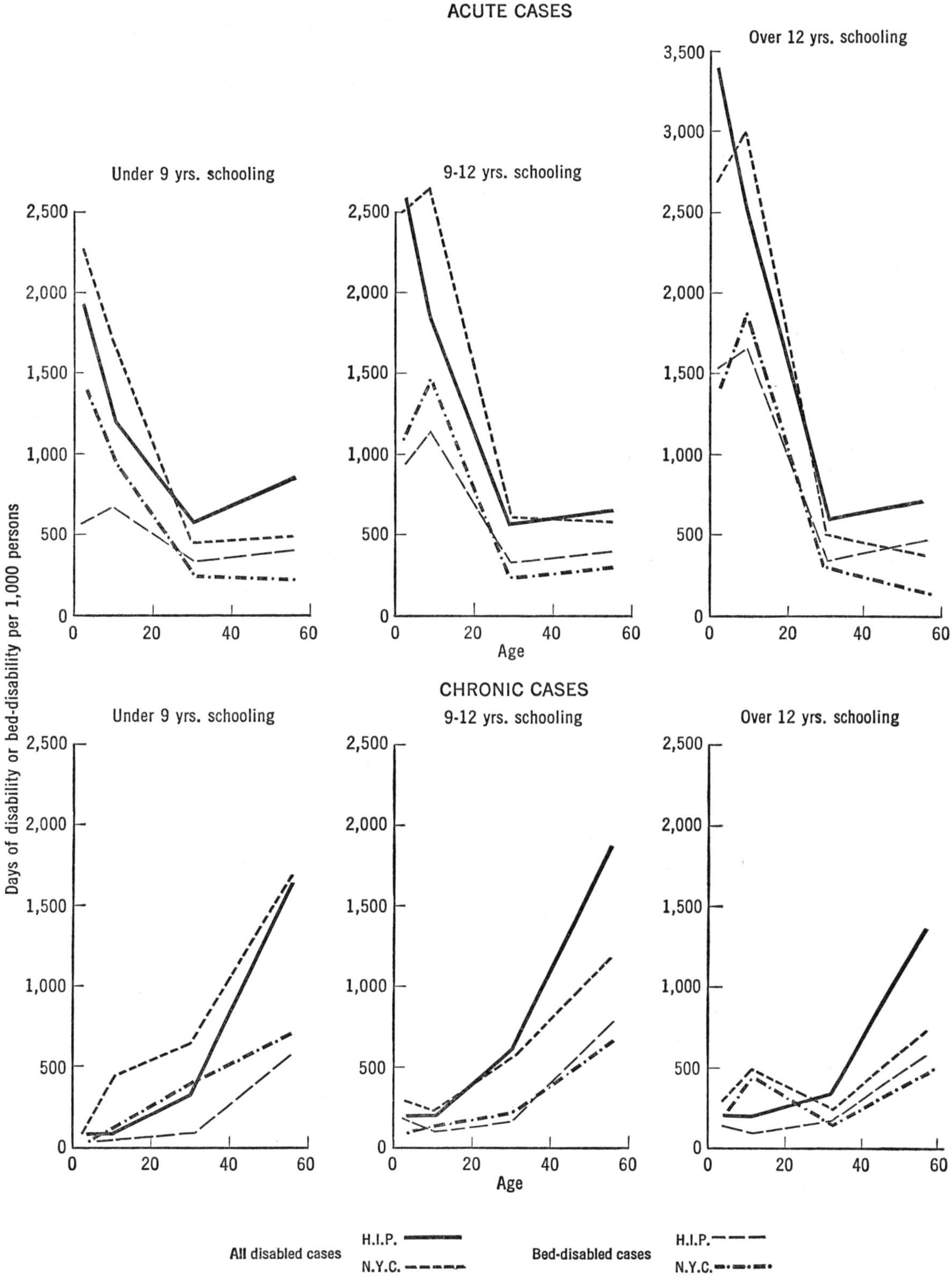

educated, especially in the New York City sample (Table x–14, Figure x–11).

4. Persons in the labor force lost more time because of acute illness than because of chronic illness (Table x–15). For persons not in the labor force, disability rates were far higher for the chronic diseases than for the acute diseases.

5. For persons not in the labor force, the days of disability resulting from chronic diseases were greatest in the least-educated group (Table x–15). Persons in the labor force showed no consistent trend with education of the head of the household in days lost from chronic illness.

In order to facilitate a comparison of the experiences of H.I.P. enrollees and persons in the New York City sample, the findings are again summarized in tabular form (see below and on opposite page).

Again resorting to standardized rates as a convenient device for summarizing the many detailed comparisons of the accompanying tabular arrangement, the over-all impression gathered from Table x–16 of the differences between the two samples is that the frequency of disability tended to be slightly higher among persons in the H.I.P. sample than in the New York City sample with the exception of bed-disabling chronic illness, which showed very similar rates in the two samples. The days lost from usual activity were higher in the H.I.P. sample than in the New York City sample for acute illness, but there was more time lost from chronic illness among persons in the latter sample than in the former.

Medical Care Received for Specific Illness Conditions

Three measures of the amount and kind of medical care received were obtained in the survey.

Tabular comparison, H.I.P. enrollees and New York City sample, respect of disability

COMPARISON	DEGREE OF SEVERITY		
	Disabling illness	*Bed-disabling illness*	*Non-disabling illness*
CASES PER 1,000 SURVEYED POPULATION			
By age and sex — Acute cases	*Very little difference* between the two samples in children, but H.I.P. had a higher rate than New York City for adults of both sexes.	Same as for all disabling illness.	H.I.P. rate *higher* than New York City rate throughout age scale for both sexes.
Chronic cases	H.I.P. rate *higher* than New York City rate for males and females throughout most of age scale.	*No consistent differences* between rates for males in the two samples. Females in H.I.P. sample had *lower* rates than New York City females over most of age scale.	H.I.P. male rate *higher* than New York City male rate. Females showed *little difference* in rates in the two samples.
By education of head of household — Acute cases	H.I.P. rate *lower* than New York City rate at young age but *higher* at older ages; when rates are standardized for age, H.I.P. rates *higher* in each education class.	Same as for all disabling illness.	H.I.P. rate *higher* than New York City rate in all three education classes.
Chronic cases	Somewhat *greater* rates in H.I.P. sample in the two highest education classes.	*Very little difference* between the two samples in any of the three education classes.	Same as disabling cases.
By labor force status — Acute cases	H.I.P. *higher* than New York City both for persons in labor force and not in labor force.	Same as disabling cases.	Same as disabling cases.
Chronic cases	In labor force—H.I.P. *higher* than New York City. Not in labor force—New York City *higher* than H.I.P.	In labor force—H.I.P. and New York City *the same.* Not in labor force—New York City *higher* than H.I.P.	In labor force—H.I.P. *higher* than New York City. Not in labor force—New York City *higher* than H.I.P.

They were: (1) whether or not a doctor was seen for a particular condition, (2) the number of times a doctor was seen for the condition, and (3) the length of time between onset of symptoms and the first visit to a doctor. Each of these measures will be examined in relation to specific diagnostic conditions present during the eight-week period, and the second will also be examined for those conditions producing illness of seven or more days' duration or hospitalization in 1951.

Conditions Resulting in Physician Contacts, Eight-Week Period

The general picture of the extent to which a doctor's care was sought for broad classes of diagnoses is shown in Table x–17.[9] A more detailed picture for specific diagnostic conditions is presented in Table x–18. Table x–42 shows data on doctor visits for acute and chronic cases distributed by education of the head of the household.

Comparison of the two samples shows that, though the differences in the percentage of specified conditions seen by a doctor were small in most instances, the direction of the differences was toward a higher percentage in the H.I.P. sample than in the New York City sample in the majority of instances. The few specific conditions in which the percentage seen by a doctor was higher in the New York City sample than in the H.I.P. sample were heart disease, arthritis and rheuma-

[9] It must be remembered in interpreting this table and those that follow that the data relate to a limited time span. Thus, while 94 percent of the deliveries or complications of pregnancy were seen by a doctor during the eight-week period, it does not follow that 6 percent of the women with this condition did not see a doctor at all. They may have been seen prior to the eight-week period.

Tabular comparison, H.I.P. enrollees and New York City sample, respect of days of disability

Comparison	*Disabling illness*	*Bed-disabling illness*
DAYS LOST PER 1,000 SURVEYED POPULATION		
By age and sex — Acute cases	*No consistent differences* with age between males in H.I.P. and New York City samples. Females tended to have higher rate at young ages in New York City, but higher in H.I.P. at older ages.	Males in H.I.P. sample had *higher* rate than males in New York City sample. Rate for females higher in New York City at young age but higher in H.I.P. at older ages.
Chronic cases	Both sexes had *higher* rates in New York City sample at younger ages, but higher in H.I.P. sample at older ages.	Rates *higher* in New York City sample at every age and for both sexes.
By education of head of household — Acute cases	*No consistent difference* between the two samples when rates were standardized for age.	*Higher* rate in H.I.P. sample in highest education group when rates are standardized for age. When standardized for age and education, rates were about the same.
Chronic cases	In lowest education group New York City sample had *higher* rate of days lost than H.I.P. sample. For middle and highest education groups, H.I.P. rate exceeded that of New York City when rates were standardized for age.	Same as for disabling illness.
By labor force status — Acute cases	Days lost for persons in labor force *greater* for H.I.P. sample than for New York City sample; reverse true for persons not in labor force. New York City rate for persons not in labor force *greatly exceeded* that for persons in labor force.	H.I.P. rate *higher* than New York City for persons in labor force; rate about the same for both H.I.P. and New York City persons not in labor force. H.I.P. rates did not differ with labor force status, but New York City rate *higher* for persons not in labor force than for persons in labor force.
Chronic cases	H.I.P. rate *higher* than New York City for persons in labor force, *lower* for persons not in labor force.	H.I.P. and New York City rates *the same* for persons in labor force; New York City rate *higher* than H.I.P. for persons not in labor force.

Table X–15. Days of disability and bed-disability from acute and chronic conditions (rates per 1,000 persons 14 years of age and over), H.I.P. enrollees and New York City samples, eight-week period, by labor force status and education of head of household[1]

TYPE OF CONDITION, LABOR FORCE STATUS, AND YEARS OF SCHOOLING COMPLETED BY HEAD OF HOUSEHOLD	H.I.P. ENROLLEES		NEW YORK CITY SAMPLE	
	Disability	*Bed-disability*	*Disability*	*Bed-disability*
ACUTE[2]				
In labor force	641.2	363.0	439.8	223.3
Less than 9	735.9	322.8	439.3	227.7
9 to 12	593.4	365.2	491.3	226.4
More than 12	594.2	403.0	318.0	253.5
Not in labor force	674.7	353.3	729.3	363.7
Less than 9	845.7	392.6	532.9	279.5
9 to 12	529.7	319.7	854.4	411.2
More than 12	727.2	386.8	960.1	529.5
CHRONIC[2]				
In labor force	563.9	169.8	375.9	172.5
Less than 9	539.8	213.1	414.1	170.6
9 to 12	724.4	173.9	333.2	155.1
More than 12	401.1	119.4	256.9	191.3
Not in labor force	1515.2	694.0	2228.0	932.3
Less than 9	1658.4	497.2	2627.7	1176.5
9 to 12	1517.8	770.2	1642.0	659.7
More than 12	1063.8	626.7	969.7	496.0

[1] See Table x–41 for actual numbers of days of disability and bed-disability.

[2] Includes days of disability and bed-disability in persons for whom education of head of household was not reported.

tism, and ulcer of the stomach,[10] but none of these differences was greater than would be expected by chance.

The generally higher percentage of physician contacts in the H.I.P. sample than in the New York City sample may be a reflection, at least in part, of removal of financial deterrents to the seeking of medical care. In the case of diabetes and the conditions designated as diseases of the nervous system and sense organs, the difference between the two samples was quite marked and statistically significant.

Age and sex. The variation in doctor contacts with age and sex is shown in Table x–19 and Figure x–12. The percentage of acute conditions seen by a doctor during the eight-week period varied from a low of about 53 percent to a high of about 80 percent, with the high values tending to occur at the extremes of the age scale. However, if the youngest and oldest age groups are omitted, the range of variation hardly exceeds 13 percent within either sample. The percentage of chronic conditions reported as being seen by a doctor during the eight-week period was generally

[10] Tuberculosis; other allergic, metabolic, and nutritional diseases; and gastroenteritis are also in this group, but the percentages in one or both samples are based on frequencies of less than 25.

Table X–16. Rates (cases and days lost) per 1,000 persons 14 years of age and over of acute and chronic medical conditions, H.I.P. enrollees and New York City sample, eight-week period, standardized for age, labor force status, and education of head of household

TYPE OF RATE AND STANDARDIZATION	ACUTE						CHRONIC					
	Disabling		*Bed-disabling*		*Non-disabling*		*Disabling*		*Bed-disabling*		*Non-disabling*	
	H.I.P. enrollees	N.Y.C. sample	H.I.P. enrollees	N.Y.C. sample	H.I.P. enrollees	N.Y.C. sample	H.I.P. enrollees	N.Y.C. sample	H.I.P. enrollees	N.Y.C. sample	H.I.P. enrollees	N.Y.C. sample
Cases per 1,000 population												
Standardized for age and education of head of household	159.1	142.8	122.7	113.5	55.3	45.2	55.8	50.9	35.4	38.4	159.6	147.4
Standardized for education of head of household and labor force status	98.7	76.3	78.9	60.1	56.0	49.1	63.2	57.9	40.4	43.5	344.5	342.9
Days lost per 1,000 population												
Standardized for age and education of head of household	1075.9	1044.7	573.3	547.9	—	—	720.8	834.8	283.2	382.0	—	—
Standardized for education of head of household and labor force status	675.1	553.9	359.5	290.5	—	—	954.5	1009.2	359.5	452.6	—	—

Table X–17. Percentage of medical conditions seen by a doctor, H.I.P. enrollees and New York City sample, eight-week period, by broad diagnostic groups

DIAGNOSTIC CONDITION	TOTAL PERSONS WITH SPECIFIED CONDITION		PERCENTAGE OF CONDITIONS SEEN BY DOCTOR	
	H.I.P. enrollees	*N.Y.C. sample*	*H.I.P. enrollees*	*N.Y.C. sample*
Infective and parasitic diseases	221	375	81.4	77.3
Neoplasms	29	64	96.6	90.6
Allergic, metabolic, endocrine, and nutritional diseases	431	623	44.6	33.4
Diseases of blood and blood-forming organs	24	36	95.8	88.9
Mental, psychoneurotic, and personality disorders	33	60	69.7	58.3
Diseases of nervous system and sense organs	172	232	83.7	62.0
Diseases of circulatory system	573	1,282	22.5	20.2
Diseases of respiratory system	1,311	1,799	62.2	55.6
Diseases of digestive tract	351	506	44.4	40.7
Disorder of genito-urinary tract	211	367	54.0	44.7
Deliveries and complications of pregnancy	33	64	93.9	93.8
Diseases of skin and cellular tissue	193	270	58.5	43.0
Diseases of bones and organs of movement	684	1,232	30.3	24.4
Accidental injuries	158	260	84.2	76.5

less than for acute conditions, averaging between 30 and 40 percent.[11] Children under five with chronic conditions, however, ran well above the other ages in the proportion seeing a doctor for these conditions. Among adults with a chronic condition the percentage who saw a doctor during the eight-week period remained fairly constant or even declined slightly with age.

Males with acute conditions were somewhat more likely to be seen by a doctor than females with acute disorders. The same was true of chronic conditions. If, however, the number of physician-attended conditions during the eight-week period is related to all persons in each sample rather than to just those persons with a condition, the percentage of females in the population who saw a doctor is higher than the corresponding figure for males. This is in agreement with other reports in the literature, such as that of Collins.[12]

Comparison of the two samples in respect of conditions seen by a doctor remains essentially unchanged when age and sex are taken into account. For both acute and chronic conditions in both sexes the percentage of conditions seen by a doctor was slightly higher in the H.I.P. sample at almost every age than in the New York City sample.

Education of household head. The extent to which various education groups sought medical care is set forth in Table X–20 and Figures X–13 and X–14. Considering the chronic conditions first because they showed a similar pattern of variation with education in both samples, there was an increase in doctor contacts for these conditions with increasing education of the head of the household. This was true for both face-to-face contacts and telephone contacts. It will be recalled, however, that the frequency of chronic conditions seemed to be somewhat greater in the less-educated group and it was suggested that perhaps the diagnoses reported by the less-educated group were less specific in meaning than those reported by the better-educated groups. This would be consistent with less frequent contact with the doctor by the less-educated group.

Doctor contacts for acute conditions showed a different pattern in the two samples. In the New York City sample there was very little variation with education of the head of the household, whereas in the H.I.P. sample the percentage of acute conditions seen by a doctor decreased with increasing education. Telephone contacts for acute conditions, on the other hand, increased with greater education in the H.I.P. sample.[13] The

[11] See footnote 9.

[12] Selwyn D. Collins, "Frequency and Volume of Doctors' Calls Among Males and Females in 9,000 Families, Based on Nation-Wide Periodic Canvasses, 1928–31," *Public Health Reports*, 55, No. 44, pp. 1977–2020, November 1, 1940.

[13] This is true even after the percentages in each education group are standardized for age differences.

H.I.P. pattern is consistent with the idea expressed in the preceding section that the greater frequency of acute conditions in the better-educated group might be due to the reporting of more minor conditions by respondents in this group. On the other hand, the lack of variation with education in doctor contacts for acute conditions in the New York City sample does not support this concept. The reason for the differing pattern in the two samples is not clear. One could hypothesize that the difference reflects differing economic motivations of the physicians in the two groups, but without more direct evidence on the point it must remain in the area of speculation.

Although the differences between the two samples in the proportion of conditions receiving medical care were not very large, they were quite consistent: H.I.P. enrollees with both acute and chronic conditions generally sought a doctor's care more often than persons in the New York

Table X–18. Percentage of specific medical conditions seen by doctor, H.I.P. enrollees and New York City sample, eight-week period

DIAGNOSTIC GROUP	TOTAL PERSONS WITH SPECIFIED CONDITION		PERCENTAGE OF CONDITIONS SEEN BY A DOCTOR	
	H.I.P. enrollees	*N.Y.C. sample*	*H.I.P. enrollees*	*N.Y.C. sample*
Infective and parasitic diseases	*221*	*375*	81.4	77.3
Tuberculosis	10	28	20.0	50.0
Other	211	347	84.4	79.5
Neoplasms	*29*	*64*	96.6	90.6
Allergic, metabolic, endocrine, and nutritional diseases	*431*	*623*	44.6	33.4
Asthma	115	189	29.6	22.2
Other allergies	100	81	73.0	60.5
Diabetes	65	133	41.5	24.0
Obesity	131	191	33.6	29.8
Other	20	29	70.0	96.6
Diseases of blood and blood-forming organs	*24*	*36*	95.8	88.9
Mental, psychoneurotic, and personality disorders	*33*	*60*	69.7	58.3
Diseases of nervous system and sense organs	*172*	*232*	83.7	62.0
Vascular lesions and inflammatory disorder of C.N.S.	41	88	65.9	52.3
Diseases of ear	68	79	86.7	73.4
Diseases of eye	63	65	92.1	61.5
Diseases of circulatory system	*573*	*1,282*	22.5	20.2
Heart disease	135	364	33.3	34.3
Hypertension	158	382	23.4	18.8
Other	280	536	16.8	11.5
Diseases of respiratory system	*1,311*	*1,799*	62.2	55.6
Acute upper respiratory infection	795	1,101	50.2	41.8
Other	516	698	80.8	77.5
Diseases of digestive tract	*351*	*506*	44.4	40.7
Ulcer of stomach and ulcerative colitis	40	42	55.0	66.7
Gastroenteritis	21	13	33.3	84.6
Functional disorder of stomach and intestines[1]	194	307	33.5	28.7
Other	96	144	64.6	54.9
Disorder of genito-urinary tract	*211*	*367*	54.0	44.7
Disorder of menstruation and menopause	155	287	39.3	32.4
Other	56	80	94.6	88.8
Deliveries and complications of pregnancy	*33*	*64*	93.9	93.8
Delivery without complication	18	46	100.0	97.8
Other	15	18	86.7	83.3
Diseases of skin and cellular tissue	*193*	*270*	58.5	43.0
Diseases of bones and organs of movement	*684*	*1,232*	30.3	24.4
Arthritis and rheumatism	272	669	16.9	18.8
Disorders of back and symptoms referable to limbs or back	221	312	41.6	35.3
Other	191	251	36.1	25.9
Accidental injuries	*158*	*260*	84.2	76.5
All other	*224*	*316*	70.1	62.0

[1] Includes gastritis and symptoms referable to gastrointestinal tract.

Table X–19. Percentage of acute and chronic medical conditions seen by a doctor, H.I.P. enrollees and New York City sample, eight-week period, by age and sex

TYPE OF CONDITION, AGE, AND SEX	TOTAL SPECIFIED CONDITIONS		PERCENTAGE OF CONDITIONS SEEN BY A DOCTOR	
	H.I.P. enrollees	*N.Y.C. sample*	*H.I.P. enrollees*	*N.Y.C. sample*
ACUTE				
All ages	*1,770*	*2,471*	68.3	62.4
Male	919	1,203	69.5	64.2
Female	851	1,268	67.0	60.6
Under 5	*368*	*553*	72.0	68.9
Male	217	312	71.4	65.4
Female	151	241	72.8	73.4
5 to 14	*494*	*721*	71.9	62.3
Male	275	387	73.8	63.8
Female	219	334	69.4	60.5
15 to 44	*557*	*720*	60.9	58.3
Male	242	307	60.3	65.5
Female	315	413	61.3	53.0
45 to 64	*307*	*304*	70.0	58.6
Male	158	125	71.5	59.2
Female	149	179	68.4	58.1
65 and over	*34*	*124*	73.5	62.1
Male	26	51	80.8	62.7
Female	8	73	[1]	61.6
Not reported	*10*	*49*	[1]	73.5
Male	1	21	[1]	66.7
Female	9	28	[1]	78.6
CHRONIC				
All ages	*2,580*	*4,626*	42.2	33.9
Male	1,150	1,521	43.6	36.4
Female	1,430	3,105	41.2	32.7
Under 5	*91*	*101*	64.8	51.5
Male	60	69	58.3	53.6
Female	31	32	77.4	46.9
5 to 14	*172*	*222*	48.8	41.9
Male	96	122	53.1	40.2
Female	76	100	43.4	44.0
15 to 44	*1,095*	*1,597*	42.6	37.1
Male	377	469	43.2	42.6
Female	718	1,128	42.3	34.8
45 to 64	*11,064*	*1,657*	39.7	33.1
Male	508	494	40.9	34.8
Female	556	1,163	38.5	32.3
65 and over	*145*	*912*	36.6	24.6
Male	103	333	40.8	25.5
Female	42	579	26.2	24.0
Not reported	*13*	*137*	[1]	43.1
Male	6	34	[1]	29.4
Female	7	103	[1]	47.6

[1] Percentage less than 0.05.

Figure X–12. Percentage of acute and chronic conditions seen by doctor, H.I.P. enrollees and New York City sample, eight-week period, by age and sex

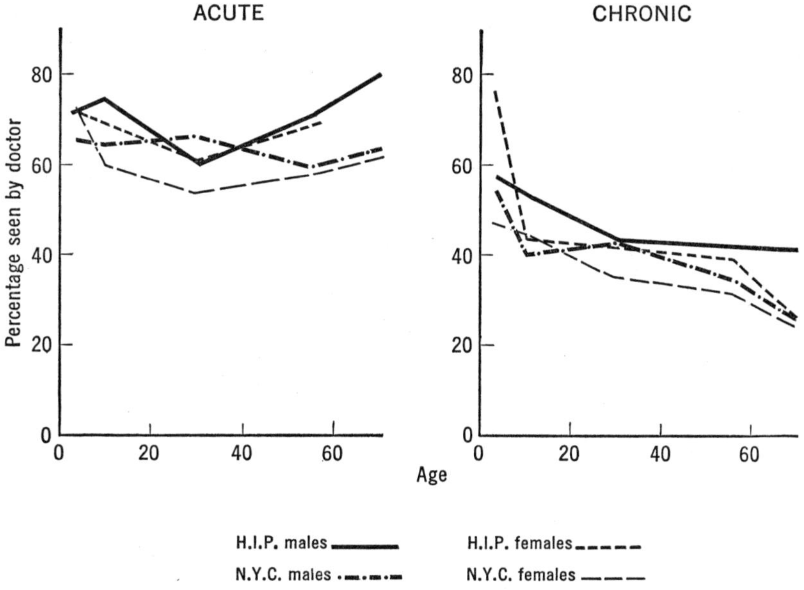

Table X–20. Acute and chronic medical conditions, H.I.P. enrollees and New York City sample, eight-week period, by age, education of head of household, and known extent of physician contact

TYPE OF CONDITION, AGE, AND YEARS OF SCHOOLING COMPLETED BY HEAD OF HOUSEHOLD	H.I.P. ENROLLEES				NEW YORK CITY SAMPLE			
	Total	*Extent of physician contact*			Total	*Extent of physician contact*		
		None	Phone only	Saw M.D.		None	Phone only	Saw M.D.
ACUTE								
All ages								
Less than 9	417	24.9	3.4	71.7	834	34.0	3.5	62.5
9 to 12	684	25.3	5.0	69.7	1,055	33.0	4.4	62.6
More than 12	648	27.0	8.3	64.7	486	33.5	3.9	62.6
Under 5								
Less than 9	44	13.6	2.3	84.1	157	29.3	4.4	66.2
9 to 12	180	21.1	8.9	70.0	257	24.5	5.4	70.0
More than 12	143	17.5	11.9	70.6	120	22.5	7.5	70.0
5 to 14								
Less than 9	103	20.4	9.7	69.9	240	39.6	5.0	55.4
9 to 12	199	23.1	2.5	74.4	337	30.6	4.4	65.0
More than 12	190	21.6	7.9	70.5	128	28.9	2.3	68.8
15 to 44								
Less than 9	113	36.3	0.8	62.8	216	34.6	3.2	62.0
9 to 12	216	31.9	4.6	63.4	317	38.8	4.4	56.8
More than 12	219	35.6	6.8	57.5	165	39.4	3.0	57.6
45 to 64								
Less than 9	137	23.5	1.4	75.2	156	28.2	1.9	70.0
9 to 12	78	20.5	3.8	75.6	88	47.7	2.3	50.0
More than 12	86	34.9	8.1	57.0	42	57.1	4.8	38.1
65 and over								
Less than 9	19	21.0	—	78.9	59	35.6	—	64.4
9 to 12	11	[1]	[1]	[1]	35	40.0	—	60.0
More than 12	2	[1]	[1]	[1]	17	35.3	—	64.7
Not reported								
Less than 9	1	[1]	[1]	[1]	6	[1]	[1]	[1]
9 to 12	—	—	—	—	21	14.3	4.7	81.0
More than 12	8	[1]	[1]	[1]	14	[1]	[1]	[1]
CHRONIC								
All ages								
Less than 9	860	61.4	0.1	38.5	2,228	68.5	0.6	30.8
9 to 12	884	55.9	0.4	43.7	1,490	62.4	0.9	36.6
More than 12	766	54.0	0.9	45.0	557	60.3	2.0	37.7
Under 5								
Less than 9	11	[1]	[1]	[1]	19	57.9	—	42.1
9 to 12	40	32.5	—	67.5	60	41.7	6.7	51.7
More than 12	40	32.5	2.5	65.0	17	35.3	11.8	52.9
5 to 14								
Less than 9	32	78.1	—	21.9	78	59.0	—	41.0
9 to 12	55	52.7	1.8	45.5	103	53.4	3.9	42.7
More than 12	83	38.6	—	61.4	39	48.7	7.7	43.7
15 to 44								
Less than 9	256	56.6	—	43.4	559	62.4	0.2	37.4
9 to 12	446	58.1	0.4	41.5	699	64.1	0.7	35.2
More than 12	370	54.6	1.6	43.8	262	58.0	1.9	40.1
45 to 64								
Less than 9	491	62.5	0.2	37.3	975	67.9	1.1	31.0
9 to 12	293	56.0	0.3	43.7	389	62.2	0.3	37.5
More than 12	241	59.3	—	40.7	148	64.9	0.6	34.5
65 and over								
Less than 9	68	67.6	—	32.4	563	78.3	0.4	21.3
9 to 12	46	56.4	—	43.5	193	71.0	—	29.0
More than 12	25	76.0	—	24.0	72	70.8	—	29.2
Not reported								
Less than 9	2	[1]	[1]	[1]	34	52.9	—	47.1
9 to 12	4	[1]	[1]	[1]	46	50.0	—	50.0
More than 12	7	[1]	[1]	[1]	19	63.2	—	36.8

[1] Percentage less than 0.05.

Figure X–13. Percentage of acute conditions seen by doctor, H.I.P. enrollees and New York City sample, eight-week period, by education of head of household and age

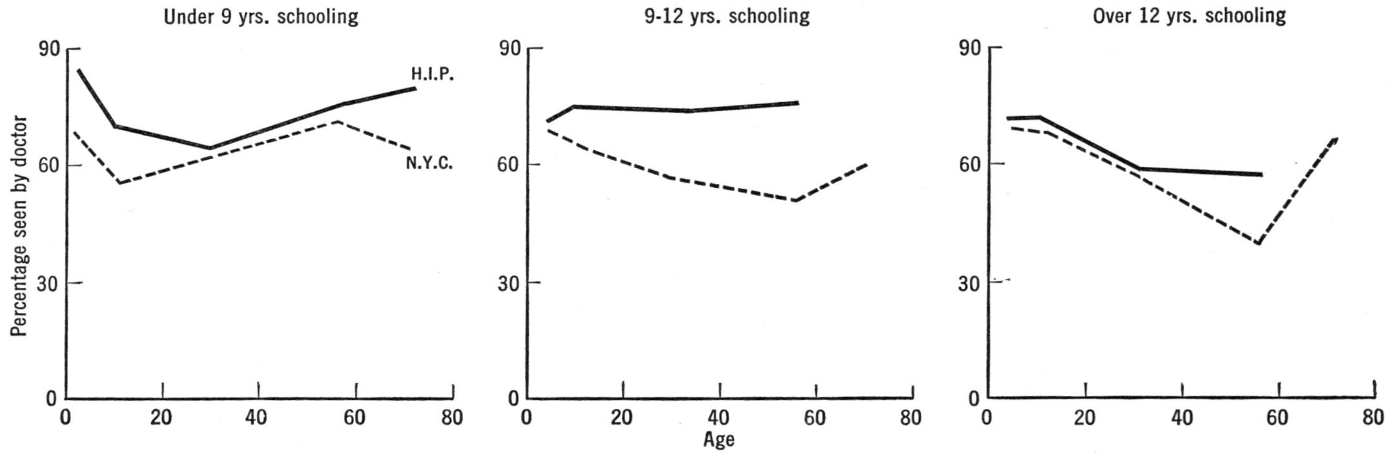

Figure X–14. Percentage of chronic conditions seen by doctor, H.I.P. enrollees and New York City sample, eight-week period, by education of head of household and age

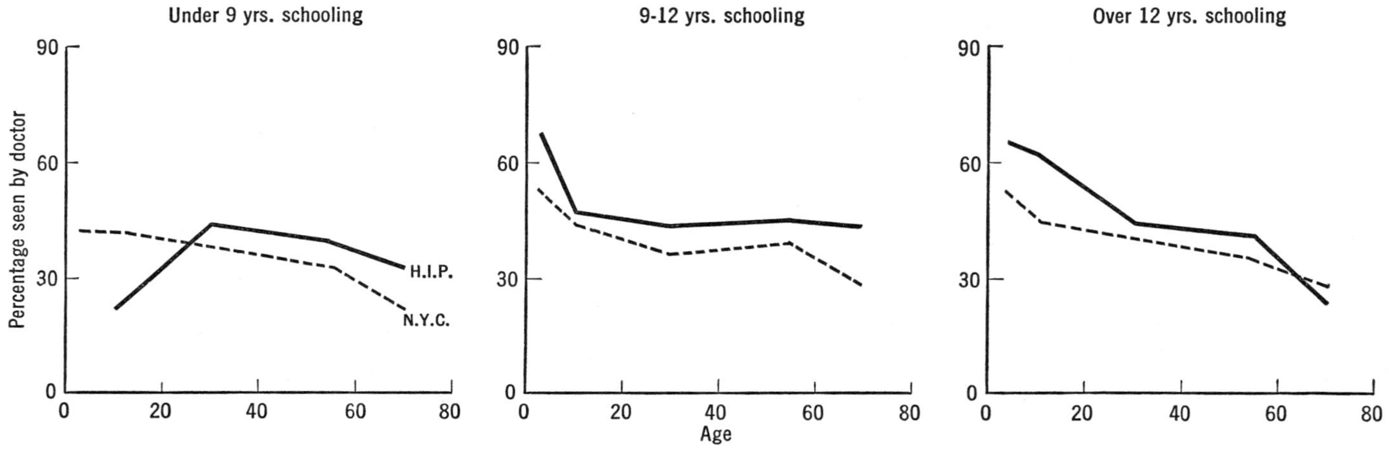

Table X–21. Percentage of persons with selected medical conditions, having specified number of physician visits, H.I.P. enrollees and New York City sample, eight-week period

DIAGNOSIS	H.I.P. ENROLLEES								NEW YORK CITY SAMPLE							
	Total conditions seen by M.D.	*Total with known number of medical visits*	*Percentage of total with known number of M.D. visits*						*Total conditions seen by M.D.*	*Total with known number of medical visits*	*Percentage of total with known number of M.D. visits*					
			1	2	3	4	5 to 9	10 or more			1	2	3	4	5 to 9	10 or more
Asthma	34	33	30.3	18.2	3.0	6.1	27.3	15.1	42	40	30.0	10.0	5.0	12.5	32.5	10.0
Other allergies	73	73	41.1	11.0	9.6	6.8	31.5	—	49	48	33.3	27.1	6.2	12.5	12.5	8.3
Diseases of ear	59	58	50.0	20.7	13.8	1.7	10.3	3.4	58	58	50.0	12.1	12.1	18.6	13.8	3.4
Diseases of eye	58	57	66.7	17.5	7.0	1.8	5.3	1.8	40	39	43.6	20.5	17.9	2.6	10.3	5.1
Heart disease	45	44	50.0	2.3	6.8	18.2	11.4	11.4	125	115	30.4	13.0	8.7	16.5	22.6	8.7
Hypertension	37	36	36.1	22.2	5.6	16.7	16.7	2.8	72	67	34.3	14.9	14.9	10.4	22.4	3.0
Acute upper respiratory infection	399	386	69.2	19.4	6.2	3.4	1.6	0.3	460	450	70.7	19.3	5.3	3.1	1.3	0.2
Other respiratory disease	417	407	59.5	20.9	10.6	2.2	4.9	2.0	541	517	47.0	21.5	10.8	7.4	7.5	5.8
Functional disorder of stomach and intestines[1]	65	64	82.8	9.4	—	1.6	6.3	—	88	75	60.0	17.3	8.0	5.3	8.0	1.3
Diseases of skin and cellular tissue	113	104	50.0	16.3	7.7	3.8	19.2	2.9	116	115	43.5	25.2	6.1	4.3	16.5	4.3
Arthritis and rheumatism	46	46	39.1	13.0	10.9	4.3	26.1	6.5	126	122	36.9	12.3	6.6	13.1	18.0	13.1

[1] Includes gastritis and symptoms referable to gastrointestinal tract.

Figure X–15. Average number of physician visits for specific conditions, H.I.P. enrollees and New York City sample, eight-week period

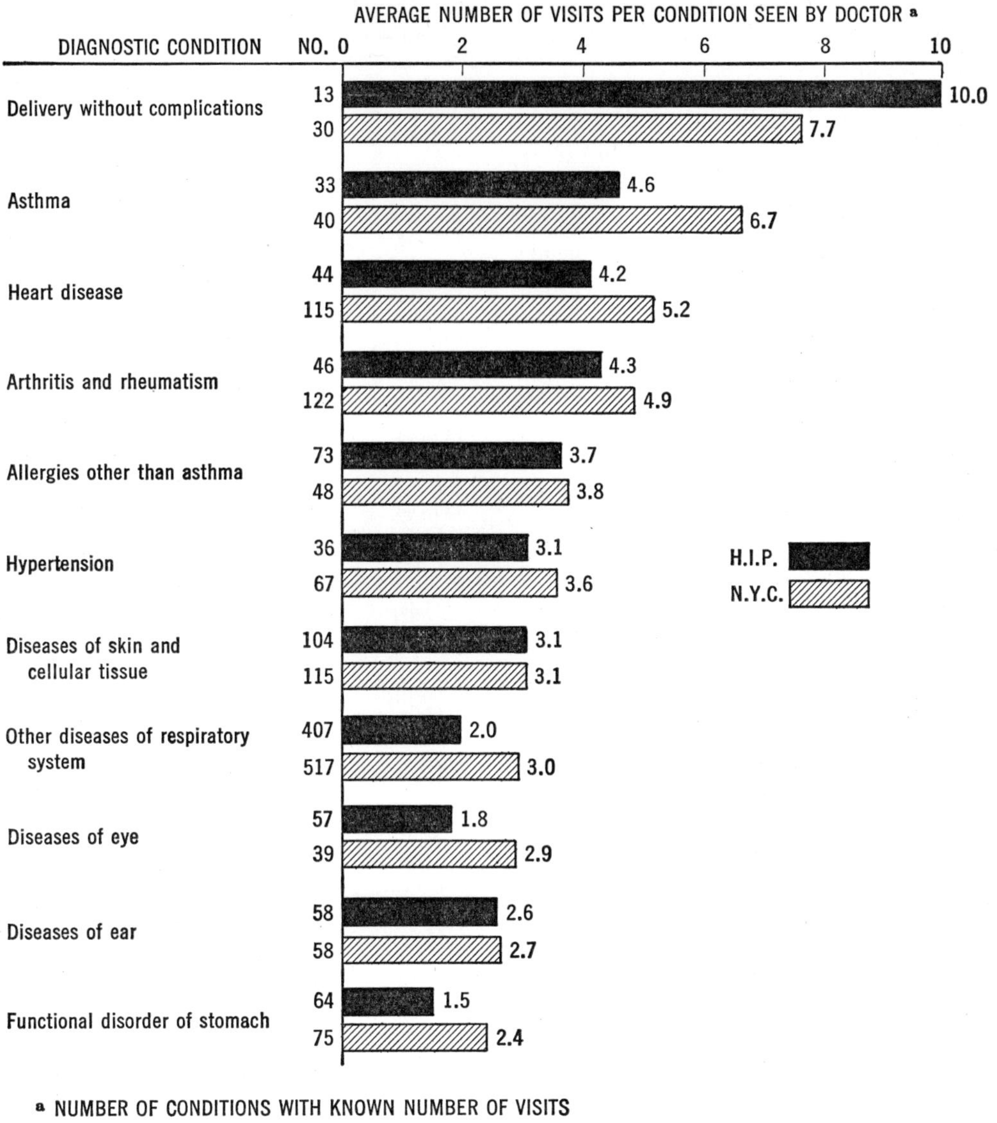

City sample, almost irrespective of age or education of the head of the household.

Number of Physician Contacts for Selected Conditions, Eight-Week Period

The second measure of amount of medical care received—the number of times a doctor was seen—is shown for selected conditions present during the eight-week period in Table x–21 (distribution by number of doctor visits) and in Figure x–15 (average number of visits per condition seen by doctor). The average number of visits per condition was greater for individuals in the New York City sample than in the H.I.P. sample for most of the conditions listed. The only condition for which the number of visits was greater in the H.I.P. sample was delivery without complications, the H.I.P. sample showing 10 visits per condition, while the corresponding figure in the New York City sample was only eight. The data presented in Chapter XIII, later, bring out that a greater proportion of H.I.P. enrollees who were pregnant were seen during the first trimester of pregnancy than was the case among the pregnant women in the New York City sample.

Average Number of Physician Contacts for Acute and Chronic Conditions, Eight-Week Period, by Age, Sex, and Education of Household Head

The average number of doctor visits showed an upward trend with age (Table x–22 and Figure x–16). This upward trend in doctor visits during the eight-week period was not as marked for chronic[14] as for acute conditions, although chronic conditions generally required more visits than acute conditions.

Males with acute conditions had more doctor visits than females with this class of condition, in both the H.I.P. and the New York City samples. This was also generally true for chronic conditions in the New York City sample but less so in the H.I.P. sample.

Both acute and chronic conditions showed a higher average number of doctor visits per condition in the New York City sample than in the H.I.P. sample, irrespective of age or sex. This is in contrast to the finding that the proportion of persons with a condition who called a doctor at all was higher in the H.I.P. sample. Thus, for those conditions present during the eight-week period it appears that the persons in the H.I.P. sample may have been more likely to contact a doctor in the first place, but once having contacted him they may not have seen him quite as often.

There was not a great deal of variation with education in the average number of doctor visits for acute conditions (Table x–23 and Figures x–17 and x–18). With the exception of a possibly higher number of visits in the highest education group in the New York City sample, the same was true of chronic diseases. It appears that education may exercise more influence on whether a doctor is seen at all than on how often he is seen once he is called in. In all education groups the New York City sample showed a generally higher average number of visits than the H.I.P. sample for both acute and chronic conditions.

Table X–22. Average number of physician visits per acute and chronic condition, H.I.P. enrollees and New York City sample, eight-week period, by age and sex

TYPE OF CONDITION,[1] AGE, AND SEX	NUMBER OF CONDITIONS		AVERAGE VISITS PER CONDITION	
	H.I.P. enrollees	*N.Y.C. sample*	*H.I.P. enrollees*	*N.Y.C. sample*
ACUTE				
All ages[2]				
Male	619	750	2.3	2.6
Female	561	749	1.8	2.5
Under 5				
Male	150	199	2.1	2.2
Female	110	173	1.5	2.2
5 to 14				
Male	198	237	1.5	1.9
Female	148	195	1.6	2.0
15 to 44				
Male	144	197	2.9	3.3
Female	189	212	1.7	2.6
45 to 64				
Male	106	72	3.1	3.4
Female	102	103	2.2	2.8
65 and over				
Male	20	31	3.4	4.7
Female	4	44	2.0	2.4
CHRONIC				
All ages[2]				
Male	479	529	3.6	4.4
Female	568	967	3.4	4.1
Under 5				
Male	32	34	3.5	2.4
Female	24	15	1.9	2.1
5 to 14				
Male	50	47	3.8	4.9
Female	33	42	2.9	4.0
15 to 44				
Male	154	195	3.2	4.8
Female	292	379	3.5	4.0
45 to 64				
Male	204	165	3.9	3.7
Female	207	356	3.3	4.1
65 and over				
Male	37	79	3.2	5.7
Female	10	130	4.1	4.7

[1] Excludes obstetric and puerperal conditions.
[2] Includes persons whose age was not reported.

Number of Physician Contacts for Acute and Chronic Conditions, 1951

The number of times a doctor was seen was also determined for those conditions producing seven or more days of bed-disability or hospitalization in 1951. The average number of doctor visits in a year for many of these conditions is very high (Figure x–19) and could result in considerable expense to families not covered by insurance.

Unlike most of the eight-week conditions, several conditions producing hospitalization or seven or more days of bed-disability in 1951 showed a higher average number of visits to the doctor

[14] See footnote 9.

Figure X–16. Average number of physician visits per acute and chronic condition (excluding obstetric and puerperal conditions), H.I.P. enrollees and New York City sample, eight-week period, by age and sex

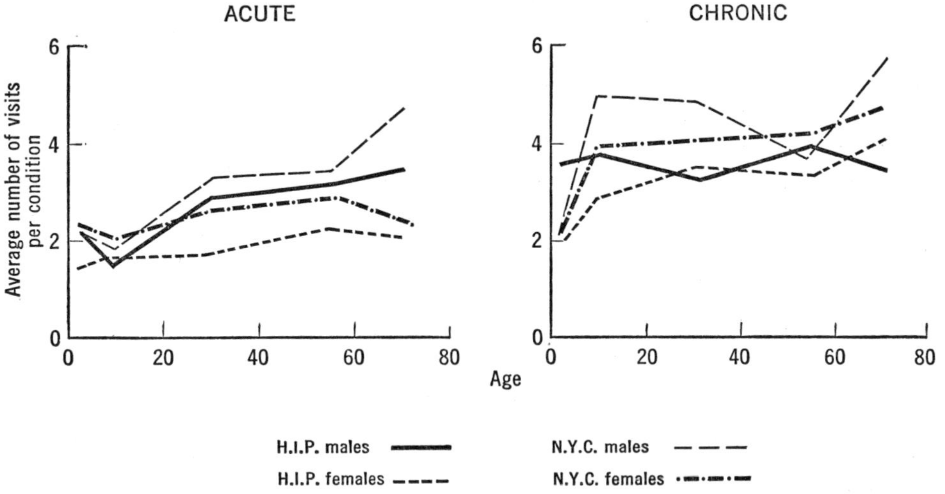

Figure X–17. Average number of physician visits per acute condition, H.I.P. enrollees and New York City sample, eight-week period, by education of head of household and age

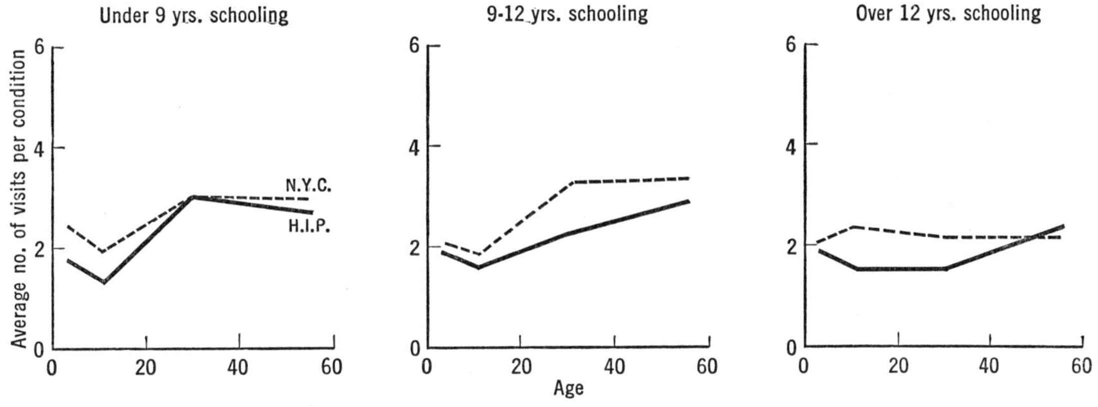

Figure X–18. Average number of physician visits per chronic condition, H.I.P. enrollees and New York City sample, eight-week period, by education of head of household and age

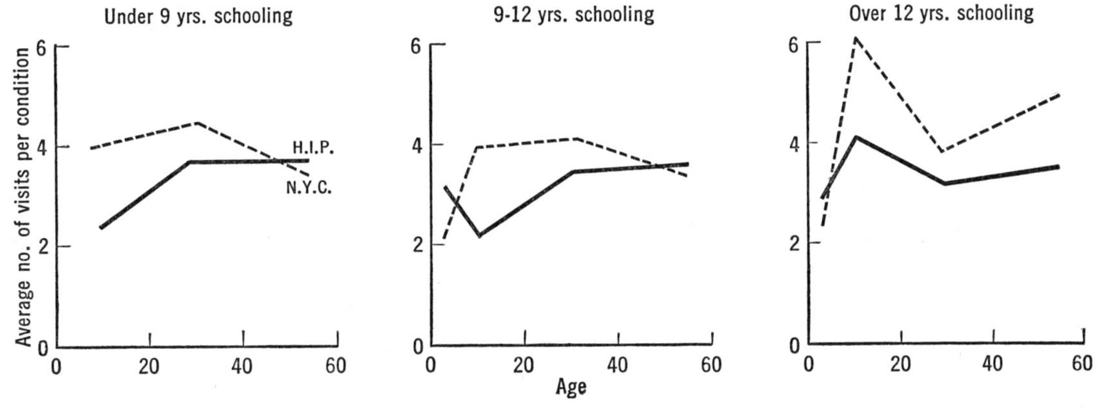

Table X–23. Average number of physician visits per acute and chronic condition, H.I.P. enrollees and New York City sample, eight-week period, by age and education of head of household

TYPE OF CONDITION, AGE, AND YEARS OF SCHOOLING COMPLETED BY HEAD OF HOUSEHOLD	NUMBER OF CONDITIONS		NUMBER OF M.D. VISITS		AVERAGE VISITS PER CONDITION	
	H.I.P. enrollees	*N.Y.C. sample*	*H.I.P. enrollees*	*N.Y.C. sample*	*H.I.P. enrollees*	*N.Y.C. sample*
ACUTE						
All ages[1]						
Less than 9	291	507	702	1,281	2.4	2.5
9 to 12	470	644	966	1,581	2.0	2.4
More than 12	406	294	729	791	1.8	2.7
Under 5						
Less than 9	37	103	64	245	1.7	2.4
9 to 12	122	175	227	368	1.9	2.1
More than 12	100	81	190	172	1.9	2.1
5 to 14						
Less than 9	69	127	89	229	1.3	1.8
9 to 12	146	213	237	378	1.6	1.8
More than 12	130	83	212	201	1.6	2.4
15 to 44						
Less than 9	70	129	214	394	3.0	3.0
9 to 12	137	175	319	571	2.3	3.3
More than 12	121	94	193	209	1.6	2.2
45 to 64						
Less than 9	99	107	266	317	2.7	3.0
9 to 12	58	44	171	148	2.9	3.4
More than 12	47	15	114	33	2.4	2.2
65 and over						
Less than 9	15	38	59	89	[2]	[2]
9 to 12	7	20	12	48	[2]	[2]
More than 12	1	11	3	99	[2]	[2]
CHRONIC						
All ages[1]						
Less than 9	325	665	1,180	2,782	3.6	4.2
9 to 12	372	529	1,255	2,017	3.4	3.8
More than 12	330	198	1,128	954	3.4	4.8
Under 5						
Less than 9	6	7	6	17	[2]	[2]
9 to 12	26	30	83	65	3.2	2.2
More than 12	24	9	68	21	2.8	2.3
5 to 14						
Less than 9	7	29	16	119	2.3	4.1
9 to 12	25	43	54	171	2.2	4.0
More than 12	50	17	208	106	4.2	6.2
15 to 44						
Less than 9	109	202	405	904	3.7	4.5
9 to 12	174	238	586	1,005	3.4	4.2
More than 12	155	101	504	449	3.2	4.4
45 to 64						
Less than 9	179	296	663	1,018	3.7	3.4
9 to 12	127	139	451	486	3.6	3.5
More than 12	95	48	337	240	3.5	5.0
65 and over						
Less than 9	22	15	85	606	[2]	5.3
9 to 12	19	56	65	243	[2]	4.3
More than 12	5	16	9	120	[2]	7.5

[1] Includes persons whose age was not reported.
[2] Average not computed.

in the H.I.P. sample than in the New York City sample. Among these were diseases of the liver, gallbladder and pancreas,[15] diseases of the heart,[15] and ulcer of the stomach.[15] The rest of the conditions shown in Figure x–19 had about the same frequency of visits for both the H.I.P. and New York City samples, although neoplasms,[15] other respiratory infection,[16] and infective and parasitic disease other than tuberculosis[16] showed a slightly higher number of visits per condition in the New York City sample.

[15] The small number of conditions on which these averages are based does not permit ruling out the possibility that these differences may be accounted for by chance alone.

[16] For these conditions the difference is statistically significant.

Figure X–19. Average number of physician visits for specific conditions producing hospitalization or seven or more days of bed-disability, H.I.P. enrollees and New York City sample, 1951

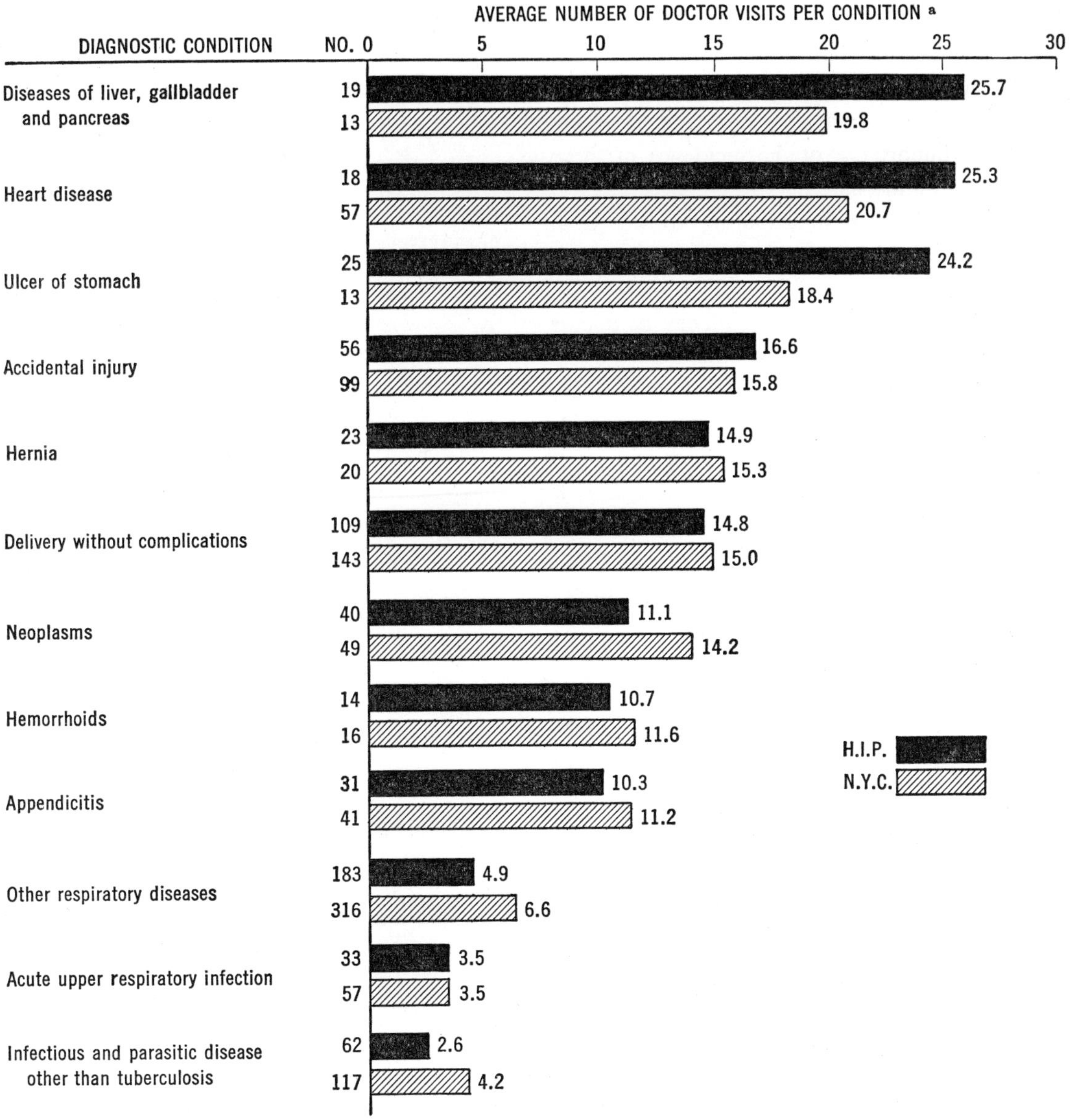

a NUMBER OF CONDITIONS WITH KNOWN NUMBER OF VISITS

Average Number of Physician Visits for Acute and Chronic Conditions, 1951, by Age, Sex, and Education of Household Head

Returning to the grouping into acute and chronic conditions in order to examine trends, it is seen that with the exception of New York City males (Figure x–20 and Table x–24) there appeared a small upward trend with age in the average number of doctor visits for acute conditions of this degree of disability. Chronic conditions, however, showed a very marked rise in the volume of medical care received with advancing age. It will be recalled that the frequency of chronic disease also rose with age. It would be of considerable importance in the planning of programs for chronic diseases and for the aged to assess the relative importance of the incidence of these diseases and of the amount of care needed once they are acquired in contributing to the total volume of care which must be furnished.[17]

For this class of conditions it is difficult to examine the variation in the frequency of doctor visits by age and education of the head of the household because of the small numbers in many age groups (Table x–42). If all ages are considered together and the rates within each education group are standardized for age (Table x–25), it is found that the number of doctor visits per acute condition in the lowest education group was about the same in the two samples, but as one progresses up the education scale the difference between the two samples widens, about five visits per acute condition being found in the highest education group in the H.I.P. sample and seven in the New York City sample. For chronic conditions there was a general decrease with education in the number of visits per condition. The averages were lower in the H.I.P. sample than in the New York City sample in the lowest education group, about the same in the middle group, and a little higher in the H.I.P. sample in the highest education group.

Table X–24. Average number of physician visits per attended acute and chronic condition producing hospitalization or seven or more days of bed-disability, H.I.P. enrollees and New York City sample, 1951, by age and sex

TYPE OF CONDITION, AGE, AND SEX	NUMBER OF CONDITIONS		AVERAGE VISITS PER CONDITION	
	H.I.P. enrollees	*N.Y.C. sample*	*H.I.P. enrollees*	*N.Y.C. sample*
ACUTE				
All ages				
Male	195	290	6.8	7.8
Female	166	308	6.7	8.8
Under 5				
Male	28	58	8.7	6.4
Female	16	32	2.8	4.9
5 to 14				
Male	59	87	4.2	4.7
Female	48	68	4.2	4.8
15 to 44				
Male	48	96	6.3	12.1
Female	62	101	8.0	9.8
45 to 64				
Male	55	34	8.6	7.1
Female	38	75	8.7	10.9
65 and over				
Male	[1]	12	—	4.2
Female	[1]	26	—	11.2
CHRONIC				
All ages				
Male	166	237	17.3	18.5
Female	175	268	14.7	15.5
Under 5				
Male	15	17	9.5	5.1
Female	[1]	16	—	7.1
5 to 14				
Male	20	39	10.4	11.5
Female	16	23	7.2	7.3
15 to 44				
Male	37	80	19.6	20.2
Female	83	111	13.4	16.4
45 to 64				
Male	83	64	16.6	24.3
Female	65	84	18.3	17.2
65 and over				
Male	[1]	32	—	20.1
Female	[1]	25	—	17.6

[1] Number less than 10.

Interval between Onset of Symptoms and First Physician Contact

Presumably if there is no economic barrier to seeking medical care, then the third measure of medical care—length of time between onset of a particular condition and the seeking of medical care for that condition—should be less than when such a barrier is present. This point is examined in Table x–26 for those conditions in which it was thought that the date of onset of symptoms could be accepted.[18]

[17] It was not possible to do this from the present survey because data on the number of doctor visits required for *all* chronic diseases during 1951 were not obtained.

[18] These are largely acute conditions. It would be desirable to test the hypothesis for chronic conditions, but the necessary data are difficult to obtain through the survey method.

Figure X–20. Average number of physician visits per acute and chronic condition producing hospitalization or seven or more days of bed-disability, H.I.P. enrollees and New York City sample, 1951, by age and sex

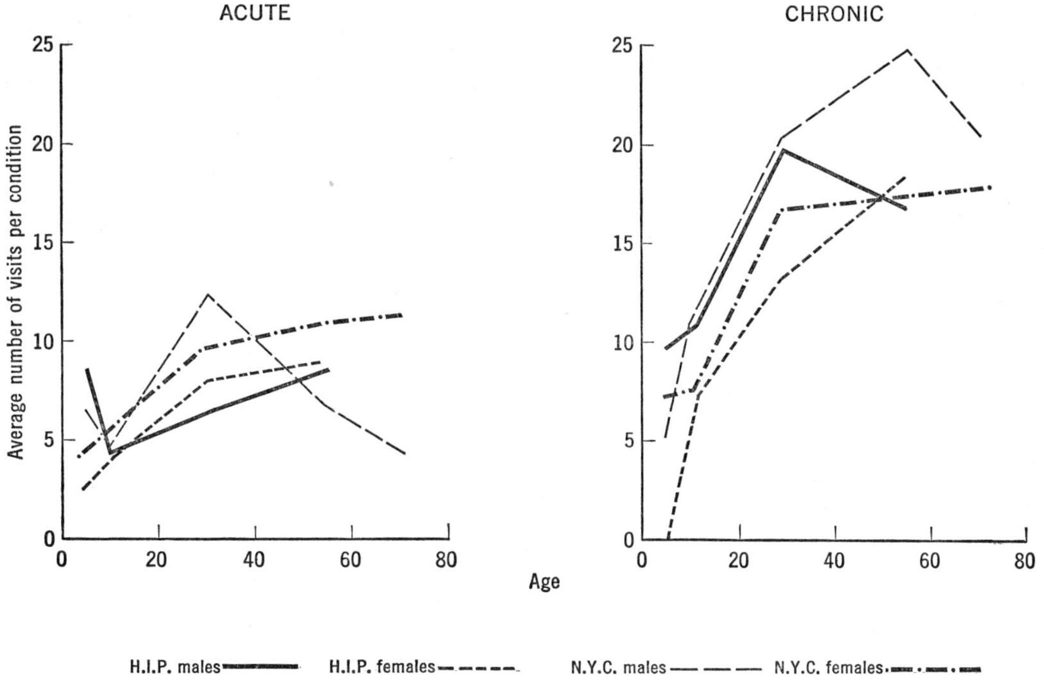

Table X–25. Average number of physician visits per attended acute and chronic condition producing hospitalization or seven or more days of bed-disability, H.I.P. enrollees and New York City sample, 1951, by education of head of household

TYPE OF CONDITION AND YEARS OF SCHOOLING COMPLETED BY HEAD OF HOUSEHOLD	NUMBER OF CONDITIONS		AVERAGE NUMBER OF DOCTOR VISITS PER CONDITION			
			Unadjusted for age		*Adjusted for age*[1]	
	H.I.P. enrollees	N.Y.C. sample	H.I.P. enrollees	N.Y.C. sample	H.I.P. enrollees	N.Y.C. sample
ACUTE						
Less than 9	113	204	7.6	7.9	6.5	6.6
9 to 12	120	265	8.1	8.8	7.3	8.5
More than 12	121	109	4.8	8.0	4.9	7.3
CHRONIC						
Less than 9	115	233	16.4	20.3	12.1	16.9
9 to 12	125	174	14.4	15.1	12.7	13.6
More than 12	91	66	14.8	10.8	7.5	5.4

[1] Adjusted only for those ages in which the number of conditions was sufficiently large to compute a rate. Detailed data are shown in Table x–42.

With the exception of the conditions called "functional disorder of the stomach" the proportion of persons seeing a doctor within less than one day of onset of the condition was greater for the H.I.P. sample than for the New York City sample. This holds true also if one combines the one-day percentages with the less-than-one-day figures. Conversely, the percentage waiting two or more days to see a doctor was less in the H.I.P. sample than in the New York City sample.

Since diseases of the respiratory system and accidents make up the great bulk of conditions

Table X–26. Time lag in physician contact for selected medical conditions with acceptable date of onset reported, H.I.P. enrollees and New York City sample, eight-week period

DIAGNOSTIC CONDITION	H.I.P. ENROLLEES				NEW YORK CITY SAMPLE			
	Total conditions	*Time lag in doctor contact*			*Total conditions*	*Time lag in doctor contact*		
		Less than 1 day	1 day	2 or more days		Less than 1 day	1 day	2 or more days
Infective and parasitic diseases other than tuberculosis	170	52.4	32.9	14.7	262	43.5	36.6	19.8
Diseases of ear	30	53.3	36.7	10.0	44	45.4	25.0	29.5
Acute upper respiratory infection	374	46.5	30.2	23.3	429	42.9	27.0	30.1
Other respiratory diseases	338	46.2	31.1	22.8	427	42.2	30.7	27.2
Functional disorder of stomach	34	50.0	14.7	35.3	30	53.3	20.0	26.7
Diseases of skin and cellular tissue	26	26.9	23.1	50.0	20	20.0	25.0	55.0
Disorders of back	25	44.0	24.0	32.0	19	21.0	26.3	52.6
Accidental injuries	127	70.9	17.3	11.8	184	67.4	20.6	12.0
All other conditions with acceptable onset date	42	61.9	11.9	26.2	50	48.0	16.0	36.0

Table X–27. Persons with acute upper respiratory infection who saw doctor, H.I.P. enrollees and New York City sample, eight-week period, by age and length of time between onset and physician visit

AGE	H.I.P. ENROLLEES						NEW YORK CITY SAMPLE					
	Number of conditions	*Percentage with specified time between onset and physician visit*					*Number of conditions*	*Percentage with specified time between onset and physician visit*				
		Total	Less than 1 day	1 day	2 to 3 days	4 or more days		Total	Less than 1 day	1 day	2 to 3 days	4 or more days
All ages[1]	374	100.0	46.5	30.2	17.8	5.4	429	100.0	42.9	27.0	19.3	10.8
Under 5	95	100.0	62.0	20.0	18.0	—	137	100.0	51.0	24.1	15.4	8.8
5 to 14	103	100.0	53.1	31.2	12.7	2.9	122	100.0	49.1	35.2	12.3	3.3
15 to 44	96	100.0	36.6	33.3	20.8	9.4	89	100.0	28.1	23.9	32.0	15.9
45 to 64	67	100.0	31.4	37.5	19.4	11.8	56	100.0	25.0	25.0	25.0	25.0

[1] Includes persons 65 and over and those whose age was not reported.

Table X–28. Persons with acute upper respiratory infection who saw doctor, H.I.P. enrollees and New York City sample, eight-week period, by education of head of household and length of time between onset and physician visit

YEARS OF SCHOOLING COMPLETED BY HEAD OF HOUSEHOLD	H.I.P. ENROLLEES						NEW YORK CITY SAMPLE					
	Number of conditions	*Percentage with specified time between onset and physician visit*					*Number of conditions*	*Percentage with specified time between onset and physician visit*				
		Total	Less than 1 day	1 day	2 to 3 days	4 or more days		Total	Less than 1 day	1 day	2 to 3 days	4 or more days
All years[1]	374	100.0	46.5	30.2	17.8	5.4	429	100.0	42.9	27.0	19.3	10.8
Less than 9	98	100.0	45.0	30.3	16.3	8.4	156	100.0	28.7	31.4	25.5	14.4
9 to 12	134	100.0	43.0	30.7	22.4	3.8	179	100.0	47.5	28.4	14.6	9.5
More than 12	136	100.0	48.5	30.9	15.4	5.1	89	100.0	57.7	16.8	17.8	7.7

[1] Includes persons for whom educational status of head of household was not reported.

for which an acceptable date of onset was obtained, these will be examined in more detail.

There was a general decline with age in the proportion of persons with acute upper respiratory infections seeking care shortly after onset of the illness. These conditions were generally seen earlier in the H.I.P. sample than in the New York City sample (Table x–27). This was particularly true for children less than five years of age. Furthermore, the proportion waiting four days or longer to call a doctor was greater in the New York City sample than in the H.I.P. sample.

When the same cases are classified by education of the head of the household (Table x–28) it is seen that there was relatively little variation in the time lag among the three education groups for the H.I.P. sample. However, in the New York City sample there was a fairly pronounced increase with education in the proportion of persons seeking medical care in less than one day after onset of the illness. Even if the figures for less than one day and one day are combined there is still an increase from 60 percent in the lowest education group to 75 percent in the highest education group seeing the doctor in less than two days. The greatest difference between the H.I.P. sample and the New York City sample occurred in the lowest education group, the percentage seeing a doctor in less than two days being 75.3 percent for the H.I.P. sample and 60.1 percent for the New York City sample. In the highest education group, although the percentage seeing a doctor in less than one day was greater for New York City than for H.I.P., combined figures for less than one day and one day were not very different—79.4 percent for H.I.P. and 74.5 percent for New York City.

Respiratory conditions other than acute upper respiratory infections (Table x–29), conditions called largely "grippe" and some pneumonia, showed a decline with age in the proportion seeking early medical care similar to that seen for acute upper respiratory conditions. However, except for the age group 5 to 14 there was very little difference between the two samples in the two shortest time-lag groups combined. In the 5 to 14 age group the percentage seeing a doctor in less than two days is 82.6 for H.I.P. and 70.8 for New York City.

The variation with education in the length of time between onset and seeking a doctor's care (Table x–30) was very much the same for "other respiratory conditions" as for acute upper respiratory infection—relatively little change with education for H.I.P., and for New York City an increase with education in the percentage with less than two days' time lag. As before, the greatest difference occurred in the lowest education group—78.7 percent for H.I.P. and 69.4 percent for New York City. In the highest education group the percentage was lower for H.I.P. (75.4 percent) than for New York City (80.2 percent).

Accidents, by their very nature, require medical care very shortly after the event, and because of the immediacy of the problem, one would not expect much difference between the two samples or much variation with age, education, or eco-

Table X–29. Persons with respiratory conditions other than acute upper respiratory infection who saw doctor, H.I.P. enrollees and New York City sample, eight-week period, by age and length of time between onset and physician visit

AGE	H.I.P. ENROLLEES: *Number of conditions*	*Percentage with specified time between onset and physician visit*: Total	Less than 1 day	1 day	2 to 3 days	4 or more days	NEW YORK CITY SAMPLE: *Number of conditions*	*Percentage with specified time between onset and physician visit*: Total	Less than 1 day	1 day	2 to 3 days	4 or more days
All ages[1]	338	100.0	46.2	31.1	17.2	5.6	427	100.0	42.2	30.7	20.1	7.0
Under 5	55	100.0	60.0	27.3	12.7	—	67	100.0	46.3	40.3	8.9	4.5
5 to 14	80	100.0	56.3	26.3	16.2	1.2	120	100.0	43.3	27.5	25.0	4.2
15 to 44	116	100.0	44.0	33.6	16.4	6.0	139	100.0	45.3	33.8	15.1	5.8
45 to 64	78	100.0	33.3	32.1	21.8	12.8	59	100.0	32.2	30.5	23.7	13.6

[1] Includes persons 65 and over and those whose age was not reported.

Table X–30. Persons with respiratory conditions other than acute upper respiratory infection who saw doctor, H.I.P. enrollees and New York City sample, eight-week period, by education of head of household and length of time between onset and physician visit

YEARS OF SCHOOLING COMPLETED BY HEAD OF HOUSEHOLD	H.I.P. ENROLLEES						NEW YORK CITY SAMPLE					
	Number of conditions	*Percentage with specified time between onset and physician visit*					*Number of conditions*	*Percentage with specified time between onset and physician visit*				
		Total	Less than 1 day	1 day	2 to 3 days	4 or more days		Total	Less than 1 day	1 day	2 to 3 days	4 or more days
All years[1]	338	100.0	46.2	31.1	17.2	5.6	427	100.0	42.2	30.7	20.1	7.0
Less than 9	75	100.0	42.7	36.0	12.0	9.3	134	100.0	37.3	32.1	21.6	9.0
9 to 12	128	100.0	48.4	29.7	16.4	5.5	191	100.0	44.0	29.3	19.4	7.3
More than 12	130	100.0	47.7	27.7	20.8	3.8	86	100.0	45.3	34.9	17.4	2.3

[1] Includes persons for whom educational status of head of household was not reported.

Table X–31. Persons with accidents who saw doctor, H.I.P. enrollees and New York City sample, eight-week period, by age and length of time between accident and physician visit

AGE	H.I.P. ENROLLEES						NEW YORK CITY SAMPLE					
	Number of conditions	*Percentage with specified time between accident and physician visit*					*Number of conditions*	*Percentage with specified time between accident and physician visit*				
		Total	Less than 1 day	1 day	2 to 3 days	4 or more days		Total	Less than 1 day	1 day	2 to 3 days	4 or more days
All ages[1]	127	100.0	70.9	17.3	4.7	7.1	184	100.0	67.4	20.7	5.4	6.5
Under 5	11[2]	100.0					17[2]	100.0				
5 to 14	35	100.0	77.1	5.7	2.9	14.3	31	100.0	64.5	22.6	9.7	3.2
15 to 44	51	100.0	60.8	29.4	7.8	2.0	79	100.0	65.8	24.1	2.5	7.6
45 to 64	25	100.0	72.0	12.0	4.0	12.0	35	100.0	62.9	14.3	11.4	11.4

[1] Includes persons 65 and over and those whose age was not reported.
[2] Number too small to permit computation of percentages.

Table X–32. Persons with accidents who saw doctor, H.I.P. enrollees and New York City sample, eight-week period, by education of head of household and length of time between accident and physician visit

YEARS OF SCHOOLING COMPLETED BY HEAD OF HOUSEHOLD	H.I.P. ENROLLEES						NEW YORK CITY SAMPLE					
	Number of conditions	*Percentage with specified time between accident and physician visit*					*Number of conditions*	*Percentage with specified time between accident and physician visit*				
		Total	Less than 1 day	1 day	2 to 3 days	4 or more days		Total	Less than 1 day	1 day	2 to 3 days	4 or more days
All years[1]	127	100.0	70.9	17.3	4.7	7.1	184	100.0	67.4	20.7	5.4	6.5
Less than 9	46	100.0	78.3	4.3	10.9	6.5	58	100.0	70.7	19.0	8.6	1.7
9 to 12	48	100.0	66.7	25.0	—	8.3	84	100.0	67.9	17.9	4.7	9.5
More than 12	32	100.0	68.8	21.9	3.1	6.2	26	100.0	53.8	34.6	—	11.5

[1] Includes persons for whom educational status of head of household was not reported.

nomic status. Such seems to be the case (Tables X–31 and X–32), particularly if one combines the data for less than one day and one day. The picture for accidents, therefore, is different from that for the other two conditions considered.

So far as the data for these three conditions are concerned, they are consistent with the hypothesis that if there is no economic barrier to seeking medical care, people will reduce the length of time between onset of a condition and the seeking of medical care for that condition. However, similar information regarding a number of other conditions combined with direct observations concerning income must be obtained before the hypothesis may be considered as proven.

Summary and Discussion

A large mass of material on the reported frequency of specific illnesses, on the degree of disability resulting from these illnesses, and on the amount of medical care sought for them has been presented in this chapter. We shall seek here to distill the essence of this material so as to (1) present a summary of the health problems of New York City and the factors influencing their nature and magnitude, and (2) consider the extent to which they throw light upon the effect, if any, of a comprehensive medical care plan such as H.I.P. upon the health of its enrollees.

The Health Problems of New York City and Factors Influencing Their Nature and Magnitude

It was shown in Chapter III that the New York City sample was reasonably representative of the city as a whole. To the extent that this fact holds, the findings for the sample reflect the health problems of the community. Among the most important of these, judging by their frequency during the eight-week period of the inquiry, were respiratory conditions, diseases of the bones and organs of movement, especially arthritis and rheumatism, and back conditions. Functional disorders of the stomach, diseases of the circulatory system, and accidents also were responsible for a large amount of illness.

The amount and kinds of illness reported and the degree of disability resulting from them varied among different segments of the population. In so far as age and sex are concerned, the pattern of variation was similar to that found in other reports. In general, acute illnesses and allergic conditions other than asthma were found with greatest frequency at the younger ages and the amount of time lost from these conditions decreased with advancing age. Chronic conditions, on the other hand, increased in frequency and caused an increasing amount of lost time with increasing age.

Females showed a higher reported frequency of illness for such conditions as obesity, diseases of the blood, hypertension, circulatory conditions other than heart disease, respiratory conditions, minor digestive disorders, and arthritis and rheumatism. Males, on the other hand, showed a higher rate than females for gastric ulcer, heart disease, and accidents. In the middle ranges of the age scale females lost more time from their usual activities because of illness, but at the extremes of the age scale males showed a greater degree of time lost.

When children—i.e., persons under 14 years of age—are omitted from the analysis, arthritis and rheumatism, circulatory diseases other than heart disease and hypertension, and disorders and symptoms referable to the back or limbs are found to have been the most prevalent conditions. Their frequency was very much higher among persons not in the labor force. For example, in the New York City sample among persons in the labor force the prevalence of arthritis and rheumatism on the day preceding the interview was about 38 cases per 1,000 population, while the corresponding figure among those not in the labor force was 96 per 1,000 population.

The three groups of conditions just discussed accounted for about 28 percent of all conditions reported among persons in the labor force and 33 percent of those reported for persons not in the labor force. Other conditions among the first ten in prevalence in both labor force status groups were hypertension, heart disease, obesity, diseases of the skin, acute upper respiratory infections, and other diseases of the bones and organs of movement. It is of interest that males in the labor force had a lower rate than females in the labor force for both acute and chronic diseases; for persons not in the labor force the reverse was true for acute conditions, but the rate for chronic diseases remained lower in males than in females.

These facts point up not only the need to know more about the natural history of these diseases in order to provide a firm base for treatment and alleviation of disability in the individual and for community health programs, but also the need for more knowledge about the dynamics of these diseases in relation to the economic and social standing of the family. For some conditions this relationship may very well involve an interaction between illness and economic status in which cause and effect exchange roles at different times. To take an extreme example—if the breadwinner leaves the labor force because of illness, what is the economic and social impact on the family over a period of time and how does this in turn affect the course of the condition or the development of other conditions? Cross-sectional studies such as the present one focus attention on these problems but cannot reveal how the evolutionary forces operate to produce the cross-sectional pictures. A better understanding of this evolutionary process is needed in the development of community programs aimed at chronic disease problems.

The kinds of illnesses reported as present during the eight-week period varied considerably with the education of the head of the household. The greater the education the greater the amount of acute illness reported and the more time lost from usual activity. Chronic disease, on the other hand, was reported with greater frequency and resulted in more lost time in the least-educated groups of the population.

Do the better educated really have more acute disease and less chronic disease than the less-schooled members of the population? With regard to acute illness it seems more likely that the higher rates among the better educated reflected higher standards of what constitutes good health and good care and that these higher standards led them to consider as illness, conditions which might not be so considered or might even go unrecognized among the less educated. The higher rate of chronic disease among the least-educated group, on the other hand, cannot be explained in this fashion. There may actually have been more chronic disease in this group of the population, although for particular chronic diseases the higher rates among the less educated may have reflected less specificity in the reported diagnoses than in the better-educated group.

Whatever the explanation, the fact remains that illness and disability rates vary with education; and, even though education is highly correlated with other variables, such as income, the findings of this study emphasize the importance of sociological as well as biological factors in any approach on the part of the community to meeting the health needs of the population. This is also brought out by the findings on medical care received by the population.

The medical care received by persons in the two samples during the period of the survey has been reviewed in the preceding chapter. The material presented in this chapter permits a closer examination of this care in relation to diagnosis. Thus the percentage of cases seen by a doctor during the eight-week period[19] ranged from a low of 20 to 25 percent for diseases of the circulatory system to a high of over 90 percent for neoplasms. It is of interest that the conditions reported with greatest frequency among persons 14 years of age and over both in and out of the labor force were also the conditions with the greatest proportion not seen by a doctor, at least during the eight-week period. In general, persons with acute conditions sought a doctor's care more frequently than persons with chronic conditions, the former averaging about 65 percent and the latter about 35 percent. This, of course, is partly a reflection of the fact that the period of inquiry was only eight weeks.

Males, by and large, were less likely to be seen by a doctor than females. However, if attention is concentrated on those reported as actually having an acute condition during the eight-week period, then males with such conditions not only were more likely to be seen by a doctor but they also had a higher average number of visits than females with acute conditions. This is also true of chronic conditions.

The variation with education in medical care received for a condition seems to depend largely on whether a doctor is contacted at all rather than on the number of times he is seen once he has been called. With increasing education of the head of the household, there was an increase in the proportion of chronic conditions for which both face-to-face and telephone contacts with a physician were sought. A smaller proportion of chronic conditions were attended by a doctor in

[19] It should be borne in mind that those cases reported as not having seen a doctor may have been seen by a physician before or after the eight-week period.

the lowest education group than in the two higher education groups in both the H.I.P. and New York City samples. Since presumably there should be no financial deterrent to seeking medical care in the H.I.P. sample, one is led to conclude that these findings must to some extent reflect different attitudes toward illness, or different concepts of health, among the several education groups. This emphasizes once again that programs aimed at bringing our growing knowledge of the biological aspects of chronic disease to bear in the control of these diseases in the population must also give consideration to the health mores of that population, especially since it is in the lowest education group that the highest frequency of chronic disease is found.

In respect of acute conditions there was little variation with education of the head of the household in the proportion of these attended by a doctor, even though such conditions are more frequent among the better educated. That a lower threshold for recognition of illness may account for this higher frequency is suggested by the direct variation of telephone contacts and inverse variation of face-to-face contacts with increasing education in the H.I.P. sample. On the other hand, these variations were not observed in the New York City sample. Whether they did not exist, or whether they were obscured by other factors, possibly of an economic nature, cannot be determined from these data. In any event, the hypothesis that there are differential meanings placed on the terms "illness" and "health" in different educational strata of the population has sufficiently broad implications in relation to the development of community health programs to make it desirable to find ways of testing the hypothesis wherever possible.

Effect of Prepaid Medical Care Plan on Health of Its Enrollees

Prepaid medical care plans available to large segments of the population are a recent phenomenon in the United States.[20] It is natural, therefore, that attention has been focused largely upon the economic and administrative aspects of these plans. Their impact on the health of the population has received relatively little attention. Indeed, the criteria by which to measure this impact, and the period of time over which it is necessary to observe them, are largely unknown. The Steering Committee believed that a comparison of the H.I.P. and New York City samples not only would throw light upon the influence of a comprehensive care plan such as H.I.P. on the patterns of medical care, but might also lead to the discovery of measurements pertinent to the question of the influence of the Plan on health itself.

It may be said at the outset that provision of medical care through a prepayment group practice plan which seeks to provide comprehensive coverage does modify the medical care behavior patterns of its members in comparison with similar groups of the population not covered by the plan. The principal differences observed between the H.I.P. and the New York City samples are as follows:

1. Although most specific conditions were reported with about the same frequency in the two samples, the kinds of conditions for which the H.I.P. rate was higher are generally thought of by the public as run of the mill, whereas those for which the New York City rate was higher are generally considered to be serious. Thus the H.I.P. sample showed a higher rate of reported illness from acute upper respiratory infections, influenza and grippe, allergies other than asthma, and hemorrhoids. The New York City rate, on the other hand, was higher for arthritis and rheumatism, hypertension, heart disease, arteriosclerosis, and peripheral vascular disease.

2. Considered as a group, acute conditions were more frequent in the H.I.P. sample than in the New York City sample, irrespective of labor force status. Chronic conditions as a group were also higher in the H.I.P. sample for persons in the labor force, but for persons not in the labor force the rates were higher in the New York City sample.

3. The greatest difference between the two

[20] Provision for prepayment of hospitalization began in 1933 with the establishment of the Blue Cross. Prepayment of medical care is an even more recent phenomenon. Fewer than six persons per 1,000 held surgical and medical insurance in 1939.

samples in respect of the frequency of acute conditions occurred in the highest education group. In the New York City sample the frequency of chronic conditions was considerably higher in the lowest education group than in the better-educated group, but in the H.I.P. sample the rate in the lowest education group was only a little higher than in the better-educated group.

4. The number of days lost from usual activity was higher in the H.I.P. sample than in the New York City sample for acute illness, but persons in the New York City sample lost more time because of chronic illness than persons in the H.I.P. sample.

5. The frequency of all disabling[21] cases and of bed-disabling cases tended to be higher in the H.I.P. sample than in the New York City sample, although the rates for bed-disabling chronic illness were very similar in the two samples.

6. The percentage of conditions seen by a doctor during the eight-week period was higher in the H.I.P. sample than in the New York City sample for both acute and chronic conditions.

7. In the New York City sample there was very little variation with education in the percentage of acute conditions seen by a doctor. In the H.I.P. sample the percentage of acute conditions seen by a doctor during the eight-week period decreased with increasing education, but telephone contacts increased with increasing education. Chronic conditions showed an increasing frequency of doctor contacts with education in both samples.

8. Once having seen a doctor for a particular illness present during the eight-week period, persons in the H.I.P. sample on the average had a smaller number of visits than persons in the New York City sample. Although the differences were quite small, they were consistent and were present for both acute and chronic conditions irrespective of the age or sex of the individuals.

9. For conditions in which the date of onset could be fairly reliably established, the length of time between onset of illness and seeing a doctor was less in the H.I.P. sample than in the New York City sample.

These observations make it quite clear that the behavior of H.I.P. enrollees with regard to the kinds of illnesses for which medical care was sought and also the frequency with which it was sought was different from the behavior of persons in the New York City sample. How did this difference come about?

One possible explanation is that the persons in H.I.P. at any given time were a selected group in that one of the reasons for joining and remaining in H.I.P. was that they were ill. Undoubtedly, the requirement of group enrollment went far in preventing such adverse selection. Whether it succeeded entirely is dependent upon the percentage of eligibles enrolled and the representativeness of those who joined. The percentage in H.I.P. was sufficiently high so that it would have taken a markedly adverse selection to have affected the morbidity picture to an appreciable extent. However, in general there are virtually no data on this important question in the health insurance field at the present time. It may be expected that as plans for prepayment of medical care gain a backlog of experience, the necessary information will flow from their operations.

Another possible hypothesis suggested by the data is that the differences between the two samples represented a difference in health mores. Persons enrolled in H.I.P. may have changed their standard of health or, rather, may have defined illness differently from those not in the Plan, giving greater weight to relatively less severe conditions. Because the hypothesis suggests, in essence, that a lowering of the threshold for recognition of illness took place in the H.I.P. population, one might reasonably look for data to support or disprove it among the *acute* conditions reported, since it is these which were weighted with relatively less severe ailments. Changes in concept would presumably have less influence in the definition of chronic conditions.

The facts are that (1) acute non-disabling illnesses had a greater frequency in the H.I.P. sample than in the New York City sample, even when differences in labor force status, age, sex, or

[21] A disabling case is one which keeps a person from his or her usual activities for one day or longer during the eight-week period.

education of the head of the household are taken into account; (2) days lost by persons in the labor force because of acute disabling conditions were greater for the H.I.P. sample than for the New York City sample. While it is true that factors other than a person's definition of illness enter into a decision to remain home from work, the point of departure must still be the person's conclusion that he is not well. The facts cited strongly suggest that membership in a plan for prepaid comprehensive insurance has in some way produced a higher reported frequency of acute illness and of disability from such illness.

It could justifiably be asked whether the higher frequency of acute illness reported in the H.I.P. sample might be accounted for by the fact that a higher proportion of these conditions were seen by a doctor and were, therefore, more likely to be remembered than in the New York City sample. However, the size of the difference between H.I.P. and New York City in frequencies of acute illness reported was greater than that between the proportions of such conditions which were medically attended in the two samples. Therefore, the fact of doctor contact and any consequent influence on the memory of the respondent in itself does not seem to account for the differences found.

That factors other than purely economic ones influenced the amount of illness reported is indicated by the fact that within the H.I.P. sample, as in the New York City sample, the frequency of acute conditions varied directly with increasing education of the head of the household. We must conclude that education itself, or some variable related to education *other than economic status*, influences the level of recognition of illness. The hypothesis proposed suggests that the influence of H.I.P. on a population is analogous to that shown by a higher level of education of the household head: in both cases there is a higher frequency of acute illness reported which reflects a lowered threshold for recognition of deviation from "feeling well."

The hypothesis that the differences between the two samples reflect different concepts of illness can only be considered as tentative. Certainly the evidence of the study cannot be considered as proving or disproving it. This hypothesis, however, is related to the question raised earlier concerning criteria by which to measure the effect of a prepaid medical care plan on health *per se*. If the hypothesis is really true, then one might expect that in the long run the stage at which illness is first seen might be earlier among members of such a plan than among non-members; similarly, there might be differences in the frequencies and kinds of complications and in the amount of disability experienced over long time periods. Whether this is so or not can only be determined by examining particular classes of cases and following them over extended periods of time. This is a challenge for H.I.P. in the future.

Table X–33. Persons with acute and chronic medical conditions, H.I.P. enrollees and New York City sample, eight-week period, by labor force status, education of head of household, and sex

TYPE OF CONDITION AND YEARS OF SCHOOLING COMPLETED BY HEAD OF HOUSEHOLD	H.I.P. ENROLLEES									NEW YORK CITY SAMPLE								
	In labor force			*Not in labor force*			*Labor force status inapplicable*			*In labor force*			*Not in labor force*			*Labor force status inapplicable*		
	Total	Male	Female	Total	Male	Female	Total	Male	Female	Total	Male	Female	Total	Male	Female	Total	Male	Female
Total persons (base population)	*3,804*	*2,803*	*1,001*	*2,069*	*313*	*1,756*	*2,117*	*1,096*	*1,021*	*5,634*	*3,869*	*1,765*	*4,474*	*791*	*3,683*	*3,311*	*1,751*	*1,560*
Less than 9	1,295	1,013	282	726	153	573	478	224	254	2,415	1,616	799	2,068	415	1,653	1,152	587	565
9 to 12	1,328	1,017	311	757	89	677	938	500	438	2,005	1,395	610	1,525	211	1,314	1,496	800	696
More than 12	1,072	688	384	517	64	453	675	365	310	868	626	242	627	101	526	554	310	244
Not reported	109	85	24	69	16	53	26	7	19	346	232	114	254	64	190	109	54	55
Acute	*598*	*376*	*222*	*331*	*63*	*268*	*862*	*489*	*373*	*664*	*408*	*256*	*572*	*119*	*453*	*1,247*	*677*	*570*
Less than 9	178	137	41	96	26	70	148	81	67	247	148	99	213	50	163	383	208	175
9 to 12	190	127	63	121	22	99	384	228	156	253	161	92	213	39	174	590	327	263
More than 12	215	102	113	109	13	96	328	180	148	125	81	44	121	25	96	239	130	109
Not reported	15	10	5	5	2	3	2	—	2	39	18	21	25	5	20	35	12	23
Chronic	*1,341*	*889*	*452*	*1,006*	*117*	*889*	*250*	*149*	*101*	*1,600*	*934*	*666*	*2,707*	*407*	*2,300*	*312*	*188*	*124*
Less than 9	472	344	128	359	51	308	37	16	21	708	412	296	1,430	224	1,206	91	52	39
9 to 12	441	300	141	356	38	318	96	58	38	535	319	216	787	90	697	162	97	65
More than 12	395	216	179	256	21	235	115	74	41	231	136	95	269	33	236	52	35	17
Not reported	33	29	4	35	7	28	2	1	1	126	67	59	221	60	161	7	4	3

Table X–34. Selected medical conditions reported for persons 14 years of age and over, H.I.P. enrollees and New York City sample, eight-week period, by labor force status and education of head of household

SELECTED CONDITIONS	H.I.P. enrollees: In labor force: Less than 9	9 to 12	More than 12	H.I.P. enrollees: Not in labor force: Less than 9	9 to 12	More than 12	New York City sample: In labor force: Less than 9	9 to 12	More than 12	New York City sample: Not in labor force: Less than 9	9 to 12	More than 12
Obesity	19	21	22	29	18	10	28	24	9	64	30	14
Heart disease	29	21	13	28	18	17	70	32	17	132	50	20
Hypertension	37	30	23	25	21	11	53	32	17	174	59	18
Other circulatory diseases	55	50	39	55	48	26	76	59	20	185	106	38
Acute upper respiratory infection	77	92	106	42	38	51	116	104	58	96	81	56
Diseases of skin and cellular tissue	23	27	36	10	16	22	35	42	22	36	40	20
Arthritis and rheumatism	61	40	442	54	37	24	104	59	37	260	128	30
Disorders and symptoms referable to limbs or back	37	55	43	24	28	29	53	54	13	77	58	20
Other diseases of bones and organs of movement	65	92	83	34	43	52	90	89	29	124	93	29

Column heading: YEARS OF SCHOOLING COMPLETED BY HEAD OF HOUSEHOLD

Table X–35. Selected medical conditions (rates per 1,000 persons 14 years of age and over), H.I.P. enrollees and New York City sample, eight-week period, by labor force status and education of head of household

SELECTED CONDITIONS	H.I.P. enrollees: In labor force: Less than 9	9 to 12	More than 12	H.I.P. enrollees: Not in labor force: Less than 9	9 to 12	More than 12	New York City sample: In labor force: Less than 9	9 to 12	More than 12	New York City sample: Not in labor force: Less than 9	9 to 12	More than 12
Obesity	14.7	15.8	20.5	39.9	23.8	19.3	11.6	12.0	10.4	30.9	19.7	22.3
Heart disease	22.9	15.8	12.1	38.6	23.8	32.9	29.0	16.0	16.1	63.8	32.8	31.9
Hypertension	28.6	22.6	21.4	34.4	27.7	21.3	21.9	16.0	19.6	14.1	38.7	28.7
Circulatory diseases other than heart disease and hypertension	42.5	37.6	36.4	75.8	63.4	50.3	31.5	29.4	23.0	89.5	69.5	60.6
Acute upper respiratory infection	59.5	69.3	98.9	57.8	50.2	98.6	48.0	51.9	66.8	46.4	53.1	89.3
Diseases of skin and cellular tissue	17.8	20.3	33.6	13.8	21.1	42.6	14.5	20.9	25.3	17.4	26.2	31.9
Arthritis and rheumatism	47.1	30.1	39.2	74.4	48.9	46.4	43.1	29.4	42.6	125.7	83.9	47.8
Disorders and symptoms referable to limbs or back	28.6	41.4	40.1	33.1	37.0	56.1	21.9	26.9	15.0	37.2	38.0	31.9
Other diseases of bones and organs of movement	50.2	69.3	77.4	46.8	56.8	100.6	37.3	44.4	33.4	60.0	61.0	46.3

Column heading: YEARS OF SCHOOLING COMPLETED BY HEAD OF HOUSEHOLD

Table X–36. Acute and chronic medical conditions, H.I.P. enrollees and New York City sample, eight-week period, by age, sex, and degree of disability

TYPE OF CONDITION, AGE, AND SEX	H.I.P. ENROLLEES			NEW YORK CITY SAMPLE		
	Disabling	*Bed-disabling*	*Non-disabling*	*Disabling*	*Bed-disabling*	*Non-disabling*
ACUTE						
All ages[1]						
Male	680	528	254	870	683	345
Female	633	494	236	970	767	311
Under 5						
Male	180	111	42	257	185	57
Female	126	89	27	209	154	35
5 to 14						
Male	231	199	49	333	276	55
Female	196	162	32	307	270	30
15 to 44						
Male	151	125	95	171	137	139
Female	194	145	125	280	209	139
45 to 64						
Male	101	81	58	70	52	58
Female	104	87	47	106	84	75
65 and over						
Male	16	11	10	29	24	23
Female	6	5	2	48	33	26
CHRONIC						
All ages[1]						
Male	211	139	948	278	207	1,265
Female	229	146	1,225	464	339	2,658
Under 5						
Male	15	13	46	27	20	42
Female	10	4	22	10	8	22
5 to 14						
Male	27	16	70	32	24	91
Female	25	17	53	30	22	72
15 to 44						
Male	60	35	321	76	62	402
Female	121	70	608	189	142	945
45 to 64						
Male	85	61	426	74	53	424
Female	68	53	496	146	113	1,022
65 and over						
Male	24	14	79	60	42	278
Female	3	1	40	71	45	509

[1] Includes persons whose age was not reported.

Table X–37. Acute and chronic medical conditions, H.I.P. enrollees and New York City sample, eight-week period, by age, education of head of household, and degree of disability

TYPE OF CONDITION, AGE, AND YEARS OF SCHOOLING COMPLETED BY HEAD OF HOUSEHOLD	H.I.P. ENROLLEES			NEW YORK CITY SAMPLE		
	Disabling	*Bed-disabling*	*Non-disabling*	*Disabling*	*Bed-disabling*	*Non-disabling*
ACUTE						
All ages[1]						
Less than 9	298	236	113	629	506	201
9 to 12	518	392	165	799	621	237
More than 12	483	381	167	346	283	129
Under 5						
Less than 9	31	21	12	139	107	21
9 to 12	152	93	24	214	152	37
More than 12	122	85	21	97	74	18
5 to 14						
Less than 9	84	71	16	211	184	30
9 to 12	176	143	28	300	253	33
More than 12	166	146	25	115	99	11
15 to 44						
Less than 9	80	66	31	148	115	65
9 to 12	126	97	89	197	145	113
More than 12	135	103	86	95	77	68
45 to 64						
Less than 9	92	72	45	91	70	60
9 to 12	55	50	22	53	42	34
More than 12	52	41	33	19	16	21
65 and over						
Less than 9	10	5	9	37	27	22
9 to 12	9	9	2	20	14	14
More than 12	2	1	—	12	10	5
CHRONIC						
All ages[1]						
Less than 9	145	98	368	332	238	922
9 to 12	170	104	450	252	191	702
More than 12	112	74	469	84	69	271
Under 5						
Less than 9	1	1	7	4	2	9
9 to 12	14	8	22	20	15	34
More than 12	10	8	28	8	6	8
5 to 14						
Less than 9	12	11	8	26	17	37
9 to 12	15	12	25	25	20	47
More than 12	25	10	47	10	9	22
15 to 44						
Less than 9	45	22	132	107	76	303
9 to 12	82	45	268	114	91	396
More than 12	48	33	249	32	28	165
45 to 64						
Less than 9	76	57	197	122	91	406
9 to 12	48	34	126	56	42	158
More than 12	27	23	130	21	16	58
65 and over						
Less than 9	11	7	21	69	49	146
9 to 12	10	4	9	33	21	44
More than 12	1	—	14	7	6	17

[1] Includes persons whose age was not reported.

Table X–38. Acute and chronic medical conditions, persons 14 years of age and over, H.I.P. enrollees and New York City sample, eight-week period, by labor force status, education of head of household, and degree of disability

TYPE OF CONDITION, LABOR FORCE STATUS, AND YEARS OF SCHOOLING COMPLETED BY HEAD OF HOUSEHOLD	H.I.P. ENROLLEES			NEW YORK CITY SAMPLE		
	Disabling	*Bed-disabling*	*Non-disabling*[1]	*Disabling*	*Bed-disabling*	*Non-disabling*[1]
ACUTE[2]						
In labor force	380	311	218	382	300	282
Less than 9	112	86	66	150	121	97
9 to 12	122	102	68	144	107	109
More than 12	136	114	79	69	60	56
Not in labor force	207	160	124	372	288	200
Less than 9	72	60	24	142	109	71
9 to 12	69	54	52	141	108	72
More than 12	64	44	45	73	59	48
CHRONIC[2]						
In labor force	190	119	1,151	211	171	1,389
Less than 9	68	42	404	85	63	623
9 to 12	77	44	364	78	69	457
More than 12	38	28	357	29	27	202
Not in labor force	166	110	840	432	294	2,275
Less than 9	62	41	297	217	154	1,213
9 to 12	60	39	296	129	87	658
More than 12	38	26	218	38	28	231

[1] Includes conditions in persons for whom fact of disability was not reported.

[2] Includes conditions in persons for whom education of head of household was not reported.

Table X–39. Days of disability and days in bed for acute and chronic conditions, H.I.P. enrollees and New York City sample, eight-week period, by age and sex

TYPE OF CONDITION, AGE, AND SEX	H.I.P. ENROLLEES		NEW YORK CITY SAMPLE	
	Days of disability	*Days in bed*	*Days of disability*	*Days in bed*
ACUTE				
All ages[1]				
Male	4,618	2,401	6,131	3,225
Female	4,023	2,156	7,615	3,916
Under 5				
Male	1,293	522	1,800	888
Female	887	336	1,612	799
5 to 14				
Male	1,441	912	2,381	1,385
Female	1,211	718	2,373	1,309
15 to 44				
Male	896	561	1,040	551
Female	1,020	561	1,794	863
45 to 64				
Male	744	371	633	205
Female	797	470	954	482
65 and over				
Male	235	32	247	171
Female	44	26	520	226
CHRONIC				
All ages[1]				
Male	2,830	1,211	5,395	2,126
Female	2,962	1,127	7,747	3,460
Under 5				
Male	105	85	246	119
Female	37	29	77	29
5 to 14				
Male	108	68	419	164
Female	119	52	273	182
15 to 44				
Male	544	159	974	442
Female	1,046	321	2,039	1,102
45 to 64				
Male	1,578	564	1,674	719
Female	1,683	691	2,744	1,420
65 and over				
Male	495	335	1,891	667
Female	56	21	2,223	689

[1] Includes persons whose age was not reported.

Table X–40. Days of disability and days in bed for acute and chronic conditions, H.I.P. enrollees and New York City sample, eight-week period, by age and education of head of household

TYPE OF CONDITION, AGE, AND YEARS OF SCHOOLING COMPLETED BY HEAD OF HOUSEHOLD	H.I.P. ENROLLEES		NEW YORK CITY SAMPLE	
	Days of disability	*Days in bed*	*Days of disability*	*Days in bed*
ACUTE				
All ages[1]				
Less than 9	2,275	1,025	4,409	2,430
9 to 12	3,274	1,737	6,276	3,089
More than 12	3,015	1,741	2,471	1,430
Under 5				
Less than 9	236	69	870	537
9 to 12	1,033	376	1,683	719
More than 12	901	410	769	398
5 to 14				
Less than 9	486	267	1,452	823
9 to 12	1,040	636	2,315	1,292
More than 12	1,125	726	906	545
15 to 44				
Less than 9	488	269	919	527
9 to 12	789	472	1,357	584
More than 12	616	359	479	279
45 to 64				
Less than 9	818	376	776	332
9 to 12	363	226	461	234
More than 12	333	218	141	60
65 and over				
Less than 9	219	23	376	200
9 to 12	49	27	193	94
More than 12	4	4	89	70
CHRONIC				
All ages[1]				
Less than 9	2,018	680	6,763	2,908
9 to 12	2,305	946	3,587	1,488
More than 12	1,183	533	1,056	658
Under 5				
Less than 9	7	5	18	12
9 to 12	80	68	174	51
More than 12	55	41	85	57
5 to 14				
Less than 9	31	17	360	97
9 to 12	104	63	187	122
More than 12	92	40	144	127
15 to 44				
Less than 9	297	66	1,418	856
9 to 12	846	224	1,287	504
More than 12	343	180	217	133
45 to 64				
Less than 9	1,567	543	2,648	1,094
9 to 12	1,054	440	947	533
More than 12	632	272	280	168
65 and over				
Less than 9	116	49	2,277	809
9 to 12	205	138	986	275
More than 12	56	—	202	165

[1] Includes persons whose age was not reported.

Table X–41. Days of disability and days in bed for acute and chronic medical conditions, persons 14 years of age and over, H.I.P. enrollees and New York City sample, eight-week period, by labor force status and education of head of household

TYPE OF CONDITION, LABOR FORCE STATUS, AND YEARS OF SCHOOLING COMPLETED BY HEAD OF HOUSEHOLD	H.I.P. ENROLLEES		NEW YORK CITY SAMPLE	
	Days of disability	*Days in bed*	*Days of disability*	*Days in bed*
ACUTE[1]				
In labor force	2,439	1,381	2,478	1,258
Less than 9	953	418	1,061	550
9 to 12	788	485	985	454
More than 12	637	432	276	220
Not in labor force	1,396	731	3,263	1,627
Less than 9	614	285	1,102	578
9 to 12	401	242	1,303	627
More than 12	376	200	602	332
CHRONIC[1]				
In labor force	2,145	646	2,118	972
Less than 9	699	276	1,000	412
9 to 12	962	231	668	311
More than 12	430	128	223	166
Not in labor force	3,135	1,436	9,968	4,171
Less than 9	1,204	361	5,434	2,433
9 to 12	1,149	583	2,504	1,006
More than 12	550	324	608	311

[1] Includes days of disability and bed-disability in persons for whom education of head of household was not reported.

Table X–42. Average number of physician visits per attended acute and chronic condition producing hospitalization or seven or more days of bed-disability, H.I.P. enrollees and New York City sample, 1951, by age and education of head of household

TYPE OF CONDITION, AGE, AND YEARS OF SCHOOLING COMPLETED BY HEAD OF HOUSEHOLD	NUMBER OF CONDITIONS		AVERAGE NUMBER OF PHYSICIAN VISITS PER CONDITION	
	H.I.P. enrollees	*N.Y.C. sample*	*H.I.P. enrollees*	*N.Y.C. sample*
ACUTE				
All ages				
Less than 9	113	204	7.6	7.9
9 to 12	120	265	8.1	8.8
More than 12	121	109	4.8	8.0
Under 5				
Less than 9	[1]	21	—	5.1
9 to 12	17	51	7.9	6.5
More than 12	19	17	5.7	3.4
5 to 14				
Less than 9	22	52	4.2	4.4
9 to 12	33	76	5.4	5.1
More than 12	50	26	3.5	4.6
15 to 44				
Less than 9	22	50	12.9	9.0
9 to 12	49	94	6.5	11.6
More than 12	38	44	5.1	11.7
45 to 64				
Less than 9	56	57	7.0	9.8
9 to 12	20	28	14.6	11.8
More than 12	13	19	7.4	7.9
65 and over				
Less than 9	[1]	22	—	11.6
9 to 12	[1]	10	—	3.9
More than 12	[1]	[1]	—	—
CHRONIC				
All ages				
Less than 9	115	233	16.4	20.3
9 to 12	125	174	14.4	15.1
More than 12	91	66	14.8	10.8
Under 5				
Less than 9	[1]	12	—	9.5
9 to 12	[1]	12	—	3.7
More than 12	10	[1]	12.0	—
5 to 14				
Less than 9	[1]	18	—	11.7
9 to 12	16	35	9.1	9.9
More than 12	13	[1]	8.2	—
15 to 44				
Less than 9	25	77	13.4	23.5
9 to 12	53	72	14.8	15.6
More than 12	39	34	17.0	12.1
45 to 64				
Less than 9	73	89	17.7	21.5
9 to 12	44	35	17.6	21.0
More than 12	28	[1]	16.1	—
65 and over				
Less than 9	[1]	33	—	19.3
9 to 12	[1]	14	—	18.1
More than 12	[1]	[1]	—	—

[1] Number less than 10.

CHAPTER XI

Hospital Experience, 1951

THE role of the hospital in modern medical care has undergone considerable change in the last several decades, in large part as a result of advances in medical knowledge, changing patterns of disease in the population, and the growth of hospital insurance. The relation of the hospital to the total health picture has come under closer scrutiny not only by the medical profession and the hospital administrator, but also by the economist, the sociologist, the civic-minded individual concerned with community planning, and the general public. Factual information is essential to guide the thinking of these groups in their efforts to meet hospital needs.

Information regarding hospitalization is ordinarily obtainable from one (or more) of three general sources: (1) hospital records, (2) the experience of various health programs having hospitalization insurance as an integral part of the plan, and (3) surveys of various population groups.

Hospital records provide much information regarding diagnoses of persons admitted to the hospital and about their length of stay, but the lack of a population base to which to relate such data makes them seriously deficient as a source of information with respect to the frequency of hospitalization in the population—what the actuaries refer to as the "risk of hospitalization"—and how it varies with the demographic, social, and economic characteristics of the population.

Potentially, the records of hospital insurance programs, such as Blue Cross, are capable of contributing considerable knowledge on the subject of hospitalization. With an increasing proportion of the population having hospital insurance, knowledge derived from these sources should become more representative of the population. Until now, however, such organizations have not generally engaged in research related to their experience. In addition, such data as have become available from this source have, in the nature of the case, been examined in relation to only a very few population characteristics.

The third source of data on hospitalization is the survey method. This is the method of the present study. With the increasing utilization of sampling procedures, it has gained in popularity. Although it is usually a costly procedure, it has the advantage of referring to a definite population base and of not being limited in the population and illness characteristics about which inquiry can be made except by the willingness, patience, and memory of the respondent and by the layman's knowledge of disease.

Foci of Interest in Present Survey

Of the many questions on hospitalization toward which this survey might have directed attention, the principal foci of interest were, first, the broad picture of the extent of hospitalization in the general population; second, the extent of hospitalization among persons covered by insurance as compared with those uninsured for all or a part of any hospital costs that they might incur; and, third, the relative amount of hospitalization in the H.I.P. and the New York City populations.

Since it was doubted that the size of the samples set up for the collection of morbidity data during the eight-week period would yield a volume of hospitalization sufficient to be statistically significant, it was decided to inquire about all members of households who had been in hospitals at any time during the previous calendar year. The general nature of the survey has been described earlier. All informants were asked the following question: "Did anybody in this household spend at least one night in a hospital during 1951?" If the answer was "yes," an Illness and Medical Care Memorandum (Appendix A, Schedule 3) was filled out describing the hospitalization. The general facts covered were the place of hospitalization, the nature of the diagnosis, duration of disability and hospitalization, and medical care received. Inquiry was also made as to whether insurance covered any part of the cost of medical care for the condition (Schedule 3, Question 16).

All illness reported for the eight-week period preceding the interview was described in detail on the Illness and Medical Care Memorandum (Appendix A, Schedule 2), and hospitalizations related to any such illness were noted (Schedule 2, Questions 10–15 and Question 21).

Since the questions regarding hospitalization referred to persons present in the household at the time of the survey, information was not obtained about persons hospitalized in 1951 who had died or moved out of the household prior to the time of the survey. Also, persons hospitalized in mental hospitals, tuberculosis hospitals, and other such institutions for the care of the chronically ill were not considered members of the household or included in the counts of persons hospitalized.[1] Thus, the data of this survey refer only to persons hospitalized in general hospitals who remained members of the household to the time of the survey.

Frequency of Hospitalization, New York City Sample

The response to the question on hospitalization in 1951 as defined above yielded an annual hospitalization rate of 6.7 percent for the 13,558 persons in the New York City sample.

Through the courtesy of the Hospital Council of Greater New York, data were obtained on the number of admissions to general hospitals in New York City in 1951. These data give an annual admission rate of 11.1 percent, which, after correction to remove the admissions of non-residents[2] of the city, becomes 10.5 percent. This correction is based on 1933 data, and the movement of population may have increased since then, particularly to the nearby suburbs. It would appear, however, that the figure of approximately 7 percent for the annual hospitalization rate obtained from the household survey is an underestimation of the true rate for the New York City population.

There are several factors which must be considered in interpreting the rate obtained from the survey as an estimate of the annual rate of hospitalization for the city as a whole. As has been said, persons who were hospitalized in 1951 and who died prior to the survey were not included in the survey rate. Using the total death rate for New York City as a basis, an estimate was made of the expected number of hospitalized deaths in the New York City sample in 1951.[3] After adjustment for these deaths, the hospitalization rate for the New York City sample became 7.4 percent.

Another factor tending to make the observed hospitalization rate of the survey lower than the actual rate is that in order for a household to be counted in the survey it must be present. Thus, the survey misses the hospital experience of individuals who have moved out of the area, and of households which have disintegrated, and often of single-person households; consequently the observed rate is too low. The necessary data to correct the observed rate for these factors are missing.

Although the rate from the survey includes such readmissions as were reported, it is believed that readmissions tend generally to be underreported in surveys. The extent of this underreporting is also unknown.

[1] Hospitalizations in 1951 in tuberculosis or mental hospitals of persons who had been discharged by the time of the survey were, however, included in the total count. However, such persons constituted less than 1 percent of both the H.I.P. and New York City samples, and these hospitalizations accounted for less than 1.4 percent of all 1951 hospitalizations.

[2] Based on the only available data, it is estimated that 6.7 percent of discharges from voluntary hospitals and 0.8 percent of discharges from municipal hospitals are non-residents. The figures for voluntary hospitals were also applied to proprietary hospitals. Neva R. Deardorff, and Marta Fraenkel, *Hospital Discharge Study, 1933*, published by Works Progress Administration for Welfare Council of New York City, 1942, Vol. 1, pp. 38–40.

[3] This probably underestimates the number of deaths in hospitals, since the death rate in hospitals is greater than in the general population.

Hospitalization and Insurance Status, New York City Sample

About 49 percent of the persons in the New York City sample were reported on Schedule 1 as having hospital insurance.[4] The crude figures for this sample show a hospitalization rate of 6.2 per 1,000 persons covered by hospital insurance and a rate of 7.5 for those without such coverage. This latter figure was an unexpected finding, because most published data indicate a higher hospitalization rate for persons with hospital insurance than for those without it. It gave rise to further doubts regarding the validity of the data on insurance status as recorded for persons on Schedule 1 and resulted in more intensive examination of available material on the problem. The results of the examination are set forth below.

As noted above, about half of the New York City sample reported having some hospital insurance. This contrasts with a figure of 63 percent reported for persons in urban areas of the United States by the Health Information Foundation and about 60 percent reported for the total population by the Health Insurance Council. These discrepancies increased our concern about the reliability of the rate of hospitalization for the insured population, because, if it is assumed that the proportion covered by hospital insurance is larger, then the observed rate for them will be even further decreased with adjustment made for underreporting.

When a hospitalization rate for the eight-week period is computed for the New York City sample, the rate for the insured (1.7 per 1,000 population), though not very different from that for the uninsured (1.6), bears the same relation to it as that reported in the literature. This still leaves suspect the annual hospital rates by insurance status in this sample.

Data from other sources on the hospitalization rate by insurance status were then examined. Through the courtesy of the Associated Hospital Service (Blue Cross), information was obtained on claims of H.I.P. enrollees as contrasted with non-H.I.P. members of the A.H.S. In 1953 a rate of 253.2 claims per 1,000 contracts was reported for non-H.I.P.–Blue Cross members, which yields an annual utilization rate of 11.4 persons per 1,000 covered.[5] It will be noted that this rate is higher than that found by the survey procedure, and slightly higher than the hospitalization rate of 10.5 percent for New York City as a whole estimated in the preceding section. Certainly there is nothing in these data from the A.H.S. to suggest that the hospitalization rate for persons *not* covered by hospital insurance should be higher than the rate for those having such insurance.

In a house-to-house survey conducted by the Health Information Foundation, the annual hospital admission rate for urban areas was found to be 13 percent for the insured population and 10 percent for the uninsured group. In the studies in the Arsenal Health District of Pittsburgh, also based on a household survey, the hospitalization rates for 1952 were 9.6 percent for the insured persons and 7.2 percent for the uninsured. It is findings such as these that have made the results of this study unexpected.

It is perhaps worth while to speculate on the possible reasons for the results observed in this study on hospitalization in relation to insurance. These are that (1) some respondents' knowledge of the hospital insurance status of the several members of the household was poor, (2) the enumerators failed to understand the question and to record data properly, and (3) the New York City population is peculiar, say, in respect of such factors as the availability of municipal hospital beds. It is conceivable that all three conditions were operating in some degree.

In view of the questions raised here about the reliability of the data on insurance status in this study and the difficulties in interpreting other available data, no attempt will be made in later sections of this chapter to classify the data on hospitalization by insurance status except in the discussion of length of hospital stay.

Frequency of Hospitalization, H.I.P. Enrollees

Before undertaking the comparison of the

[4] See Chapter II and Appendix D for discussion of character and quality of insurance data.

[5] After taking account of the average number of persons covered in each contractual unit.

H.I.P. and New York City sample hospitalization rates it is in order to scrutinize the H.I.P. rates, as was done for the New York City rates.

For 1951 the rate of hospitalization for the H.I.P. population was 7.4 percent. After adjustment for the expected number of hospitalized deaths in 1951, which were not reported in the survey, the rate becomes 8.1 percent.

In an effort to check this hospitalization rate, data from a number of sources were examined. The Associated Hospital Service reported a figure of 250.6 claims per 1,000 joint H.I.P.-A.H.S. contracts in 1953. Converted to a per-person basis, this figure yields an annual hospitalization rate of 10.6 percent for the H.I.P. population.

The 8.1 percent hospitalization rate also contrasts with the 13 percent rate for urban insured persons reported by the Health Information Foundation and the Arsenal Health District of Pittsburgh figure of 9.6 percent for insured persons.

The Report of the President's Commission on the Health Needs of the Nation cites data on the hospitalization rates of various medical care plans in comparison with the rate for the United States as a whole.[6] These data are shown in the accompanying tabulation.

Population group	*Time period*	*Percentage of population hospitalized (annual rate)*
United States	1951	11.5
Blue Cross members	1951	12.0
Kaiser Foundation Health Plan (Permanente)	1949–1950	10.4
Group Health Cooperative of Puget Sound, Seattle, Wash.	1950	8.0
Labor Health Institute, St. Louis, Mo.	1950	7.0

It will be noted that the three medical care plans have lower rates than either the United States population or the Blue Cross plan. The Kaiser Foundation operates its own hospitals, while Group Health Cooperative of Puget Sound, in Seattle and the Labor Health Institute of St. Louis have their own hospital insurance programs. Part of the reason for the lower rates of the medical care plans may be that they have a high proportion of employed persons among their membership. This suggests that any comparison of this sort should take labor force status into account. At the same time, there may be other reasons, such as family composition, for the lower rate of hospitalization for those medical plans than that for the United States as a whole. Until it is possible to examine the hospitalization data of such plans and of the population on axes of classification such as age, education, labor force status, family status, etc., the meaning of the observed variations in hospitalization rates will remain obscure. There is great need for the development of better data in this area.

Finally, the H.I.P. data confirm our suspicions with regard to the unreliability of the replies on hospital insurance status. It was shown in Chapter IV that although the persons in the H.I.P. sample are almost entirely covered by hospital insurance, only 60.2 percent were reported as having such hospital insurance. These data, coupled with those discussed for the New York City sample, make it clearly unwise to attempt further analysis of the frequency of hospitalization in relation to hospital insurance status.

Frequency of Hospitalization, H.I.P. Enrollees and New York City Sample

With the foregoing discussion in mind, we come to the point of comparing the hospital experience of persons in the two samples. The hospitalization rates of the two samples are remarkably similar. The alignment of the several rates of hospitalization during the period expressed as percentage of persons in the two samples are shown in the accompanying tabulation.

	H.I.P. ENROLLEES	NEW YORK CITY SAMPLE		
		Total	*Insured*	*Uninsured*
Crude rate	7.4	6.7	6.2	7.5
Rate adjusted for deaths, 1951	8.1	7.4	—	—
Rate for eight-week period, 1952	1.4	1.6	1.7	1.6

Whether or not the annual hospitalization rate for the two samples of 7 to 8 percent may be

[6] *Building America's Health: America's Health Status, Needs and Resources, Vol. 3, H Statistical Appendix.* Washington, D.C., U.S. Government Printing Office, 1952, Table 379.

considered as reflecting the true incidence of hospitalization, whatever bias results from the survey method as employed in this study is present in both the H.I.P. and New York City samples (although not necessarily to the same extent). Comparison of the frequency of hospitalization in relation to various characteristics of the surveyed populations would therefore seem warranted.

Reported Hospitalizations, H.I.P. Enrollees and New York City Sample, by Age and Sex

The pattern of hospitalization by age and sex for the two samples is shown in Table XI–1 and Figure XI–1. This pattern is generally similar to that found in other reports, such as those of Collins et al.[7] and of Councell.[8] Males in both samples tend to have a relatively high rate at the very early ages, after which the rate declines until about age 30 and then rises again. The peak rate for females is, of course, in the reproductive ages, but if obstetric and puerperal conditions are excluded, the rate remains fairly stable until after age 30, when, like the rate for males, it rises.

In the H.I.P. sample the rate for females is higher than for males over most of the age span. In the New York City sample, however, the rate for females, after exclusion of obstetric and puerperal conditions, is lower at almost all ages than the rate for males. When the two samples are compared, however, there is very little difference in the hospitalization rate for the males, but both the rate for all ages and the age-specific hospitalization rates among females appear to be higher in the H.I.P. sample (except for the age group under five). The reason for this differential among the female rates in the two samples may become more apparent when the influence of other variables is examined.

Reported Hospitalizations, H.I.P. Enrollees and New York City Sample, by Education of Household Head

The variation in hospitalization rates with education of the head of the household is not great in either sample. Although in both samples there

Table XI–1. Persons hospitalized, H.I.P. enrollees and New York City sample, 1951, by age and sex

AGE AND SEX	H.I.P. ENROLLEES		NEW YORK CITY SAMPLE	
	Total persons	*Percentage hospitalized*	*Total persons*	*Percentage hospitalized*
All ages	*8,040*	7.4	*13,558*	6.7
Male	4,229	4.9	6,446	5.0
Female[1]	3,811	10.1	7,112	8.3
Under 5	*798*	5.5	*1,392*	4.6
Male	432	7.9	730	5.5
Female	366	2.7	662	3.6
5 to 14	*1,435*	4.3	*2,095*	3.9
Male	735	4.2	1,109	4.6
Female	700	4.4	986	3.0
15 to 44	*3,489*	9.6	*5,757*	9.1
Male	1,684	3.4	2,589	4.5
Female[2]	1,805	15.3	3,168	12.8
45 to 64	*2,082*	6.6	*2,961*	5.4
Male	1,220	6.1	1,417	5.2
Female	862	7.2	1,544	5.6
65 and over	*195*	7.7	*903*	6.8
Male	143	7.7	413	7.5
Female	52	7.7	490	6.1
Not reported	*41*	2.4	*450*	4.7
Male	15	[3]	188	4.8
Female	26	3.8	262	4.6

[1] The rate for females, all ages, exclusive of obstetric and puerperal conditions, was 5.1 for the H.I.P. sample and 4.2 for the New York City sample.

[2] The rate for females in the age group 15 to 44, exclusive of obstetric and puerperal conditions, was 4.6 for the H.I.P. sample and 3.4 for the New York City sample.

[3] Percentage less than 0.05.

Figure XI–1. Percentage of persons hospitalized, H.I.P. enrollees and New York City sample, 1951, by age and sex

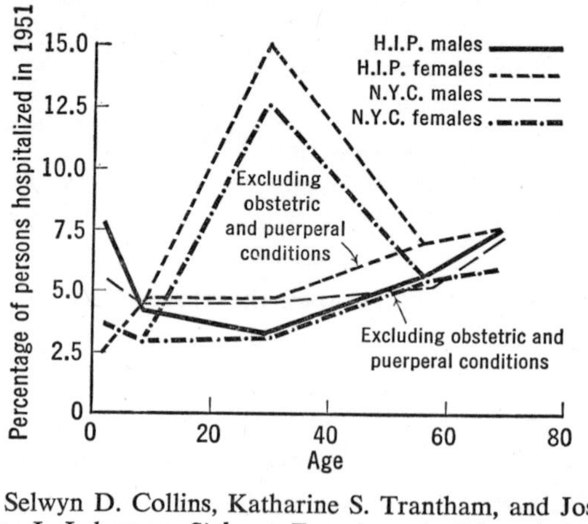

[7] Selwyn D. Collins, Katharine S. Trantham, and Josephine L. Lehmann, *Sickness Experience in Selected Areas of the United States,* Public Health Monograph No. 25 (Public Health Service Publication No. 390). Washington, D.C., U.S. Government Printing Office, 1955.

[8] C. E. Councell, "Hospital Records as a Source of Morbidity Statistics," *American Journal of Public Health,* Vol. 31, pp. 1044–1050, October 1941.

appears to be a somewhat lower hospitalization rate among individuals in the lowest education group than in either of the other two education groups, the difference could easily have arisen by chance and, in fact, when obstetric and puerperal conditions are excluded from the computation the differences by education group are even less (Table XI–2 and Figure XI–2).[9]

In each education group, however, the hospitalization rate for the H.I.P. sample is slightly higher than for the New York City sample even after adjusting for differences in age composition of the two samples. Individual age- and education-specific rates do not show consistent differences between the two samples (Figure XI–3).

Conditions Leading to Hospitalization

The annual hospital admission rate for broad classes of diagnostic conditions and for certain specific diagnoses within these classes is shown in Table XI–3 and Figure XI–4. Aside from obstetric and puerperal conditions, the four diagnostic groups with the highest rates—diseases of the digestive tract, diseases of the respiratory system, diseases of the circulatory system, and accidents—account for about 60 percent of all the conditions producing hospitalization in both the H.I.P. and New York City samples.[10]

The frequency of hospitalization for diseases of the digestive tract was greater for persons in the H.I.P. sample than in the New York City sample. The specific conditions contributing to the higher H.I.P. hospitalization rate for this group were hernias; ulcers of the stomach and ulcerative colitis; diseases of the liver, gallbladder, and pancreas; and appendicitis. The differences in the hospital admission rate for any one of these conditions, with the possible exception of ulcer of the stomach, could readily occur just by chance. It is worth noting, however, that in every instance the rate was higher for the H.I.P. sample—this made the difference in rates for this group of diseases as a whole statistically significant. For each of the conditions mentioned the surgical rate was also higher in the H.I.P. sample.

By far the greater part of the hospitalization for diseases of the respiratory system was accounted for by tonsillectomies and related surgical procedures. In contrast to diseases of the digestive tract, the admission rate for such conditions was less in the H.I.P. sample than in the New York City sample, although the difference might be due to chance both for the group as a whole and for the individual condition.

It might be expected that there would be little difference between the two samples in the admission rate for accidents since the bulk of such conditions would be of an emergency character. This proves to have been the case, the difference between the rates for the two samples being small and not significant.

The hospital admission rates for diseases of the circulatory system did not differ greatly in the two samples. All the differences observed might easily have occurred by chance. It will be recalled, however, that heart disease was the only condition in which the prevalence appeared to be greater in the New York City sample both for persons in the labor force and those not in the labor force. Whether the apparently lower hospitalization rate for heart disease in the H.I.P. sample has any relation to this is impossible to say.

In seeking to judge the meaning of the variations just described, one would like to examine the data in respect of such factors as the influence

[9] Curiously, the data show a distinctly higher hospitalization rate for obstetric and puerperal conditions in both samples in the better-educated groups (Figure XI–3). It is this that produces the apparently higher over-all hospitalization rate in the two highest education groups (Figure XI–2). Although in recent years there have been shifts in the proportionate contribution to the total births by the different socioeconomic groups, they are not of an order which would account for the findings here, in which the hospitalization rate for obstetric and puerperal conditions is about 13 per 100 women 15 to 44 in the highest education group and 6.5 in the lowest.

The 1950 census for New York City shows that within the age-sex group of women 15 to 44 years old, there are wide differences in the education groups, in the proportions of women under and over 35 years. The group with the least education is weighted with a high proportion of women over 35. The differences among the education groups may arise in part at least from differing age composition and not wholly from socioeconomic factors. (*Annual Report*, Department of Health, City of New York, 1950, p. 46.)

[10] It should be remembered that no attempt was made to verify diagnoses by reference to hospital records.

Table XI–2. Persons hospitalized, H.I.P. enrollees and New York City sample, 1951, by age and education of head of household

AGE AND YEARS OF SCHOOLING COMPLETED BY HEAD OF HOUSEHOLD	H.I.P. ENROLLEES		NEW YORK CITY SAMPLE	
	Total persons	*Percentage hospitalized*[1]	*Total persons*	*Percentage hospitalized*[1]
All ages				
Less than 9	2,506	6.5 (5.3)	5,698	5.9 (4.7)
9 to 12	3,047	7.9 (5.3)	5,068	7.4 (4.5)
More than 12	2,278	7.7 (4.6)	2,071	7.4 (4.1)
Not reported	209	7.6 (6.7)	721	6.5 (5.5)
Under 5				
Less than 9	124	5.6	389	5.6
9 to 12	404	5.4	666	4.6
More than 12	266	5.6	286	3.5
Not reported	4	[2]	51	2.0
5 to 14				
Less than 9	405	3.4	863	3.8
9 to 12	566	4.4	876	4.2
More than 12	438	4.8	299	3.3
Not reported	26	7.7	57	1.8
15 to 44				
Less than 9	894	7.3 (4.1)	2,176	7.4 (4.2)
9 to 12	1,451	10.1 (4.5)	2,365	10.1 (3.9)
More than 12	1,064	10.9 (4.3)	960	10.4 (3.5)
Not reported	80	8.8 (6.4)	256	9.4 (6.1)
45 to 64				
Less than 9	965	6.9	1,583	5.4
9 to 12	569	7.7	805	5.0
More than 12	467	4.7	376	6.9
Not reported	81	4.9	197	4.1
65 and over				
Less than 9	111	7.2	557	5.2
9 to 12	46	6.5	198	8.6
More than 12	23	4.3	70	8.6
Not reported	15	20.0	78	11.5
Not reported				
Less than 9	7	14.3	130	4.6
9 to 12	11	[2]	158	5.7
More than 12	20	[2]	80	2.5
Not reported	3	[2]	82	4.9

[1] Figures in parentheses are the hospitalization percentage rates computed exclusive of obstetric and puerperal conditions.
[2] Percentage less than 0.05.

of education of the head of the household on the frequency of hospitalization for specific conditions. This degree of refinement is not possible with the numbers involved. However, an attempt can be made to relate the usual demographic characteristics of this study to diagnoses by grouping the latter into acute, chronic, and obstetric and puerperal conditions.

Hospitalization of Acute and Chronic Conditions, by Age, Sex, and Education of Household Head

The pertinent facts regarding the hospitalization of acute and chronic conditions by age are set forth in Table XI–4. The definitions of acute and chronic are those used in the previous chapter and detailed in Appendix H.

The over-all hospitalization rate was less for acute than chronic conditions, and while the former decreased with advancing age, the latter showed a marked increase in both samples (Figure XI–5).

The age-specific hospitalization rates for acute conditions were essentially the same in both samples and this is true for both sexes (Table XI–4). In contrast, the rate for chronic conditions was higher at every age in the H.I.P. sample than in the New York City sample and the difference

Figure XI–2. Percentage of persons hospitalized, H.I.P. enrollees and New York City sample, 1951, by education of head of household

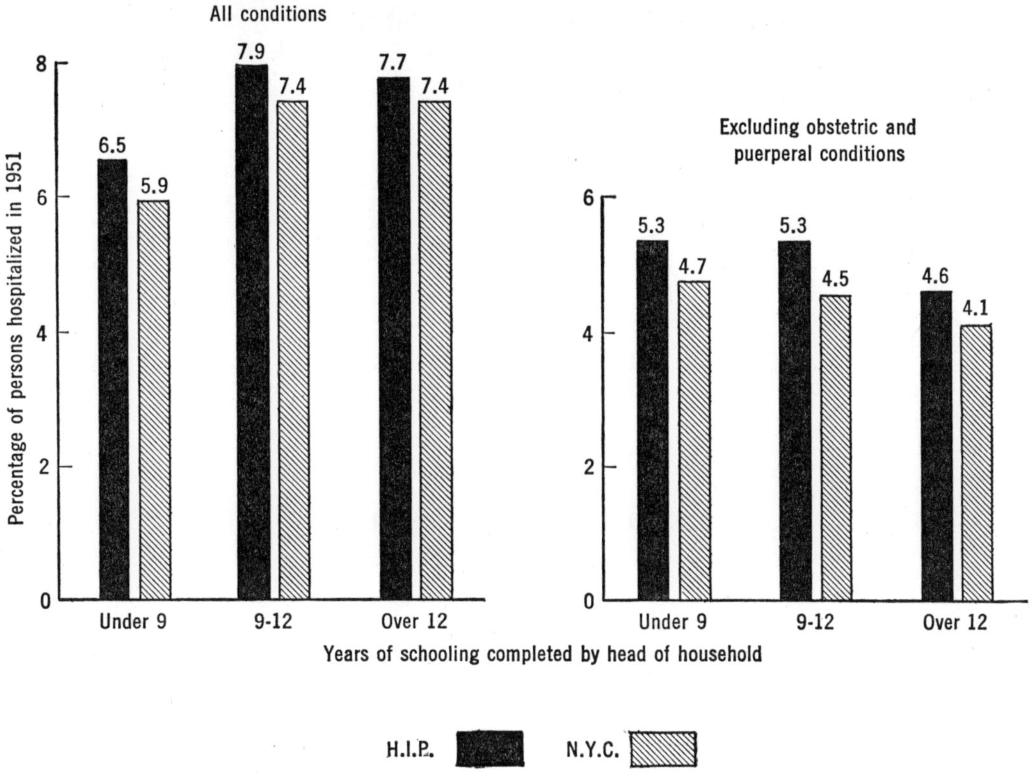

between the two samples increased with age. This difference between the samples in hospitalization of chronic conditions is especially noticeable for females; for males the picture is not as consistent.

The higher hospitalization rate for chronic diseases among females in the H.I.P. sample prompted an examination by sex of the diagnoses responsible for hospitalization. The rates appropriate to this examination are shown in Table XI–5, in which the analysis is limited to persons 15 years of age or over.

It is clearly seen that the greatest differences between the two samples occurred in regard to hospitalization for diseases of the digestive tract, the rates being consistently higher in the H.I.P. sample for both sexes, both for the more specific conditions and for the disease group as a whole. Thus, the higher hospitalization rate for these conditions persists even when examined separately for each sex.

The relatively higher hospitalization rates among females, in comparison with males, for neoplasms, allergic and metabolic disorders, diseases of the nervous system and sense organs, varicose veins, and disorders of the genito-urinary tract resulted in the generally higher hospitalization rate for chronic diseases in the H.I.P. sample.

The variation in the hospitalization rate with educational status was less than with age and showed no consistent patterns for either acute or chronic conditions, the differences among the several education groups being easily explainable on a chance basis. The hospitalization rate for obstetric and puerperal conditions, however, showed a marked increase with increasing education of the head of the household. As said earlier, it is probable (see footnote 9) that this increase reflected differences in age composition of the female population in the highest and lowest education groups.

The hospitalization rate for acute conditions showed no consistent difference between the two

Figure XI–3. Hospitalization (rate per 100 persons), H.I.P. enrollees and New York City sample, 1951, by education of head of household and age

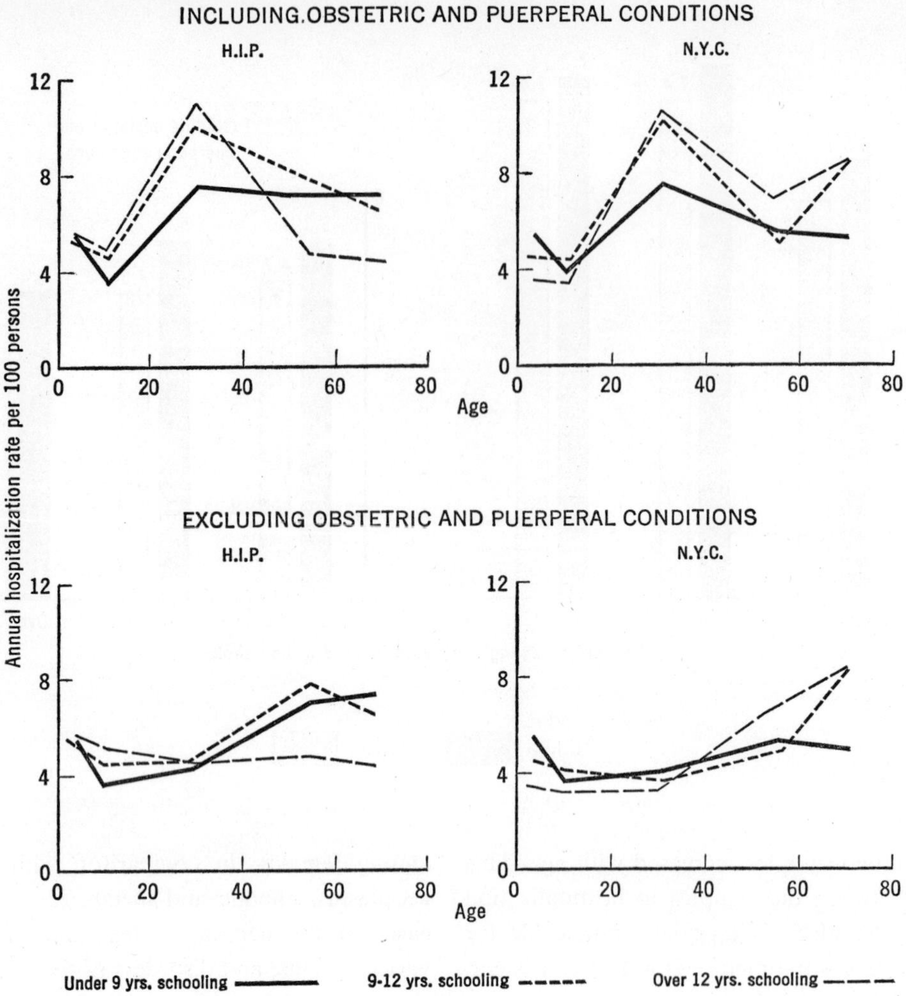

samples. Although the greatest difference occurred in the lowest education group, the difference was within the range of sampling variation. For chronic conditions, on the other hand, there was a consistently higher rate in the H.I.P. sample in each education group, with the differences tending to be greater in the two higher education groups.

Frequency of Surgery

Some data on the frequency of surgery in the two samples have already been presented in the section dealing with specific diagnostic conditions related to hospitalization. Here we shall present a general view of the frequency of surgery as well as a consideration of certain specific operations.

The general picture of hospitalized surgery by age and sex (Table XI–6) and by education (Table XI–7), is similar to that for hospitalization itself. About 40 out of every 1,000 H.I.P. enrollees were reported as having undergone some form of surgery in the hospital in 1951; the corresponding figure for the New York City sample is about 32. The difference between the two samples was greater for females than for males and there was some tendency in each education group for the surgical rate to be higher for the H.I.P. sample than for the New York City sample.

The frequency of certain operations is presented in Table XI–8. Whether attention is focused on the frequency rate or on the percentage rela-

Table XI–3. Diagnostic conditions producing hospitalization and related surgery (number and rates per 1,000 population) H.I.P. enrollees and New York City sample, 1951

DIAGNOSTIC GROUP	CONDITIONS PRODUCING HOSPITALIZATION IN 1951		NUMBER OF SURGICAL PROCEDURES[1]		HOSPITAL ADMISSIONS PER 1,000 POPULATION[2]		SURGICAL PROCEDURES PER 1,000 POPULATION[1]	
	H.I.P. enrollees	*N.Y.C. sample*	*H.I.P. enrollees*	*N.Y.C. sample*	*H.I.P. enrollees*	*N.Y.C. sample*	*H.I.P. enrollees*	*N.Y.C. sample*
Infective and parasitic diseases	5	15	—	2	0.6	1.1	—	0.2
Tuberculosis	2	7	—	2	0.2	0.5	—	0.2
Neoplasms	42	54	43	50	5.2	4.0	5.3	3.8
Allergic, metabolic, and nutritional diseases	20	19	12	5	2.5	1.4	1.5	0.4
Mental, psychoneurotic, and personality disorders	4	7	—	—	0.5	0.5	—	—
Diseases of nervous system and sense organs	15	26	12	9	1.9	1.9	1.5	0.7
Diseases of eye	11	14	11	7	1.4	1.0	1.4	0.5
Diseases of circulatory system	39	65	21	30	4.8	4.8	2.6	2.3
Hemorrhoids	15	18	16	18	2.0	1.3	2.0	1.3
Heart disease	12	29	—	—	1.4	2.1	—	—
Varicose veins and phlebitis	6	6	5	5	0.7	0.4	0.6	0.4
Hypertension	2	5	—	2	0.2	0.4	—	0.2
Diseases of respiratory system	56	116	33	80	7.0	8.6	4.1	5.9
Hypertrophied tonsils; other chronic respiratory disease	31	79	33	80	3.9	5.9	4.1	5.9
Pneumonia	14	27	—	—	1.7	2.0	—	—
Diseases of digestive tract	112	122	88	101	13.9	9.0	10.9	7.5
Appendicitis	32	44	29	44	4.0	3.2	3.6	3.2
Hernia	25	23	25	22	3.1	1.7	3.1	1.6
Ulcer of stomach and ulcerative colitis	21	10	8	2	2.6	0.8	1.0	0.2
Diseases of liver, gallbladder, and pancreas	18	15	14	15	2.2	1.1	1.7	1.1
Disorder of genito-urinary tract	35	67	29	54	4.4	4.9	3.6	4.0
Diseases of breast and other female genital organs	22	30	20	31	2.8	2.2	2.5	2.3
Diseases of kidney, bladder, and urinary tract	9	25	6	13	1.1	1.8	0.7	1.0
Deliveries and complications of pregnancy	191	305	24	32	23.8	22.5	3.0	2.4
Diseases of skin and cellular tissue	5	18	4	10	0.6	1.3	0.5	0.7
Diseases of bones and organs of movement	23	26	13	8	2.9	1.9	1.6	0.6
Accidental injuries	48	68	27	36	6.0	5.0	3.4	2.7
All other	24	32	10	7	3.0	2.4	1.2	0.1

[1] The count of surgical procedures includes multiple operations in the same individual wherever they occurred. It is for this reason that the number of surgical procedures may exceed the number of conditions reported (as for neoplasms in the H.I.P. sample).

[2] The sum of rates for all conditions exceeds the rates of hospitalization shown on p. 157 because in this table each condition present was counted. Some persons had more than one condition.

Figure XI–4. Hospitalization by diagnostic categories (rate per 1,000 persons), H.I.P. enrollees and New York City sample, 1951

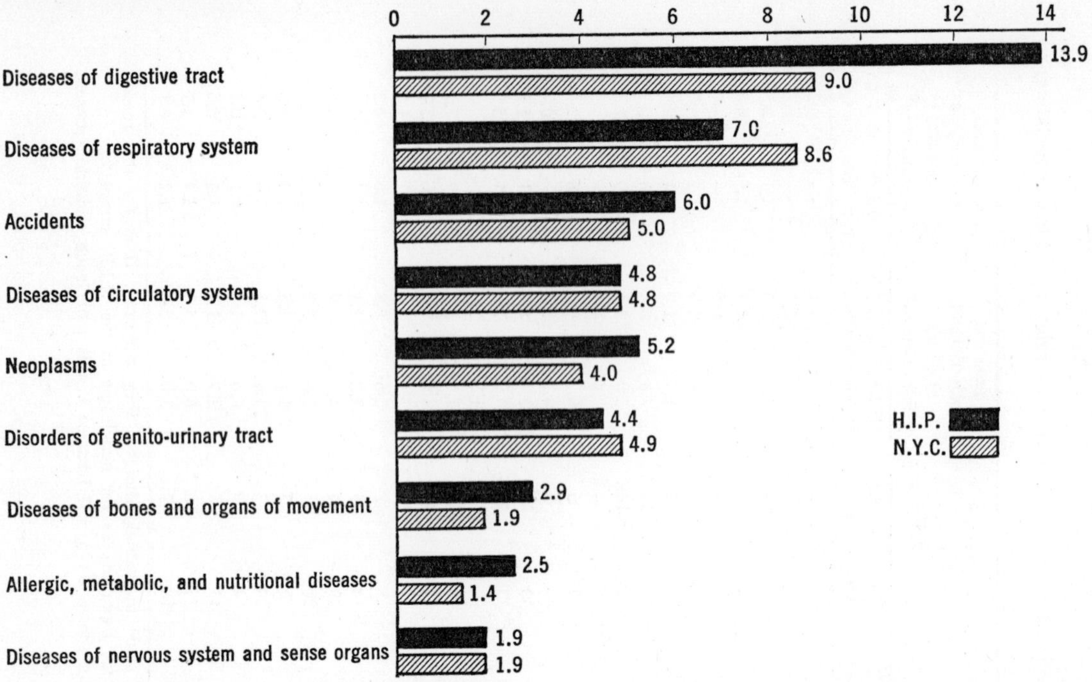

tive to all operations, the relative importance of each class of operation in the two samples is essentially the same. Gastrointestinal and abdominal operations accounted for a major portion of all operations; eye, ear, nose, and throat operations, chiefly tonsillectomies, came next in the New York City sample; and third in frequency in the New York City sample were operations for gynecological and obstetric conditions. The order of these last two groups was reversed in the H.I.P. sample. Orthopedic surgery ranked fourth in both samples.

Operations on the respiratory system (principally tonsillectomies) and genito-urinary surgery appear to have been more frequent in the New York City sample than in the H.I.P. sample, though the small numbers in the sample leave open the possibility that the difference may have been due to chance.

Gastrointestinal operations showed a distinctly higher frequency in the H.I.P. sample than in the New York City sample. It will be recalled that the hospitalization rates for gastrointestinal diseases were also greater in the H.I.P. sample, particularly among females.

The balance of the operations shown in Table XI–8 had higher rates in the H.I.P. sample, but again the differences fell within the range expected by chance.

In Table XI–9 data are presented for H.I.P. enrollees according to the H.I.P. status of the surgeon. About 63 percent of all operations on H.I.P. enrollees were performed by H.I.P. surgeons. However, when the data are examined by years of schooling completed by the household head it is seen that the higher the educational level the greater the proportion of operations performed by H.I.P. surgeons.

It is of interest to see how the proportion of operations performed by H.I.P. surgeons varied with the class of operation. This is shown in Table XI–10. It will be recalled that programs for crippled children and compensation cases fell largely in the field of orthopedic care.

Duration of Hospital Stay

The general findings with respect to length of hospital stay are quite similar to those reported in other studies (Table XI–11). The over-all average length of stay for H.I.P. was 10.6 days and

Table XI–4. Persons hospitalized for acute and chronic conditions and for obstetric conditions, H.I.P. enrollees and New York City sample, 1951, by age and sex

H.I.P. STATUS, TYPE OF CONDITION, AND SEX	NUMBER OF CONDITIONS PRODUCING HOSPITALIZATION							ANNUAL HOSPITAL RATE PER 1,000 POPULATION						
	All ages	Under 5	5 to 14	15 to 44	45 to 64	65 and over	Not reported	All ages	Under 5	5 to 14	15 to 44	45 to 64	65 and over	Not reported
H.I.P. ENROLLEES														
Acute	*115*	*20*	*26*	*42*	*22*	*4*	*1*	14.3	25.1	18.1	12.0	10.6	—	—
Male	68	15	12	22	16	3	—	16.1	34.7	16.3	13.1	13.1	—	—
Female	47	5	14	20	6	1	1	12.3	13.7	20.0	11.1	7.0	—	—
Chronic	*308*	*25*	*36*	*114*	*121*	*11*	*1*	38.3	31.3	25.1	32.7	58.1	—	—
Male	144	20	19	34	63	8	—	34.1	46.3	25.8	20.2	51.6	—	—
Female	164	5	17	80	58	3	1	43.0	13.7	24.3	44.3	67.3	—	—
Obstetric and puerperal[1]	*191*	—	—	*191*	—	—	—	50.1	—	—	105.8	—	—	—
NEW YORK CITY SAMPLE														
Acute	*181*	*34*	*31*	*72*	*29*	*11*	*4*	13.4	24.4	14.8	12.5	9.8	—	—
Male	104	26	18	45	11	3	1	16.1	35.6	16.2	17.4	7.8	—	—
Female	77	8	13	27	18	8	3	10.8	12.1	13.2	8.5	11.6	—	—
Chronic	*446*	*37*	*51*	*164*	*131*	*51*	*12*	32.9	26.6	24.3	28.5	44.2	56.5	—
Male	219	19	33	71	60	28	8	34.0	26.0	29.8	27.4	42.3	67.8	—
Female	227	18	18	93	71	23	4	31.9	27.2	18.2	29.4	46.0	46.9	—
Obstetric and puerperal[1]	*305*	—	—	*300*	—	—	*5*	42.9	—	—	94.7	—	—	19.1

[1] The rate for obstetric and puerperal conditions is expressed per 1,000 females in the indicated age group.

Figure XI–5. Hospitalization for acute and chronic conditions (rate per 1,000 persons), H.I.P. enrollees and New York City sample, 1951, by age

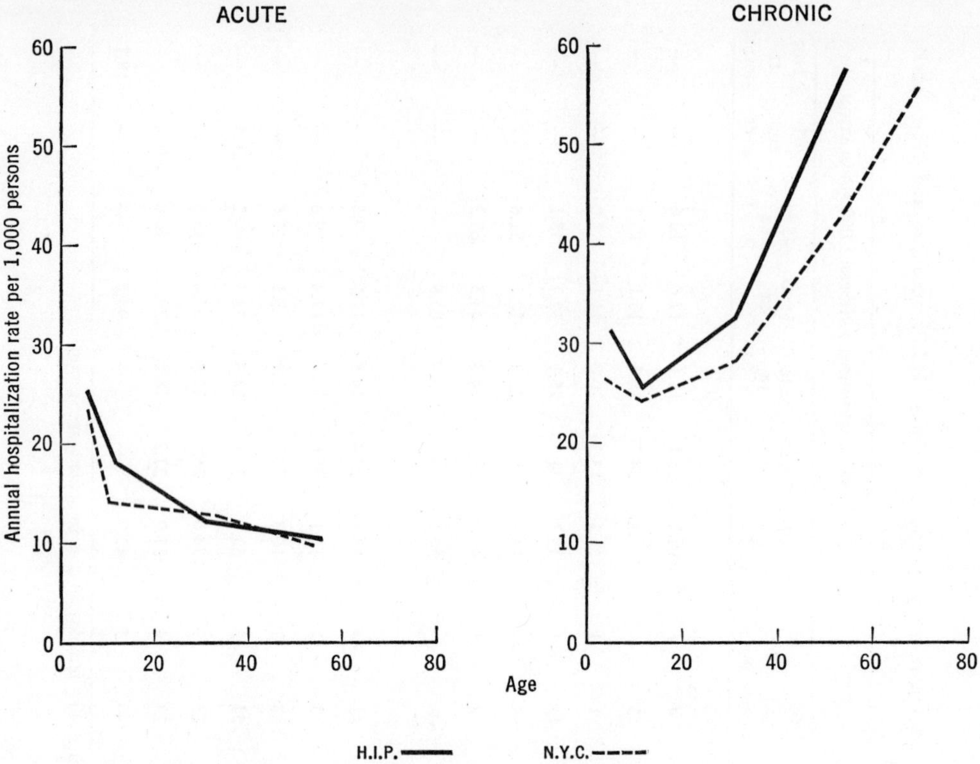

Table XI–5. Number of hospitalizations and rates per 1,000 hospitalized persons 15 years of age and over, H.I.P. enrollees and New York City sample, 1951, by diagnosis and sex

DIAGNOSTIC GROUP	NUMBER OF HOSPITALIZATIONS				RATE PER 1,000 POPULATION			
	H.I.P. enrollees		*N.Y.C. sample*		*H.I.P. enrollees*		*N.Y.C. sample*	
	Male	Female	Male	Female	Male	Female	Male	Female
Infective and parasitic diseases	—	1	4	5	—	0.3	0.6	0.7
Tuberculosis	—	1	3	4	—	0.3	0.5	0.6
Neoplasms	8	29	9	45	1.9	7.7	1.4	6.6
Allergic, metabolic, endocrine, and nutritional diseases	6	11	1	13	1.4	2.9	0.2	1.9
Diseases of nervous system and sense organs	3	8	9	14	0.7	2.1	1.4	2.0
Diseases of eye	2	5	4	10	0.5	1.3	0.6	1.4
Diseases of circulatory system	24	12	32	32	5.7	3.2	5.1	4.7
Heart disease	7	2	23	5	1.7	0.5	3.7	0.7
Hypertension	2	—	1	4	0.5	—	0.2	0.6
Hemorrhoids	11	4	6	12	2.6	1.0	1.0	1.8
Varicose veins	2	4	2	4	0.5	1.0	0.3	0.6
Diseases of respiratory system	4	8	23	22	0.9	2.1	3.7	3.2
Pneumonia	2	2	10	10	0.5	0.5	1.6	1.4
Chronic and other upper respiratory disease	1	3	15	10	0.2	0.8	2.4	1.4
Diseases of digestive tract	60	44	60	34	14.2	11.6	9.6	5.0
Ulcer of stomach and ulcerative colitis	15	6	8	2	3.6	1.6	1.3	0.3
Appendicitis	14	6	16	10	3.3	1.6	2.6	1.4
Hernia	15	6	18	1	3.6	1.6	2.9	0.1
Diseases of liver, gallbladder and pancreas	4	14	3	12	0.9	3.7	0.5	1.8
Disorder of genito-urinary tract	4	28	20	37	0.9	7.4	3.2	5.4
Diseases of breast and female genital organs	—	22	—	30	—	5.8	—	4.4
Diseases of kidney, bladder, and urinary tract	4	5	17	5	0.9	1.3	2.7	0.7
Deliveries and complications of pregnancy	—	191	—	302	—	50.5	—	44.1
Diseases of skin and cellular tissue	3	1	8	6	0.7	0.3	1.3	0.9
Diseases of bones and organs of movement	11	11	16	8	2.6	2.9	2.6	1.2
Accidental injuries	22	15	28	23	5.2	4.0	4.5	3.4

Table XI–6. All operations in hospitals, and rates per 1,000 population, H.I.P. enrollees and New York City sample, 1951, by age and sex

AGE AND SEX	NUMBER OF OPERATIONS		RATE PER 1,000 POPULATION	
	H.I.P. enrollees	*N.Y.C. sample*	*H.I.P. enrollees*	*N.Y.C. sample*
All ages	*324*	*433*	40.3	31.9
Male	133	192	31.4	29.8
Female	191	241	50.1	33.9
Under 5	*21*	*39*	26.3	28.0
Male	15	21	34.7	28.8
Female	6	18	16.4	27.2
5 to 14	*45*	*61*	31.4	29.1
Male	23	39	31.3	35.2
Female	22	22	31.4	22.3
15 to 44	*165*	*211*	47.3	36.7
Male	49	83	29.1	32.1
Female	116	128	64.3	40.4
45 to 64	*88*	*86*	42.3	29.0
Male	45	34	36.7	24.0
Female	43	52	49.9	33.7
65 and over	*3*	*27*	15.4	29.9
Male	1	11	7.0	26.6
Female	2	16	38.5	32.7
Not reported	*2*	*9*	48.9	20.0
Male	—	4	—	21.3
Female	2	5	76.9	19.1

Table XI–7. All operations in hospitals, and rates per 1,000 population, H.I.P. enrollees and New York City sample, 1951, by education of head of household

YEARS OF SCHOOLING COMPLETED BY HEAD OF HOUSEHOLD	NUMBER OF OPERATIONS		RATE PER 1,000 POPULATION	
	H.I.P. enrollees	*N.Y.C. sample*	*H.I.P. enrollees*	*N.Y.C. sample*
Less than 9	92	167	36.7	29.3
9 to 12	128	183	42.0	36.1
More than 12	96	62	42.1	29.9

for New York City 11.6 days. The difference between the two samples is not statistically significant. Average length of stay was three to four days greater for males than for females and slightly higher in the New York City sample than in the H.I.P. sample for each sex. However, if obstetric and puerperal conditions are excluded, the average length of stay of females becomes 12.7 days for the H.I.P. sample and 13.7 for the New York City sample, very close to the average for males.

The average length of stay increased with age (Figure XI–6). Comparison between the two samples is sharpened by considering the distribution of persons by length of stay. These distributions are shown in Table XI–12, and the cumulated distributions are presented in Figure XI–7. There was a noticeably higher proportion of males with short stays in the H.I.P. sample than in the New York City sample. Thus, while nearly a third of the hospitalized males in the H.I.P.

Table XI–8. All operations, rates per 1,000 persons, and percentage distribution, H.I.P. enrollees and New York City sample, 1951, for broad classes of operations and selected specific operations

CLASS OF OPERATION AND SELECTED SPECIFIC OPERATION	NUMBER OF OPERATIONS		RATE PER 1,000 PERSONS		PERCENTAGE OF ALL OPERATIONS	
	H.I.P. enrollees	*N.Y.C. sample*	*H.I.P. enrollees*	*N.Y.C. sample*	*H.I.P. enrollees*	*N.Y.C. sample*
All operations	*324*	*433*	40.3	31.9	100.0	100.0
Eye, ear, nose, and throat	*46*	*91*	5.7	6.7	14.2	21.0
T&A or tonsillectomy	27	66	3.4	4.9	8.7	15.3
Gastrointestinal and abdominal	*114*	*124*	14.2	9.1	35.2	28.6
Hernioplasty	25	22	3.1	1.6	7.4	5.1
Appendectomy[1]	29	44	3.6	3.2	9.0	10.2
Gallbladder operation	13	15	1.6	1.1	4.0	3.5
Hemorrhoidectomy	16	18	2.0	1.3	5.0	4.2
Genito-urinary	*10*	*22*	1.2	1.6	3.1	5.1
Gynecological and obstetric	*63*	*75*	7.8	5.5	19.4	17.3
Dilatation and curettage	9	22	1.1	1.6	2.8	5.2
Hysterectomy	13	11	1.6	0.8	4.0	2.6
Caesarean section	4	8	0.5	0.6	1.2	1.8
Orthopedic	*32*	*28*	4.0	2.1	9.9	6.5
Reduction of fracture	17	16	2.1	1.2	5.3	3.8
All other operations	*59*	*93*	7.3	6.8	18.2	21.5

[1] Does not include those appendectomies secondary to other operations.

Table XI–9. All operations in hospitals, H.I.P. enrollees, 1951, by H.I.P. status of surgeon and education of head of household

YEARS OF SCHOOLING COMPLETED BY HEAD OF HOUSEHOLD	NUMBER OF OPERATIONS				PERCENTAGE OF OPERATIONS		
	Total	H.I.P. status of surgeon			Total[1]	H.I.P. status of surgeon	
		H.I.P.	Non-H.I.P.	Not reported		H.I.P.	Non-H.I.P.
Total	*324*	*185*	*108*	*31*	100.0	63.1	36.9
Less than 9	92	45	31	16	100.0	59.2	40.8
9 to 12	128	76	47	5	100.0	61.8	38.2
More than 12	96	60	28	8	100.0	68.2	31.8
Not reported	8	4	2	2	—	—	—

[1] Operations for which status of surgeon was not reported have been eliminated from this total.

Table XI–10. Specified types of operations in hospitals, H.I.P. enrollees, 1951, by H.I.P. status of surgeon

TYPE OF OPERATION	NUMBER OF OPERATIONS				PERCENTAGE OF OPERATIONS		
	Total	H.I.P. status of surgeon			Total[1]	H.I.P. status of surgeon	
		H.I.P.	Non-H.I.P.	Not reported		H.I.P.	Non-H.I.P.
Eye, ear, nose, and throat	46	25	16	5	100.0	61.0	39.0
Gastrointestinal and abdominal	114	70	32	12	100.0	68.6	31.4
Gynecological and obstetric	63	38	21	4	100.0	64.4	35.6
Orthopedic	32	14	14	4	100.0	50.0	50.0
All other	69	38	25	6	100.0	60.3	39.7

[1] Operations for which status of surgeon was not reported have been eliminated from this total.

Table XI–11. Average duration[1] of hospital stay, H.I.P. enrollees and New York City sample, 1951, by age and sex

AGE AND SEX	H.I.P. ENROLLEES			NEW YORK CITY SAMPLE		
	Persons	Total days	Average days	Persons	Total days	Average days
All ages	*571*	*6,075*	10.6	*873*	*10,133*	11.6
Male	196	2,551	13.0	301	4,356	14.5
Female	375	3,524	9.4	572	5,777	10.1
Under 5	*44*	*372*	8.5	*63*	*569*	9.0
Male	34	239	7.0	40	426	10.7
Female	10	133	13.3	23	143	6.2
5 to 14	*56*	*437*	7.8	*81*	*860*	10.6
Male	29	189	6.5	51	685	13.4
Female	27	248	9.2	30	175	5.8
15 to 44	*327*	*2,843*	8.7	*503*	*4,586*	9.1
Male	53	739	13.9	108	1,288	11.9
Female	274	2,104	7.7	395	3,298	8.3
45 to 64	*129*	*1,869*	14.5	*151*	*2,937*	19.4
Male	70	973	13.9	67	1,405	21.0
Female	59	896	15.2	84	1,532	18.2
65 and over	*14*	*491*	35.1	*56*	*848*	15.1
Male	10	411	41.1	27	495	18.3
Female	4	80	20.0	29	353	12.2
Not reported	*1*	*63*	63.0	*19*	*333*	17.5
Male	—	—	—	8	57	7.1
Female	1	63	63.0	11	276	25.1

[1] Persons with duration of hospital stay not reported are excluded from this table.

Table XI–12. Percentage of persons hospitalized, H.I.P. enrollees and New York City sample, 1951, by duration of hospital stay, sex, and education of head of household

DAYS IN HOSPITAL	H.I.P. ENROLLEES						NEW YORK CITY SAMPLE					
	Male	*Female*		*Years of schooling completed by head of household*			*Male*	*Female*		*Years of schooling completed by head of household*		
		Total	Excluding obstetric	Less than 9	9 to 12	More than 12		Total	Excluding obstetric	Less than 9	9 to 12	More than 12
1	18.4	5.1	11.1	6.0	12.6	8.4	15.6	7.2	13.9	8.1	11.9	10.9
2	4.6	4.5	4.3	5.3	5.9	1.8	2.3	3.5	5.9	2.8	2.5	4.8
3 to 4	9.7	11.7	7.7	4.6	13.0	14.4	6.6	11.5	8.2	10.9	10.2	7.5
5 to 6	9.2	29.3	10.6	15.2	25.6	25.1	13.6	25.0	10.6	15.0	27.3	19.0
7 to 9	18.4	24.3	23.1	19.9	20.2	26.3	18.9	28.3	21.4	21.6	25.1	34.6
10 to 13	12.2	10.9	15.4	19.2	9.3	8.4	10.6	7.9	11.2	11.5	5.2	8.8
14 to 20	11.7	5.3	10.1	15.9	2.5	7.2	14.0	7.0	11.9	14.4	6.0	4.1
21 or more	15.8	8.8	17.8	13.9	10.9	8.4	18.3	9.6	16.8	15.6	11.9	10.2
Total persons[1]	196	375	208	151	238	167	301	572	303	320	363	147

[1] Persons with duration of hospital stay not reported are excluded.

Figure XI–6. Average duration of hospital stay, H.I.P. enrollees and New York City sample, 1951, by age and sex

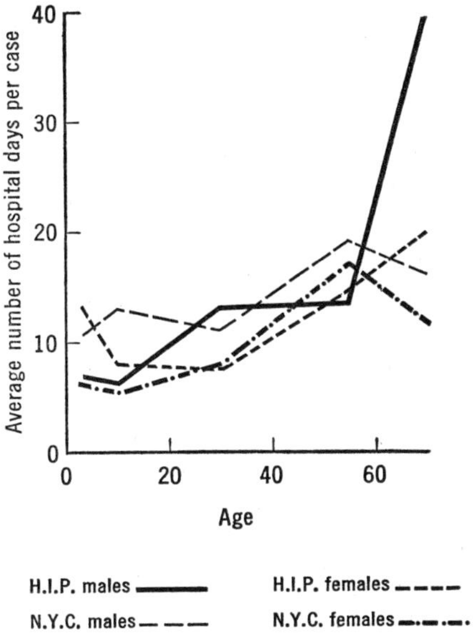

Figure XI–7. Cumulative percentage distribution of duration of hospital stay, H.I.P. enrollees and New York City sample, 1951, by sex

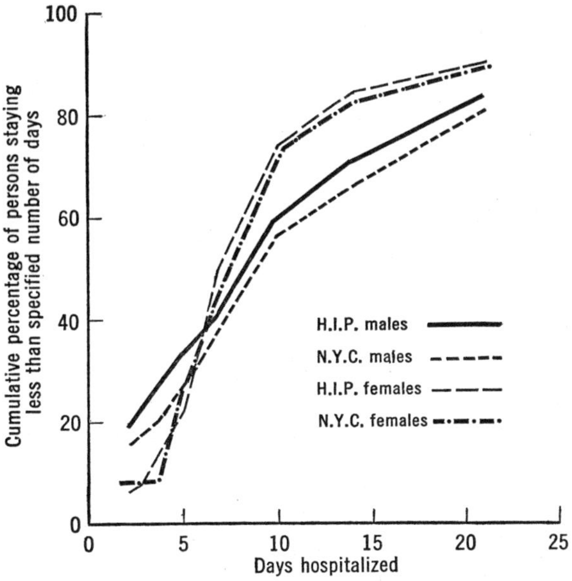

sample spent less than five days in the hospital, the corresponding figure for the New York City hospitalized males is only a fourth. The difference between the two distributions decreased, of course, with greater length of stay. However, while 73 percent of the H.I.P. male cases stayed less than two weeks, the corresponding figure for the New York City sample is 68 percent. On the other hand, there was little difference in the cumulative distributions for length of stay of females in the two samples. However, if obstetric and puerperal conditions are excluded, the females in the New York City sample have a higher proportion of very short lengths of stay and also very long lengths of stay.

The variation in length of stay with education of the head of the household is shown in Table XI–13. In both samples the lowest education group

Table XI–13. Persons hospitalized, H.I.P. enrollees and New York City sample, 1951, by average duration of stay, age, and education of head of household

AGE AND YEARS OF SCHOOLING COMPLETED BY HEAD OF HOUSEHOLD[1]	H.I.P. ENROLLEES			NEW YORK CITY SAMPLE		
	Persons	*Total days*	*Average days*	*Persons*	*Total days*	*Average days*
All ages						
Less than 9	162	1,890	11.7	336	4,180	12.4
9 to 12	241	2,361	9.8	374	3,874	10.4
More than 12	175	1,455	8.3	154	1,681	10.9
Under 5						
Less than 9	7	148	21.1	22	167	7.6
9 to 12	22	102	4.6	31	360	11.6
More than 12	15	122	8.1	10	34	3.4
5 to 14						
Less than 9	14	158	11.3	33	428	13.0
9 to 12	25	178	7.1	37	380	10.3
More than 12	21	98	4.7	10	51	5.1
15 to 44						
Less than 9	65	591	9.1	160	1,521	9.5
9 to 12	147	1,305	8.9	240	2,020	8.4
More than 12	116	902	7.8	100	827	8.3
45 to 64						
Less than 9	67	815	12.2	86	1,538	17.8
9 to 12	44	701	15.9	40	672	16.8
More than 12	22	326	14.8	26	632	24.3
65 and over						
Less than 9	8	115	14.3	29	469	16.2
9 to 12	3	75	25.0	17	189	11.1
More than 12	1	7	7.0	6	132	22.0
Not reported						
Less than 9	1	63	63.0	6	57	9.5
9 to 12	—	—	—	9	253	28.1
More than 12	—	—	—	2	5	2.5

[1] Excludes persons for whom education of head of household was not reported in both samples.

had the longest average length of stay, when all ages are considered together. The average length of stay tended to increase with age in each of the three education groups.

The differences in duration of hospital stay in the three education groups are more readily seen if the distributions are cumulated, as in Figure XI–8. The length of stay of the lowest education group was obviously greater in both samples than that of the two higher education classes, which did not differ greatly from each other. Thus, in the H.I.P. sample, 50 percent of the cases hospitalized in the middle education group stayed less than 6.5 days, while the corresponding figure for the lowest education group is 10 days. In the New York City sample the figures are 7 and 9 days, respectively.

This greater duration of hospitalization of persons in the lowest education group is not due to differences in the age composition of the education groups. When data are adjusted to a standard age distribution, it is found that in the H.I.P. sample half the cases in the middle education group stayed less than 6.5 days, whereas in the lowest education group the corresponding figure is 9 days. In the New York City sample the figures are 7.0 and 8.3 days, respectively.

When the same data are plotted so as to emphasize the comparison of the H.I.P. and New York City samples (Figure XI–9), it is seen that the variation in length of stay among the education groups is of much greater magnitude than the variation between the two samples within each education group. In fact, the similarity between

Figure XI–8. Cumulative percentage distribution of duration of hospital stay, H.I.P. enrollees and New York City sample, 1951, by education of head of household

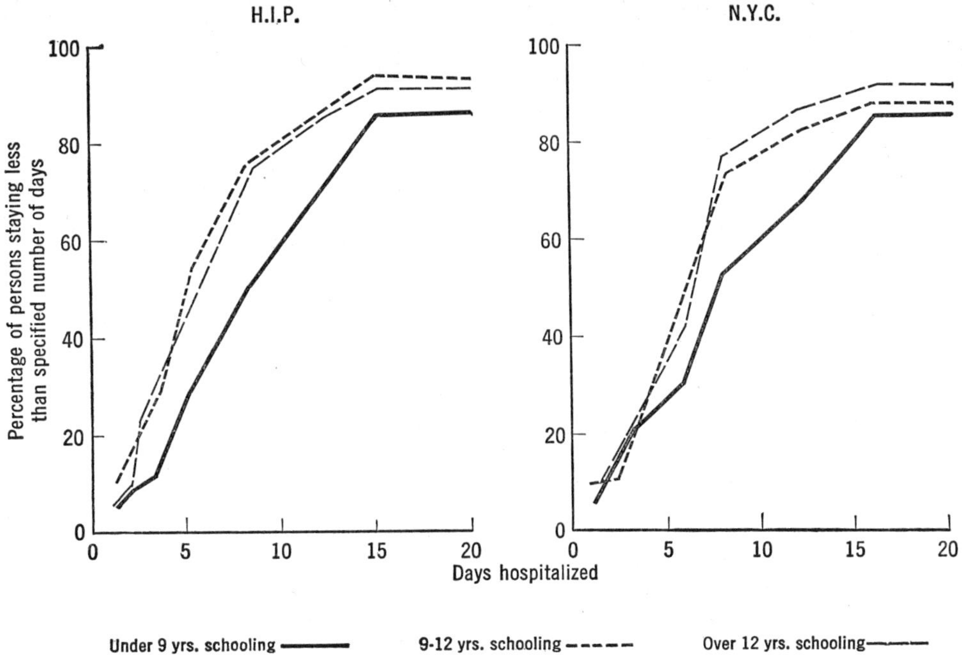

the two samples for each education group is remarkable. If anything, this similarity increases with increase in education of the household head.

Duration of Hospital Stay, by Insurance Status

Although the data on the hospital insurance status of persons in the sample are open to question, one might expect that the fact of having or not having hospital insurance would be reported reasonably accurately for those persons who were hospitalized. Assuming this to be the case, it is of interest to examine the length of stay as reported on Schedule 3 in relation to insurance status. This is done in Table XI–14. Although all H.I.P. enrollees are expected to have hospital insurance, there were still 70 hospitalized enrollees who were reported as having no hospital insurance (see Chap-

Table XI–14. Persons hospitalized, H.I.P. enrollees and New York City sample, 1951, by insurance status, education of head of household, and average length of hospital stay

H.I.P. STATUS AND YEARS OF SCHOOLING COMPLETED BY HEAD OF HOUSEHOLD	ALL GROUPS			SOME HOSPITAL INSURANCE			NO HOSPITAL INSURANCE			NOT REPORTED		
	Persons	*Days*	*Average days*	*Persons*	*Days*	*Average days*	*Persons*	*Days*	*Average days*	*Persons*	*Days*	*Average days*
H.I.P. ENROLLEES												
All education groups	*594*	*6,075*	10.1	*502*	*4,613*	9.2	*70*	*1,322*	19.0	*22*	*140*	6.4
Less than 9	162	1,890	11.6	132	1,426	10.8	28	457	16.4	2	7	3.5
9 to 12	241	2,361	9.8	210	1,925	9.2	20	380	19.0	11	56	5.0
More than 12	175	1,455	8.3	151	1,202	8.1	18	190	10.8	6	63	10.0
Not reported	16	369	23.1	9	60	6.7	4	295	73.8	3	14	4.7
NEW YORK CITY SAMPLE												
All education groups	*911*	*10,133*	11.0	*400*	*3,439*	8.6	*459*	*6,339*	14.0	*52*	*355*	6.8
Less than 9	336	4,180	12.4	109	1,096	10.0	209	2,978	14.2	18	106	5.9
9 to 12	374	3,874	10.4	195	1,691	8.7	158	2,040	14.2	21	143	6.8
More than 12	154	1,681	10.9	80	531	6.7	63	1,057	16.8	11	93	8.5
Not reported	47	398	8.5	16	121	7.6	29	264	9.1	2	13	6.5

Figure XI–9. Cumulative percentage distribution of duration of hospital stay, H.I.P. enrollees and New York City sample, 1951, by education of head of household

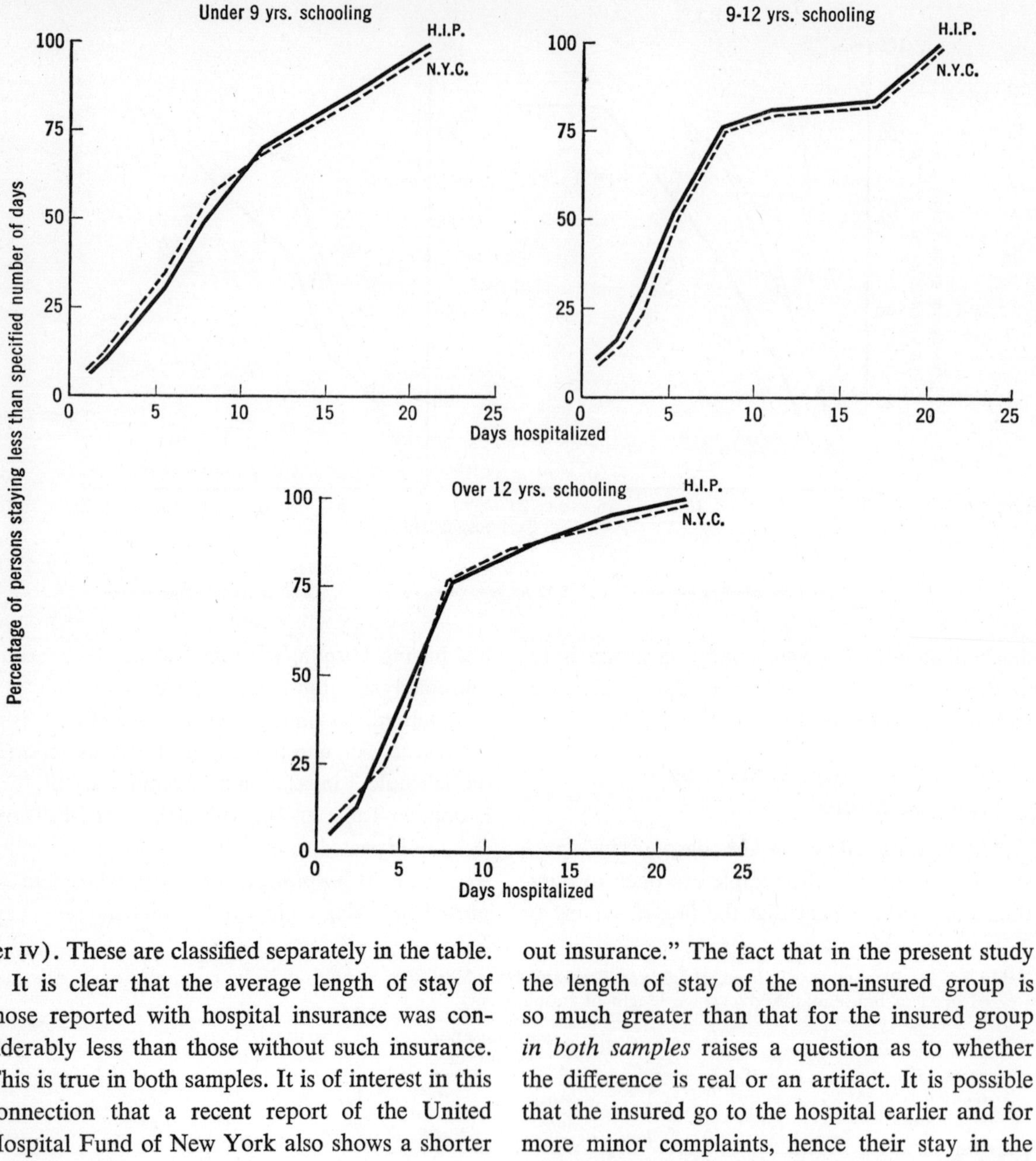

ter IV). These are classified separately in the table.

It is clear that the average length of stay of those reported with hospital insurance was considerably less than those without such insurance. This is true in both samples. It is of interest in this connection that a recent report of the United Hospital Fund of New York also shows a shorter length of stay for insured as compared with non-insured persons, although the difference between the two groups is considerably less than that of the present study.

However, the National Family Survey of Medical Costs and Voluntary Health Insurance[11] found the "average length of hospital stay for all persons hospitalized was 9.7 days with virtually no differences between those with insurance and without insurance." The fact that in the present study the length of stay of the non-insured group is so much greater than that for the insured group *in both samples* raises a question as to whether the difference is real or an artifact. It is possible that the insured go to the hospital earlier and for more minor complaints, hence their stay in the hospital is shorter than that for the uninsured. Unfortunately, the unreliable nature of the insurance data, discussed in Chapter IV, Appendix D, and earlier in this chapter, makes it impossible to examine the hypothesis. On the other hand, the comparatively long length of stay of the non-

[11] Odin W. Anderson, *National Family Survey of Medical Costs and Voluntary Health Insurance.* New York, Health Information Foundation, 1954, p. 53.

insured group may reflect the inclusion of individuals who had some insurance but whose condition was not covered or whose entire length of stay was greater than that allowed by the insurance contract.

In spite of the difficulties of interpretation just noted, it is worth remarking on certain other features of Table XI–14. The average length of stay of both the insured and non-insured groups was somewhat higher in the H.I.P. sample than in the New York City population. Also, within the insured group in both samples the average length of stay declined with increasing education of the head of the household,[12] and within each education group the H.I.P. enrollees had a longer average length of stay. For those in the "no insurance" group the trend with education was not clear nor was the direction of the difference between the two samples consistent.

Duration of Hospital Stay, by Diagnostic Condition

The variations described above would undoubtedly be easier to interpret if it were possible to examine them in relation to specific diagnostic conditions. A breakdown to this extent, however, renders the material too thin for analysis. Nevertheless, by using the grouping into "acute" and "chronic," some picture of the influence of diagnosis can be obtained. It will be remembered that

Figure XI–10. Percentage of acute and chronic conditions requiring seven or more nights of hospitalization, H.I.P. enrollees and New York City sample, 1951, by age

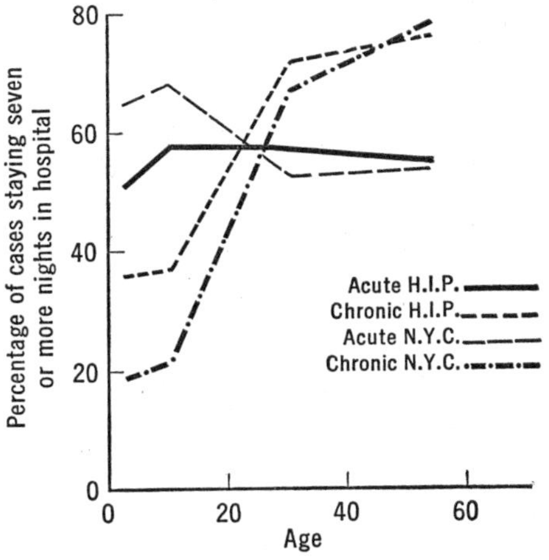

obstetric and puerperal conditions are not included in either of these two broad classes.

The distribution of length of stay for acute and chronic conditions reported in the two samples is shown in Table XI–15. Chronic conditions, of course, had somewhat higher proportions with a longer length of stay than acute conditions. In the H.I.P. sample 56.3 percent of the acute cases stayed seven days or longer and 66.0 percent of the chronic cases fell in that class. The corresponding percentages for the New York City sample were 58.8 and 62.3, respectively. The over-all differences between the two samples were not great. When examined in relation to age, the expected pattern of hospital stay is seen, acute conditions showing a slight decline with age while chronic conditions show a marked rise (Figure XI–10).

Up to the age group 45 to 64 the percentage of persons with chronic conditions who stayed in the hospital seven or more nights was greater in the H.I.P. sample than in the New York City sample. The difference between the two samples became progressively less with increasing age until in the age group 45 to 64 the curves crossed each other.

The pattern of length of stay in relation to education of household head continued to show a greater length of stay for those in the lowest education group (Table XI–16), both for the acute and chronic conditions. If anything, the differences between the lowest education group and the other two groups were accentuated when examined separately for the two broad groups of disease conditions.

Acute conditions seem to have had a slightly shorter length of stay in the New York City sample for those in the lowest education group. In the other two education groups the length of stay was shorter in the H.I.P. sample. For chronic conditions, New York City had a shorter length of stay in the highest education group, but in the two lower education groups it had a greater percentage of persons staying in the hospital 14 days or longer.

[12] It will be recalled that this trend persists even after correction for differences in age composition.

Place of Hospitalization

Nearly three-fifths of all persons hospitalized went to voluntary hospitals. There was little difference between the two samples in this respect (Table XI–17). However, a much higher proportion of hospitalized persons in the New York City sample entered municipal hospitals (19.4 percent) than in the H.I.P. sample (6.3 percent). Conversely, the percentage entering proprietary hospitals was higher for the H.I.P. sample (33.9 percent) than for the New York City sample (18.6 percent). These differences persisted throughout the age scale.

In Table XI–18 place of hospitalization is ex-

Table XI–15. Percentage distribution of acute and chronic medical conditions producing hospitalization of known duration, H.I.P. enrollees and New York City sample, 1951, by duration of related hospitalization, age, and sex

TYPE OF CONDITION, AGE, AND SEX	H.I.P. ENROLLEES					NEW YORK CITY SAMPLE				
	Total with known duration	*Nights in hospital* 1	2 to 6	7 to 13	14 or more	*Total with known duration*	*Nights in hospital* 1	2 to 6	7 to 13	14 or more
ACUTE										
All ages	*112*	13.4	30.4	30.4	25.9	*175*	10.3	30.9	34.8	24.0
Male	65	15.4	30.8	24.6	29.2	100	16.0	28.0	33.0	23.0
Female	47	10.6	29.8	38.3	21.3	75	2.7	34.7	37.3	25.3
Under 5	*20*	25.0	25.0	15.0	35.0	*34*	11.8	23.5	35.3	29.4
Male	15	26.7	20.0	13.3	40.0	26	15.4	15.4	30.8	38.5
Female	5	20.0	40.0	20.0	20.0	8	—	50.0	50.0	—
5 to 14	*26*	7.7	34.6	34.6	23.1	*31*	3.2	29.0	48.4	19.4
Male	12	8.3	33.3	25.0	33.3	18	5.6	33.3	38.9	22.2
Female	14	7.1	35.7	42.9	14.3	13	—	23.1	61.5	15.4
15 to 44	*39*	10.3	33.3	38.5	17.9	*69*	11.6	36.2	37.7	14.5
Male	19	15.8	36.8	31.6	15.8	42	16.7	38.1	33.3	11.9
Female	20	5.0	30.0	45.0	20.0	27	3.7	33.3	44.4	18.5
45 to 64	*22*	18.2	27.3	27.3	27.3	*26*	11.5	34.6	23.1	30.8
Male	16	12.5	37.5	25.0	25.0	10	20.0	20.0	30.0	30.0
Female	6	33.3	—	33.3	33.3	16	6.2	43.8	18.8	31.2
65 and over	*4*	—	25.0	25.0	50.0	*11*	18.2	18.2	9.1	54.5
Male	3	—	—	33.3	66.7	3	66.7	—	—	33.3
Female	1	—	100.0	—	—	8	—	25.0	12.5	62.5
Not reported	*1*	—	—	—	100.0	*4*	—	25.0	25.0	50.0
Male	—	—	—	—	—	1	—	—	100.0	—
Female	1	—	—	—	100.0	3	—	33.3	—	66.7
CHRONIC										
All ages	*297*	14.5	19.5	37.4	28.6	*432*	16.9	20.8	28.7	33.6
Male	136	18.4	18.4	36.0	27.2	207	15.9	19.8	26.6	37.7
Female	161	11.2	20.5	38.5	29.8	225	17.8	21.8	30.7	29.8
Under 5	*25*	52.0	12.0	20.0	16.0	*37*	59.4	21.6	16.2	2.7
Male	20	50.0	15.0	20.0	15.0	19	47.4	26.3	26.3	—
Female	5	60.0	—	20.0	20.0	18	72.2	16.7	5.6	5.6
5 to 14	*33*	45.4	18.2	15.2	21.2	*51*	58.8	19.6	9.8	11.8
Male	17	47.1	17.6	29.4	5.9	33	54.5	24.2	3.0	18.2
Female	16	43.8	18.8	—	37.5	18	66.7	11.1	22.2	—
15 to 44	*112*	8.0	20.5	50.0	21.4	*160*	8.8	25.0	32.5	33.8
Male	32	9.4	15.6	53.1	21.9	68	4.4	20.6	33.8	41.2
Female	80	7.5	22.5	48.8	21.2	92	12.0	28.3	31.5	28.3
45 to 64	*115*	5.2	20.9	39.1	34.8	*126*	4.8	17.5	27.8	50.0
Male	59	6.8	22.0	39.0	32.2	55	3.6	16.4	25.5	54.5
Female	56	3.6	19.6	39.3	37.5	71	5.6	18.3	29.6	46.5
65 and over	*11*	—	18.2	—	81.8	*47*	—	14.9	46.8	38.3
Male	8	—	12.5	—	87.5	25	—	8.0	40.0	52.0
Female	3	—	33.3	—	66.7	22	—	22.7	54.5	22.7
Not reported	*1*	—	—	—	100.0	*11*	9.1	27.3	36.4	27.3
Male	—	—	—	—	—	7	14.3	42.8	28.6	14.3
Female	1	—	—	—	100.0	4	—	—	50.0	50.0

Table XI–16. Percentage distribution of persons with acute and chronic conditions, H.I.P. enrollees and New York City sample, 1951, by duration of hospital stay and education of head of household

NIGHTS IN HOSPITAL	YEARS OF SCHOOLING COMPLETED BY HEAD OF HOUSEHOLD											
	H.I.P. enrollees						*New York City sample*					
	Acute			Chronic			Acute			Chronic		
	Less than 9	9 to 12	More than 12	Less than 9	9 to 12	More than 12	Less than 9	9 to 12	More than 12	Less than 9	9 to 12	More than 12
Total	100.0	99.9	100.0	100.0	100.0	100.0	100.0	100.0	100.0	100.0	100.0	99.9
1	10.0	19.1	—	6.5	21.4	15.4	8.5	11.0	15.0	10.6	25.4	21.5
2 to 6	17.5	36.2	43.5	12.0	23.9	21.8	28.8	33.0	20.0	20.1	17.4	27.7
7 to 13	32.5	19.1	52.2	45.6	36.8	28.2	37.3	30.8	50.0	29.1	26.8	29.2
14 or more	40.0	25.5	4.3	35.9	17.2	34.6	25.4	25.3	15.0	40.2	30.4	21.5
Number of cases	40	47	23	92	117	78	59	91	20	199	138	65

Table XI–17. Persons hospitalized, H.I.P. enrollees and New York City sample, 1951, by type of hospital and sex

TYPE OF HOSPITAL	NUMBER OF PERSONS HOSPITALIZED						PERCENTAGE OF PERSONS HOSPITALIZED[1]					
	H.I.P. enrollees			*New York City sample*			*H.I.P. enrollees*			*New York City sample*		
	Total	Male	Female	Total	Male	Female	Total	Male	Female	Total	Male	Female
All types	594	209	385	911	321	590	100.0	100.0	100.0	100.0	100.0	100.0
Municipal	35	17	18	163	60	103	6.3	9.0	4.9	19.4	20.8	18.6
Voluntary	322	111	211	497	166	331	58.0	59.0	57.5	59.0	57.4	59.9
Proprietary	188	55	133	157	48	109	33.9	29.2	36.2	18.6	16.6	19.7
Other[2]	10	5	5	25	15	10	1.8	2.7	1.4	3.0	5.2	1.8
Not reported[3]	39	21	18	69	32	37						

[1] Percentages computed exclusive of "not reported" data.
[2] Includes those hospitalized in more than one type of hospital.
[3] Includes those hospitalized outside of New York City.

Table XI–18. Persons hospitalized, H.I.P. enrollees and New York City sample, 1951, by education of head of household and type of hospital

H.I.P. STATUS AND YEARS OF SCHOOLING COMPLETED BY HEAD OF HOUSEHOLD	NUMBER OF PERSONS HOSPITALIZED						PERCENTAGE OF PERSONS HOSPITALIZED[1]				
	All hospitals	*Municipal*	*Voluntary*	*Proprietary*	*Other*[2]	*Not reported*[3]	*All hospitals*	*Municipal*	*Voluntary*	*Proprietary*	*Other*[2]
H.I.P. ENROLLEES											
Less than 9	162	18	80	46	—	18	100.0	12.5	55.6	32.0	—
9 to 12	241	13	128	80	8	12	100.0	5.7	55.9	34.9	3.5
More than 12	175	3	104	58	2	8	100.0	1.8	62.3	34.7	1.2
Not reported	16	1	10	4	—	1	100.0	6.7	66.7	26.7	—
NEW YORK CITY SAMPLE											
Less than 9	336	76	180	49	8	23	100.0	24.3	57.5	15.7	2.5
9 to 12	374	55	205	16	10	28	100.0	15.9	59.2	22.0	2.9
More than 12	154	23	88	25	6	12	100.0	17.2	12.0	19.6	4.2
Not reported	47	9	24	7	1	6	100.0	22.0	58.5	17.1	2.4

[1] Percentages computed exclusive of "not reported" data.
[2] Includes those hospitalized in more than one type of hospital.
[3] Includes those hospitalized outside of New York City.

amined in relation to education of the head of the household. Again, the proportion entering municipal hospitals was greater in each education group in the New York City sample. Moreover, the difference between the two samples became relatively greater as the education of the head of the household increased.

This pattern of place of hospitalization as a concern of hospital administrators and municipal authorities will be considered in the following pages of summary and discussion.

Summary and Discussion

The findings with respect to hospitalization of persons in the H.I.P. and New York City samples may be summarized under three headings: (1) the frequency of hospitalization, (2) the duration of hospitalization, and (3) the place of hospitalization.

Frequency of Hospitalization

The annual crude hospitalization rates in 1951 were very similar in the two samples, being 7.4 for the H.I.P. sample and 6.7 for the New York City sample.[13] For reasons discussed in the detailed text, it is believed that these figures underestimate the true incidence of hospitalization in each group.

Diseases of the digestive tract, the respiratory system, and the circulatory system, and accidents account for about 60 percent of all the conditions producing hospitalization in both the H.I.P. and New York City samples. The hospitalization rate for acute conditions is essentially the same in both samples, although there may be a lower rate in the H.I.P. sample than in the New York City sample for respiratory conditions, particularly tonsillectomies. Hospitalization for chronic disease, on the other hand, is greater in the H.I.P. sample than in the New York City sample. The difference is largely due to the higher hospitalization rate for diseases of the digestive tract in both sexes in the H.I.P. sample.

It was not possible to relate the frequency of hospitalization for a particular condition to the frequency of the condition itself in 1951, because the latter information was available only for an eight-week period in 1952. Nevertheless, if the differences between the two samples in hospitalization for gastrointestinal conditions and tonsillectomies are truly a reflection of the influence of a comprehensive medical care plan, such a finding has significance for hospital administrators and for community planners in general, since it means that as such plans take hold in a community, the distribution of diagnoses seen in the hospital may change. The differential between the two samples with respect to hospitalization for chronic diseases such as those included in the gastrointestinal group may come about in several ways. One hypothesis to account for the difference is that the condition itself may actually be more frequent in the H.I.P. population. However, it was shown in Chapter X that most conditions, including those of the gastrointestinal tract, were reported with about the same frequency in both samples. Further, those conditions reported with greater frequency in the New York City sample than in the H.I.P. sample may all be classed as chronic. It hardly seems likely, then, that this hypothesis is the explanation of the difference in the rate of hospitalization in the two samples.

A second hypothesis which could explain the higher H.I.P. hospitalization for gastrointestinal conditions is that H.I.P. enrollees, because a greater proportion have contact with a physician during a given period of time, would remember their illnesses better than persons in the New York City sample. However, as was pointed out in the summary of the previous chapter, while chronic illnesses such as gastrointestinal conditions were reported more frequently in the lowest education group, there was not a similarly greater frequency of seeing the doctor in this group. In addition, one might suppose that conditions in this group serious enough to hospitalize would be reasonably well remembered.

It was pointed out earlier that a higher proportion of H.I.P. enrollees had hospital insurance than persons in the New York City sample. Since it is known that the frequency of hospitalization is greater for persons with such insurance, the higher rate of hospitalization for chronic condi-

[13] The difference between these two figures can easily be accounted for by chance alone.

tions in the H.I.P. sample may simply reflect these general facts rather than any special aspect of comprehensive medical care. Unfortunately, the unreliability of the insurance data obtained in this study leaves this hypothesis untested.

A fourth hypothesis which may be put forward is that the conditions of group practice make specialist care more readily available and that the preventive aspects of early hospitalization are emphasized. If this hypothesis is true it might be expected that among persons with these conditions H.I.P. enrollees would be seen at an earlier stage than non-members of the Plan. It might further be expected that the frequency of immediate and late postoperative complications would be less in the H.I.P. group. The development of ways of testing this type of hypothesis is the real challenge facing plans such as H.I.P., because such hypotheses are related to the fundamental questions of the impact of medical care plans on the health *per se* of their enrollees.

Variation in the hospitalization rate with age, sex, and education of the head of the household could be examined only in relation to the broad grouping of diagnoses into acute and chronic conditions. The frequency of hospitalization for acute conditions declined slightly with age, but there was a marked rise in the rate for chronic conditions with increasing age. This fact, of course, is of considerable importance in regard to the development of social programs designed to meet the medical care needs of aging persons.

Age- and sex-specific hospitalization rates for acute conditions were found to be essentially the same in the two samples. For chronic conditions, however, the rate was higher at every age among females in the H.I.P. sample than among females in the New York City sample. This difference was largely, though not entirely, due to the higher rate of hospitalization of H.I.P. females for gastrointestinal conditions. There were no consistent differences between the age- and sex-specific hospitalization rates of males in the two samples.

Education of the head of the household appears to influence the frequency of hospitalization much less than age, since the variation in the hospitalization with education was not nearly as marked as with age and showed no consistent pattern for either acute or chronic conditions. However, in all three education groups the hospitalization rate for chronic conditions was higher in the H.I.P. sample than in the New York City sample. There was no consistent difference between the two samples for acute conditions.

When surgery was involved, education did appear to influence whether or not an H.I.P. surgeon performed the operation on an H.I.P. enrollee. About two-thirds of all operations on H.I.P. enrollees were performed by H.I.P. surgeons, but this figure varied from 59 percent in the lowest to 68 percent in the highest education group.[14] This fact should be of significance to administrators of medical care plans, since it suggests a need for developing programs to acquaint enrollees with the qualifications of doctors participating in the plan and with the general quality of care available through the plan.

Duration of Hospital Stay

The over-all duration of hospital stay was between 10 and 11 days. Males stayed in the hospital about four days longer than females on the average, but if obstetric and puerperal conditions are excluded, the average length of stay for both sexes is about the same, between 12.5 and 13.5 days.

Males in the H.I.P. sample had a somewhat shorter length of stay than those in the New York City sample. Nearly a third of the hospitalized males in the H.I.P. sample spent less than five days in the hospital, whereas the corresponding figure for the New York City sample was only a fourth.[15] There was very little difference between the two samples in length of stay of females. When, however, attention is focused on the chronic diseases, length of stay was greater in the H.I.P. sample. This was particularly true at the younger ages. Acute conditions showed no appreciable difference in the distribution by length of stay in the two samples.

[14] It should be remembered that these percentages refer to 1951, when H.I.P. was only four years old and many of the enrollees had been in the Plan for a much shorter period.

[15] It should be borne in mind that a higher proportion of the H.I.P. males than of New York City males were employed. Analysis of hospitalization by labor force status was not possible with the limited amount of data available.

Persons in the lowest education group had longer periods in the hospital than those in the two higher education groups even after differences in age composition among the education groups were taken into account. This greater length of stay in the lowest education group was found in both samples. There was virtually no difference between the two samples in the duration of hospitalization in any of the three education groups.

It would appear that whatever it is that contributes to the longer length of stay in the lower education group, it is common to all persons in the group and is not brought about by membership in a plan like H.I.P. It is true that chronic disease was reported with greater frequency in the lowest education class, but on the other hand there was no noticeably greater rate of hospitalization in that education group than in the two other education groups. It may be that the home accommodations of persons in the lowest education group are such as to make it easier or necessary for them to stay in the hospital a little longer. In this connection it was found that among persons with hospital insurance length of stay was greatest in the least-educated group. Or, possibly, the better-educated group feel the need to get back on the job more quickly. In any event, the facts should prove of interest to administrators of home care programs and others concerned with the duration of hospital stay. Certainly the special significance of this finding needs appraisal.

Assuming that the fact of having or not having hospital insurance would be reported reasonably accurately for those persons in the New York City sample who were hospitalized, it was found that the average length of stay of those reported with hospital insurance was less than those without insurance. Within the insured group the average length of stay was slightly higher (9.2 days) in the H.I.P. sample than in the New York City sample (8.6 days). This was true in all three education groups. Within the insured group length of stay decreased as education increased.

Place of Hospitalization

Place of hospitalization was found to be quite different in the two samples. A higher proportion of persons in the New York City sample than in the H.I.P. sample was hospitalized in municipal hospitals (19.4 and 6.3 percent, respectively). However, the N.Y.C. sample had a lower proportion of persons entering proprietary hospitals (18.6 percent and 33.9 percent, respectively). In both samples not quite 60 percent of persons hospitalized went to voluntary hospitals. The differences between the two samples were present in each education group. It should be noted that although the total proportion of persons hospitalized in voluntary hospitals was very similar in both samples, differences might exist in amount of free care required from voluntary hospitals by the two samples. The present study does not offer data for investigation of this point.

Since a higher proportion of H.I.P. enrollees than of the New York City sample are employed, it is difficult to tell how much of the differential in use of municipal hospitals and proprietary hospitals was due to the difference in the two sample population characteristics and how much was the result of membership in H.I.P. itself. Nevertheless, the fact that the difference between the two samples was large and existed even in the lowest education group suggests that some, if not all, of the difference was a reflection of membership in H.I.P. If this is true, the fact should have considerable significance for municipal planners, hospital administrators, and those concerned with hospital planning in general, since the presence of a medical care plan such as H.I.P. in the community may not only change the composition of the population using certain classes of hospitals, but may also have an influence, directly or indirectly, on the quality of hospital care because of the standards of care of the plan itself. Little research on questions of this kind has been undertaken by the field of hospital administration, yet it becomes increasingly clear from this and other studies that the forces influencing the pattern of hospitalization of the population and of hospital care rendered by the community have their origin largely outside the walls of the hospital. This fact is of great significance for the development of planning in the field of hospital care and for future research in hospital administration.

CHAPTER XII

Attended Dental Conditions

Dental Care as Reported in This Survey

Although the benefits rendered under the H.I.P. contracts do not include dental services, a comparison has been undertaken of the dental care received by the two groups here under scrutiny, that is, the sample of the New York City population and that of H.I.P. enrollees. Because it is a peripheral interest, the inquiry was sharply limited in scope. Its objective was not to find out about the dental conditions and the needs for dental care of the two populations, as in the case of the medical conditions, but rather to learn simply about the relative amounts of dental care that comparable segments of the two populations were receiving. Accordingly, the schedule was designed not to ask the respondent for the household about the condition of the teeth of its members but only whether a dental condition existed on the day preceding the interview for which a dentist was being seen and whether a dentist had been seen at any time during the preceding eight weeks. If a dentist had been seen, some further details about the contact were recorded.

A variety of reasons governed the decision not to ask about dental conditions *per se* in this one-interview contact with households. It was thought that in many of them the informant would not be fully aware of the dental conditions of the members, especially if there had been no dental examinations within the previous six months or, at most, the previous year. Attitudes vary widely among people as to the importance of dental caries as a health condition, particularly in children's deciduous teeth[1] and among adults of the absence of extracted teeth without replacement.

Aesthetic and cosmetic concern plays a considerable part in sensitivity to the need for dental care. Some people are less worried about dental disfigurement than are others and therefore less likely to report disfiguring but painless conditions as dental problems. Since this was only a collateral interest, it did not justify the time that would have been required to design and carry through an inquiry that would overcome these and other obstacles in the collection of reliable data.[2]

It was thought, however, that informants would know about fairly recent visits to the dentist by family members and that this information would be helpful in confirming or correcting the surmise made by H.I.P. that its population might be getting more dental care than comparable groups in the general population. This surmise rested on two suppositions. The first was that persons in the H.I.P. population might be referred by their physicians to dentists more often for attention to the less obvious dental conditions, and the second was that, having their medical care prepaid, more people in H.I.P. would be in a position to seek and pay for dental care. Other conditions could also have played a part in creating differences. Assuming that more H.I.P. enrollees were found to be receiving dental care than in comparable groups in the general population, there remained the possibility that the same concern that led people to enroll in H.I.P. would also lead them to seek dental care. In this connection it will be recalled that in group enrollment in voluntary health plans it is assumed that medical risks become actuarially sound if 75 percent of the eligible persons elect to join. This leaves the possibility of some self-selection among enrollees.

[1] See John O. McNeel, "Dental Program of the St. Louis Labor Health Institute," *American Journal of Public Health*, Vol. 44, No. 7, p. 880, July 1954.

[2] For a summary of the problems of planning and, by implication, of studying the distribution of dental care, see George St. J. Perrott, "Dental Care in a National Health Program," *Journal of the American Dental Association*, Vol. 26, pp. 1633–1644, October 1939.

The tabulations which follow show for each of the two samples the number of persons per 1,000 who on the day preceding the interview had dental conditions receiving dental care, with and without accompanying medical conditions. Specific rates for the day preceding the interview are shown by age, sex, labor force status (persons aged 14 years and over), and relation of the persons to the head of the family. Data for the eight-week period follow; these include rates for age, sex, education of the household head, association with medical conditions, number of visits to the dentist, and the instances in which a single visit to the dentist was made solely for the purpose of a dental check-up. As used here, the phrase "association with medical conditions" means merely that the two sets of conditions are present at the same time, not that they were all physiologically related, though some probably were.

Persons with Attended Dental Conditions, Day Preceding Interview, by Age, Sex, and Association with Medical Conditions

The attended dental conditions recorded as present on the day preceding the interview included all of those reported as receiving care at any time during the preceding eight weeks and still present on the day before the interview. The numbers of persons per 1,000 with such conditions are shown in Table XII–1, by age, sex, and presence of medical conditions.

From these data it appears that on a given day about 50 per 1,000 persons in the general population had dental conditions for which they were receiving care. In the population covered by H.I.P. approximately 60 per 1,000 were receiving such care. A wider difference was found for females than for males.

In comparing the figures for the several age groups it should be remembered that the population base for the children under five included infants under three years who rarely receive the care of a dentist. Had the rates been calculated for children aged three and over, they would have been considerably higher.[3]

Among the several age groups the discrepancy between H.I.P. and the general population was smallest for the children aged five to 14. This undoubtedly reflects the operation of the Bureau of Dentistry of the Health Department, which for the last several years has carried on a very active program for school children both in the public and parochial schools. For the school year 1951–1952 the Bureau reports that 67 percent of the children in the schools received the inspection services of the Bureau, and that over half of the children in school had the needed dental services completed. Remedial services were supplied both by dentists in private practice and by dental clinics operated on a philanthropic basis. Such massive public efforts unquestionably tended to minimize the differences between the rates for attended dental conditions in the two groups here considered.

As age increased, the differences between the rates for the two populations widened, again with the differences greater for the females in each age group than for the males. The rate for the small group of aged women in H.I.P. was six times that for aged women not so covered. The highest rate for any age-sex group of adults was that of women in the child-bearing ages of 15 to 44 years.

The accompaniment of attended dental conditions by medical conditions shows no pattern that distinguishes one population from the other. In each population group about 1 in 4 persons with attended dental conditions was reported as having one or more medical conditions as well. In the New York City sample this ratio for males was 1 to 5.6, for females 1 to 3.2; in the H.I.P. sample this ratio for males was 1 to 3.9, and for females 1 to 4.1. Thus, the males in the New York City sample, with a low total rate of attended dental care, showed such conditions *least* often associated with medical conditions. On the other hand, the females in this population, with a considerably

[3] Though different in absolute size, the rates show the same general configuration for the age-sex groups in the New York City sample as that found by Dr. Selwyn D. Collins in his analysis of the data collected by the Committee on the Cost of Medical Care which covered 38,544 person years of observation in 1928–31. See Selwyn D. Collins, "Frequency of Dental Services Among 9,000 Families, Based on Nation-Wide Periodic Canvasses, 1928–31," *Public Health Reports*, Vol. 54, No. 16, pp. 629–657, April 1939.

Table XII–1. Rates per 1,000 persons with attended dental conditions, H.I.P. enrollees and New York City sample, day preceding interview, by age, sex, and association with medical conditions

AGE AND SEX	H.I.P. ENROLLEES			NEW YORK CITY SAMPLE		
	Total with dental conditions (482 persons)	*Dental conditions only (361 persons)*	*With dental and medical conditions (121 persons)*	*Total with dental conditions (667 persons)*	*Dental conditions only (496 persons)*	*With dental and medical conditions (171 persons)*
All ages[1]	60.1	45.0	15.1	49.2	36.6	12.6
Male	51.3	38.1	13.2	43.9	36.1	7.8
Female	69.8	52.7	17.1	54.0	37.0	17.0
Under 5	11.3	11.3	—	6.5	5.8	0.7
Male	15.5	15.5	—	5.5	5.5	—
Female	5.5	5.5	—	7.6	6.1	1.5
5 to 14	73.9	58.6	15.3	69.7	64.0	5.7
Male	66.7	47.6	19.1	65.8	60.4	5.4
Female	81.4	70.0	11.4	74.0	67.9	6.1
15 to 44	77.7	61.6	16.1	66.5	47.8	18.7
Male	65.9	53.4	12.5	57.5	46.7	10.8
Female	88.6	69.2	19.4	73.9	48.6	25.3
45 to 64	42.3	25.0	17.3	35.1	20.3	14.8
Male	35.2	22.1	13.1	31.8	23.3	8.5
Female	52.2	29.0	23.2	38.2	17.5	20.7
65 and over	35.9	10.3	25.6	15.5	8.9	6.6
Male	35.0	14.0	21.0	26.6	16.9	9.7
Female	38.5	—	38.5	6.1	2.0	4.1
Age not reported	48.8	—	48.8	24.4	24.4	—
Male	133.3	—	133.3	5.3	5.3	—
Female	—	—	—	38.2	38.2	—

[1] Rates based upon population of 8,040 H.I.P. enrollees and 13,558 persons in the New York City sample.

higher rate, showed this association in the highest proportion of cases. The males and females in the H.I.P. population had about the same proportion of associated cases. This was midway between the extremes shown for the males and females in the New York City sample.

In the several age groups this ratio, that is, the total number of persons with attended dental conditions only in relation to those with dental conditions associated with medical conditions, showed a broad general tendency to increase as age advanced until the aged in the H.I.P. group showed over two-thirds of those with attended dental conditions having accompanying medical conditions. The association of attended dental conditions with degenerative medical conditions is strongly suggested by these figures for the aged in H.I.P.

Persons with Attended Dental Conditions, Day Preceding Interview, by Labor Force Status

In view of the possibility that status in the labor force might affect the rates of attended dental care, analysis was made to answer that question insofar as these data permit. It was thought that persons in each of the two samples who were in direct receipt of income from jobs or businesses and under compulsion to meet the demands of those situations might present a different picture in terms of rates than would those who were not so circumstanced. The results of this analysis appear in Table XII–2. Labor force status is applicable only to persons 14 years of age and over.

As can be seen from the table, in both population groups persons in the labor force had lower rates of attended dental conditions than did persons not in the labor force. But this large difference was achieved in both instances by reason of the very high rates for persons going to school. In this connection it will be recalled that such persons included not only the children 14 years of age and over who were attending elementary and secondary schools but also persons in local colleges, universities, and other educational institutions who were not in regular employment.[4]

[4] Persons in educational institutions away from home were not enumerated in either sample.

The difference in rates between the H.I.P. enrollees and the New York City sample was actually less for persons in the labor force (7.5 per 1,000 persons at risk) than for persons not in the labor force (23 per 1,000). For the persons in the labor force who were at work, the H.I.P. margin dropped to 5.2 per 1,000. For persons keeping house there was a difference of 13.2 persons per 1,000, again higher for the H.I.P. enrollees; and for persons going to school the difference was substantial, 40.6 more persons per 1,000 in the H.I.P. population than among persons in the general population.

The high rates for persons in school probably mirror the effect of the dental program of the Health Department, referred to above, for the younger persons in school, as well as the influence exerted by the social environment of educational institutions. The economic strength of families able to send their older children to high school and the local colleges and universities doubtless contributed to this condition. The higher rates of attended dental conditions in the H.I.P. sample in each labor force status group, particularly among those going to school, make it desirable to cross-classify by education of the head of the household since, as will be shown later (p. 176), there is a marked increase in rate with increase in education and the greatest difference between the H.I.P. and New York City samples is for the people in the highest education class. Unfortunately this was not possible, so that it is difficult to determine whether the observed differences reflect differences in population composition or whether, with medical care financed under the Plan, dental care in greater amount became feasible for these families than might otherwise be the case. As said above, the persons keeping house as well as those going to school showed higher rates in the H.I.P. enrollment than in the general population. The following presents further data on this issue.

Persons with Attended Dental Conditions, Day Preceding Interview, by Relationship to Household Head

In the preceding sections it has been shown that in both populations the rate per 1,000 for females with attended dental conditions exceeded the rate for males, that rates for children and adolescents exceeded those for older persons and, accordingly, rates for persons not in the labor force exceeded those for persons in it. The logical corollary of those findings now appears in the data on the rates for persons who stand in the several relationships to the head of the household (Table XII–3).

Table XII–2. Rates per 1,000 persons aged 14 years and over with attended dental conditions, H.I.P. enrollees and New York City sample, day preceding interview, by labor force status

LABOR FORCE STATUS	H.I.P. ENROLLEES		NEW YORK CITY SAMPLE	
	Number	*Persons per 1,000 with attended dental conditions*	*Number*	*Persons per 1,000 with attended dental conditions*
Total	*5,926*	64.8	*10,253*	51.8
In labor force	*3,804*	58.1	*5,634*	50.6
Working	3,637	58.3	5,277	53.1
Looking for work	52	39.2	248	20.2
Other	115	60.9	109	9.2
Not in labor force and other	*2,122*	77.3	*4,619*	54.3
Keeping house	1,524	59.7	3,204	46.5
Going to school	444	146.4	737	105.8
Other (including unknown labor force status)	154	46.4	678	28.3

Here the persons who stood in the relation of child to the head of the household had the highest rates but not nearly as high as those for persons attending school (Table XII–2). This is because the persons in the category of "child" were not necessarily young but instead might be adults, many in the labor force. In fact, a relatively substantial fraction of the total population consisted of persons over the age of 18 who lived with their parents; usually they were employed or in school or college. There were also the older single persons living with and supporting aged parents but still classified as children.

Comparison of the rate (56.6 per 1,000) shown here for spouses, who by definition in this survey[5] are always females, with the rate in Table XII–2 for persons keeping house (46.5 per 1,000) strongly implies that it was the *employed* married women who were responsible for the size of the rate shown here for spouses, and that among them a very high rate of attended dental conditions must have obtained.[6] It must also be remembered that the average age of employed women is less than that of those keeping house.

While the same general pattern of relationships among members of the family was shown in the two populations, it is to be noted that the H.I.P. enrollees again showed higher rates in every category set up for the analysis of the persons with attended dental conditions on the day preceding the interview.

Table XII–3. Rates per 1,000 persons with attended dental conditions, H.I.P. enrollees and New York City sample, day preceding interview, by relationship to head of household

RELATIONSHIP TO HEAD OF HOUSEHOLD	H.I.P. ENROLLEES		NEW YORK CITY SAMPLE	
	Number	*Persons per 1,000 with attended dental conditions*	*Number*	*Persons per 1,000 with attended dental conditions*
Total persons	*8,040*	60.1	*13,558*	49.2
Head	2,874	50.5	4,191	41.5
Spouse	2,114	62.9	3,111	56.6
Child	2,833	69.2	4,950	57.4
Other	219	41.1	1,306	25.3

Persons with Attended Dental Conditions, Eight-Week Period, by Age and Sex

Informants in the visited households were asked not only about the attended dental conditions present on the day preceding the interview among the household members, but also about all attended dental conditions during the prior eight weeks. It was found that approximately twice the number of persons had been in receipt of dental care during that period as was shown in the count as of a single day. While this relationship did not hold invariably throughout all of the age-sex groups in the two populations, there was a marked tendency in that direction (see Table XII–4).

When the period of observation is lengthened, the proportion of persons who had both attended dental and medical conditions becomes considerably higher than was found in the returns for a single day. This does not necessarily imply any more cases with an organic relation between medical and dental conditions than obtained for the cases reported for the one day. Over a longer period there is more opportunity for coincidental cases to increase in number.

With the exception of girls five to 14 years old and males aged 45 to 64 years—in both of which cases the differences were small—all of the age-sex classes showed higher rates for the H.I.P. enrollees during the eight-week period than for persons in the New York City population.

Persons with Attended Dental Conditions, Eight-Week Period, by Education of Household Head

When the data on persons with attended dental conditions are cast in terms of the education of the head of the household, the rate per 1,000 persons in each educational group is seen to rise materially as the years of schooling increase. This

[5] In all cases in which there was a husband in the household he was classified as head of the household, with the wife appearing as spouse.

[6] In Dr. Selwyn D. Collins' report on the data collected for the Committee on the Cost of Medical Care, women engaged in professional pursuits had a rate of attended dental care that markedly exceeded the rates for all other occupational groups of males or females. See Selwyn D. Collins, "Frequency of Dental Services Among 9,000 Families, Based on Nation-wide Periodic Canvasses, 1928–31," *Public Health Reports*, Vol. 54, No. 16, pp. 629–657, April 1939.

difference occurred in both populations but was exaggerated in the case of the H.I.P. population. In the New York City sample the range covered 48.2 persons per 1,000. Among the H.I.P. enrollees the range was 85.5 persons, with those in the best educational group showing an appreciably higher rate than the other two H.I.P. groups and the similarly educated group in the New York City sample. The number with attended dental conditions per 1,000 persons in each educational group in each sample is shown in the tabulation.

	H.I.P. enrollees	*New York City sample*
Persons with attended dental conditions per 1,000 in sample	119.8	99.1
Head of household with:		
Less than 9 years schooling	86.6	80.2
9 to 12 years schooling	113.2	111.9
Over 12 years schooling	172.1	128.4

The correlation shown here between education of the head of the household and the rate of attended dental conditions roughly parallels that found by the study of the Committee on the Cost of Medical Care when rates for family income classes are established. But the range of this difference is narrower for the New York City sample than that found in the earlier study. Several conditions doubtless have a part in the reduction of this difference. The New York City school dental care program referred to above, the presence of rural families in the earlier study, the difference in general economic conditions among people in the lower income groups in the two periods at which the data were collected, the effect of health education and the intensive advertising campaigns directed to the care of the teeth, with the possible effect on spending habits, are some of the conditions that are to be taken into account in considering this contraction in the range of rates.

Comparison of the differences between the H.I.P. enrollees and the general population in each education group shows them to be very small

Table XII–4. Rates per 1,000 persons with attended dental conditions, H.I.P. enrollees and New York City sample, eight-week period, by age, sex, and association with medical conditions

AGE AND SEX	H.I.P. ENROLLEES			NEW YORK CITY SAMPLE		
	Total with dental conditions (963 persons)	*Dental conditions only (547 persons)*	*With dental and medical conditions (416 persons)*	*Total with dental conditions (1,343 persons)*	*Dental conditions only (823 persons)*	*With dental and medical conditions (520 persons)*
All ages[1]	119.8	68.0	51.8	99.1	60.7	38.4
Male	108.5	61.9	46.6	90.3	58.8	31.5
Female	132.3	74.8	57.5	107.0	62.4	44.6
Less than 5	35.1	15.0	20.1	18.0	6.5	11.5
Male	41.6[2]	20.8	20.8	16.4[4]	5.5	10.9
Female	27.3[3]	8.2	19.1	19.6[5]	7.5	12.1
5 to 14	154.7	87.8	66.9	147.0	96.4	50.6
Male	163.2	81.6	81.6	139.8	90.2	49.6
Female	145.7	94.3	51.4	155.2	103.5	51.7
15 to 44	141.6	87.4	54.2	124.2	79.4	44.8
Male	124.7	82.5	42.2	107.4	73.0	34.4
Female	157.3	91.9	65.4	137.9	84.6	53.3
45 to 64	94.1	45.6	48.5	78.7	40.9	37.8
Male	77.9	39.4	38.5	79.0	51.5	27.5
Female	117.2	54.5	62.7	78.4	31.1	47.3
65 and over	87.2	30.8	56.4	35.4	14.4	21.0
Male	97.9	42.0	55.9	48.4	19.3	29.1
Female	57.7	—	57.7	24.5	10.2	14.3
Age not reported	146.4	73.2	73.2	66.7	46.7	20.0
Male	133.3	—	133.3	26.6	26.6	—
Female	153.8	115.4	38.4	95.4	61.0	34.4

[1] Rates based upon population of 8,040 H.I.P. enrollees and 13,558 persons in the New York City sample.
[2] This rate becomes 75.0 when based upon a population aged 2.5 to 5.
[3] This rate becomes 49.3 when based upon a population aged 2.5 to 5.
[4] This rate becomes 30.3 when based upon a population aged 2.5 to 5.
[5] This rate becomes 35.3 when based upon a population aged 2.5 to 5.

in families headed by persons with high school education or less, but very wide in favor of H.I.P. in families headed by persons with more than a high school education. Since dental care is not an H.I.P. benefit and any effect of coverage by H.I.P. is necessarily indirect, it is conceivable that in the case of families in the lowest income bracket this effect is not sufficiently great to allow them to have dental care much more frequently than they would otherwise have had it. In the case of some of these people, H.I.P. coverage means the transfer from medical indigency to medical self-support and, therefore, no greater margin in the family budget for dental expense is created by H.I.P. coverage. For families in the middle group there is little difference between the two populations, but in both instances their rates are considerably higher than those for the lowest group. These are the people who usually have higher standards of living, but often their incomes, particularly in white-collar employment, are no greater than the family incomes in the lowest group. Therefore H.I.P. coverage may not give them enough leeway to afford more dental care than they previously had been receiving. But in the case of persons with higher incomes the effect of H.I.P. coverage might mean a reallocation of the family's expenditures and a release of more resources for the pursuit of dental care. Whether these differences between the rates in the two populations arise from the effect of H.I.P. membership upon family budgeting or from other reasons cannot be determined. But the fact remains, the rate of attended dental conditions per 1,000 persons in households headed by persons with more than a high school education was one-third higher among H.I.P. enrollees than among the similarly educated persons in the general population.

Number of Dental Visits by Persons with Attended Dental Conditions, Eight-Week Period, by Sex

Persons in the New York City sample who saw dentists during the eight-week period and reported the number of visits had an average of 3.3 visits. The corresponding average for persons in the H.I.P. sample was 3.4 visits. Males and females in the general population had average numbers of visits that were alike, but in the H.I.P. sample there was a slight divergence, with 3.2 visits the average for the males and 3.5 for the females. These averages closely resemble those found in the first two studies mentioned above.

There was some variation in the average number of visits to the dentist within the eight-week period among the persons in the several age groups who saw dentists. In the New York City population the range was from an average of 2.4 visits for children under five years of age to 3.5 for persons aged 15 to 44; the range between the averages for these two age groups in the H.I.P. sample was from 2.1 to 3.6.

On the whole, the distribution of persons who saw dentists for specified numbers of times shows very close correspondence for the two population groups. In other words, although not as many people in the general population as among the H.I.P. enrollees saw dentists, when these people did see dentists they saw them about the same number of times as did the H.I.P. enrollees.

The distribution of persons seeing dentists according to the number of visits paid appears in Table XII–5.

Table XII–5. Percentage distribution of persons seeing dentist, H.I.P. enrollees and New York City sample, eight-week period, by sex and number of visits to dentist

SEX AND NUMBER OF VISITS TO DENTIST	H.I.P. ENROLLEES	NEW YORK CITY SAMPLE
Total persons[1]	100.0	100.0
1 visit	32.4	32.4
2 to 4 visits	39.0	40.8
5 or more visits	23.5	23.2
Number of visits not reported	5.1	3.6
Male	100.0	100.0
1 visit	35.8	32.5
2 to 4 visits	36.0	40.0
5 or more visits	22.3	23.7
Number of visits not reported	5.9	3.8
Female	100.0	100.0
1 visit	29.3	32.4
2 to 4 visits	41.8	41.4
5 or more visits	24.6	22.8
Number of visits not reported	4.3	3.4

[1] A total of 963 H.I.P. enrollees (459 males, 504 females) and 1,343 persons in the New York City sample (582 males, 761 females) were reported to have seen a dentist during the eight-week period.

While some slight differences in the number of times the dentist was seen appear between the distributions for the sex groups in each sample and between the distributions for the sex groups in the two populations, these differences are inconsequential. The similarity in the distributions would appear to testify to the standardization of general dental practice.

Number of Dental Visits per 1,000 Persons, Eight-Week Period, by Age

Because the age groups differed so widely in the average number of visits per person who saw a dentist, it is enlightening to see not only the number of persons per 1,000 who were in receipt of dental care but also the number of dental visits per 1,000 persons in each age group during the eight-week period. These rates are shown in Table XII–6.

The rate, in the eight-week period, for all *persons* in the H.I.P. population who saw a dentist exceeded that for all persons in the New York City population by about 21 percent (Table XII–4), but the rate of *visits* per 1,000 persons showed a difference between the two populations of about 23 percent. As in other analyses, the H.I.P. rates were higher at each age level.

Dental Check-Ups

Within the eight-week period 12.5 persons per 1,000 in the New York City sample and 13.6 persons per 1,000 H.I.P. enrollees had gone to the dentist for a check-up and had received such service together with whatever dental repairs could be attended to in a single visit. Assuming that an annual rate of service would be five times the eight-week rate,[7] about 62.5 persons per 1,000 in the New York City sample and 68.0 per 1,000 H.I.P. enrollees would have sought services that fall into the category of preventive dental care. The ratio of these persons among all persons seeking dental care of any type was about the same in both samples, that is, 12.6 percent in the New York City sample and 11.9 in the H.I.P. sample. This proportion did not vary appreciably among the age groups in the two samples that had sizable numbers of persons in them.

The question might well be raised as to whether, given greater access to dental care, the additional persons in the general population would show higher proportions whose need would be only for preventive and prophylactic services, or whether the volume of dental need for remedial service would still greatly predominate. If the H.I.P. experience can be taken as a guide, the second rather than the first condition would be found.

Summary

Examination of the returns on attended dental conditions from the survey of the samples of the two populations—the general population of New York City and the H.I.P. enrollees—reveals that:

[7] For the conversion of the eight-week rate for attended dental conditions into an annual rate, the multiple 5 has been used instead of the 6.5 ratio of eight weeks to 52. This yields a more cautious estimate which allows for possibly lower rates of utilization in other parts of the year.

Table XII–6. Dental visits (rates per 1,000 persons), H.I.P. enrollees and New York City sample, eight-week period, by age

AGE	H.I.P. ENROLLEES			NEW YORK CITY SAMPLE		
	Total persons	*Total visits*	*Visits per 1,000 persons*	*Total persons*	*Total visits*	*Visits per 1,000 persons*
Total	*8,040*	*3,100*	385.6	*13,558*	*4,245*	313.1
Under 5	798	40	50.1	1,392	52	37.4
5 to 14	1,435	667	464.8	2,095	932	444.9
15 to 44	3,489	1,699	486.9	5,757	2,415	419.5
45 to 64	2,082	637	306.0	2,961	705	251.6
65 and over	195	47	241.0	903	77	85.3
Not reported	41	10	243.9	450	64	141.8

1. About 20 percent more persons in the H.I.P. population than in the general population were receiving dental care for conditions present on a given day. In the general population 49.2 persons per 1,000 and in the H.I.P. population 60.1 persons per 1,000 had conditions which were under the care of dentists at the time of the survey.

2. The difference was least among elementary-school-aged children for whom the New York City Health Department had for several years prior to the survey been carrying on an active campaign both for the discovery of dental defects and their correction. The differences between the two populations were greatest for young children and for older persons. As age advanced after the age of 14, the rates for attended dental care declined in both groups.

3. More females than males, especially in the ages of 15 to 44, were in receipt of dental care.

4. In both populations more persons *not* in the labor force were receiving dental care than were the persons in it. This is due in large part to the high rate of attention to dental needs among persons in school. In the general population women keeping house had a lower rate than working persons in the labor force. But in the H.I.P. sample, working persons and those keeping house had approximately the same rates.

5. Wives in the general population, including those who were in the labor force, had a considerably higher rate of attended dental conditions than did the heads of families. Their rate was also considerably higher than that for women keeping house. A lesser difference, but in the same direction, was shown for the wives versus housekeepers in the H.I.P. sample. This suggests the likelihood of much higher rates for dental care for employed married women than for women at home. Age may also be a factor, since working women tend to be in the younger groups.

6. The number of persons with attended dental conditions within a period of eight weeks prior to the survey interview was approximately double that of persons with such conditions on a single day. The difference among age-sex groups in the two populations observed for the eight-week period followed the same general contours as those shown for the conditions found on the day preceding the interview.

7. There was a consistent advance in the rates of attended dental conditions as the education of the head of the household advanced from less than nine years of schooling completed to 12 years or more.

8. Since dental care is not a benefit under H.I.P. coverage, such coverage could be expected to have only an indirect effect upon the receipt of dental care. Assuming that such indirect effect was operative, it apparently became so only for persons in households headed by persons with more than 12 years of schooling completed.

9. While fewer persons in the general population saw dentists than in the H.I.P. population, when they did receive dental care they received it in amounts that very closely approximated those received by persons in the H.I.P. population.

10. The number of persons in the H.I.P. population who received preventive dental care only slightly exceeded the number found in the general population.

CHAPTER XIII

Preventive Health Services

Concept of Preventive Health Services

In health care, prevention is a word with many meanings. Fundamentally, however, these meanings cover two types of activities: (1) those intended to prevent the occurrence of disease, and (2) those aimed at halting or retarding the progression of disease. The former includes all means employed to avert the occurrence of disease, impairment of function and disability. The latter involves early detection of morbid processes, preferably before they produce symptoms, and embraces all measures which may uncover such evidence of disease.

Preventive services conceived in this sense proceed on two separate but related levels, which may be characterized as non-personal and personal. Non-personal preventive services comprise the classical activities of public health agencies, such as the disposal of sewage, the protection and provision of water supplies, the hygiene of foods, and the control of communicable diseases. Because these activities, arising out of the need for environmental sanitation and control of epidemic diseases, require organized action for the entire community, this sector of preventive service is primarily, but not wholly, the responsibility of governmental health agencies. While this group of services is concerned with people and their diseases in the mass, no hard and fast line can be drawn between them and the personal preventive services, consisting of measures applied directly to the individual.

Personal preventive services embrace those rendered directly to individuals so as to increase their ability to withstand the impact of deleterious elements (infections, nutritional abuses, intoxications, and somatic and psychic traumata), as well as the medical examination of individuals at varying age levels with a view to the early detection of physical and mental deviations from a norm so that they may be corrected as promptly and as effectively as possible. Included in these services are immunizations against specific diseases, antepartum and postpartum care, infant and child care, guidance in nutrition, and direct personalized education in all matters pertaining to the maintenance and improvement of health.

The periodic examination of presumably well individuals, as, for instance, infants, preschool children, pregnant women, industrial workers, and other adults has come to be regarded by many authorities in public health as a basic tool in the discovery of disease before it becomes overt. These authorities believe that such examinations make possible the detection in their incipiency of disorders whose onset is silent and insidious, as well as the discovery of minor but potentially detrimental defects that would otherwise be ignored.

New York City's General Program of Public Health Measures

Before the relevant data for the two samples of population are examined it is in order to review briefly the level which the public health movement in New York City had attained at the time of this survey. For half a century New York City has been aggressively engaged in the protection and improvement of health. Distinguished leadership in the municipal public health service has been supported both by deep citizen interest in the public programs and by the development of voluntary services of many kinds. Because the population was so large and so densely settled, epidemiology and the control and elimination of specifically dangerous environmental conditions have been energetically pursued. The municipal health program also encompassed several services of a personal kind: well-baby clinics, prenatal services, school health programs, immunizations, dental services, health education activities; recently a beginning at diagnostic services to aid patients has been made. For many years the Health Department has assisted physicians to improve medical care through highly competent laboratory services. Finally, as has been mentioned earlier, the City has a very large system of municipal hospitals with large out-patient departments to serve the medically indigent. These have provided hospital and sanatorium care for the tuberculous, and for all types of acute and chronic disease except long-time care of mental patients, which has been the responsibility of the State of New York.

Besides these public and voluntary programs, there has been a substantial development of industrial medicine administered through business organizations and in a few notable instances by labor unions. This for the most part has consisted of services for diagnosis and for some treatment for ambulatory patients who were employed. In this connection it is worth noting that in the survey of child health services conducted by the American Academy of Pediatrics in 1946–1947, New York was listed among the top five states providing organized well-child services.[1] The United States Public Health Service reported in 1954 that in the year 1950 the New York Basic Trading Area (25 counties) had the highest ratio of physicians and surgeons per 100,000 population of any of the 357 Rand McNally Basic Trading Areas in the United States. This ratio was 213. Washington, D.C., had a ratio of 210; Boston, 204. (The rate for Rochester, Minnesota, was 1,150, but its base population was only 65,106 and the Mayo Clinic located there is a national rather than a local institution.[2]) Studies of the resources for dental care have reported that the New York City area (one of 126 in the country) had a ratio of 104 dentists per 100,000 population, the highest in the country in 1952.[3]

In view of this background it would be expected that the sample of the New York City population would be found to have had a good measure of preventive care. Moreover, it can well be asked what it was expected that coverage in H.I.P. would add to the program of disease prevention.

H.I.P. Program for Prevention

Because they thought that preventive measures of a personal kind could be greatly strengthened through a closer integration with efforts to cure people of their illnesses, the leaders of H.I.P. have stressed from its inception the opportunity of plans for prepaid medical care to provide programs which would not only insure against the cost of care of illness, but would also put into effect procedures designed to prevent disease and disability and to serve as positive and aggressive agencies in the field of health promotion. In accordance with this postulate, H.I.P. has maintained an organized campaign of health education for the benefit of subscribers and their families. The H.I.P. has provided a central source of guidance and stimulation to the medical groups to strengthen their preventive services; it has also acted as the liaison with contractor groups, notably labor union welfare funds, to urge their beneficiaries to make full use of the services offered to them under the H.I.P. contract, which specifies that the insured persons are entitled to "periodic health examinations, immunizations, and other measures for the prevention of disease."

It has been thought that the family physician and the pediatrician were the persons best able to integrate preventive services and health education measures with routine medical care, and that family coverage greatly strengthened the situation. It was believed that a comprehensive program

[1] American Academy of Pediatrics, Committee for the Study of Child Health Services, *Child Health Services and Pediatric Education.* New York, The Commonwealth Fund, 1949, p. 25.

[2] Maryland Y. Pennell and Marion E. Altenderfer, *Health Manpower Source Book: 4. County Data from 1950 Census and Area Analysis.* Public Health Service Publication No. 263, Section 4. Washington, D.C., U.S. Government Printing Office, 1954, pp. 173–181.

[3] Elliot H. Pennell and Maryland Y. Pennell, *Health Manpower Source Book: 7. Dentists.* Public Health Service Publication No. 263, Section 7. Washington, D.C., U.S. Government Printing Office, 1955, p. 24.

would increase contacts with doctors and that the provision of health care at no further expense to the subscriber would serve to bring genuine amalgamation of health and medical care. It was also recognized that unlike the provision of medical care for the sick, the use of preventive services must in some part originate with people who have no immediate or compelling reason for seeing a doctor. Before H.I.P. was organized, the efforts made by social and health agencies, labor unions, and other groups had encountered considerable inertia and even some resistance when they tried to have well people come to their offices for health examinations. By providing that such services were to be rendered by the personal physician of the subscriber and his dependents, it was hoped that better results in preventive efforts would be forthcoming.

General Provisions for Medical Care, Both Samples

While it is still too early to expect that the results of preventive care would have become measurable, it is not too early to attempt measurement of the success of the program in terms of bringing more people under medical observation and in direct contact with health education forces. The evidence on this question falls into two classes: (1) those facts which relate to general medical care and (2) those which bear on preventive examinations of supposedly well persons. The facts found for the first of these classes have been the subject of several earlier chapters in this report, namely Chapters V, VI, VII, IX, and XII.

If it can be assumed that age for age and group for group in education, more persons under medical observation, more persons with family doctors, more children with pediatric care, and more persons receiving dental services represent more health protection, it would appear that appreciably more H.I.P. enrollees, proportionately, receive such protection than is the case with the general population of New York City.

It is now in order to examine the application of two special techniques in medical care and public health for which data were collected in the Household Survey. These are prenatal and postpartum care and health examinations of persons with no reported medical conditions.

Prenatal and Postpartum Care

In all instances in which a woman had been pregnant and delivered in 1951, a battery of six questions was asked about the care she had received in the prenatal and postpartum periods. This was part of the inquiry aimed at seeing how the care received by the H.I.P. enrollees compared with that given mothers in the general population. In some of the tabulations a distinction was made between the instances in which the mother herself was the respondent in this inquiry and those in which some other member of the family reported. That factor will be shown in Table XIII–2 relating to the components of the prenatal examinations. A total of 177 births were reported for H.I.P. enrollees and 276 for women in the New York City sample.[4]

The first item to be reviewed relates to the month of the pregnancy in which the doctor first saw the patient. This knowledge gives indication of the awareness of the benefits of early care in pregnancy on the part of the mothers as well as providing a picture of the volume of medical care rendered to these patients.

In reading these figures it is well to remember that an estimated 17 percent of the women in the H.I.P. sample who were delivered in 1951 did not have H.I.P. obstetric service, first, because they may not have been in H.I.P. for all of the period of their pregnancy, and second, because even when they had been, they did not utilize the H.I.P. obstetricians for their deliveries. It is known that some women are not willing to change to a new obstetrician until they and their families have had considerable experience with the H.I.P. physicians.[5]

It would thus appear (Table XIII–1) that 84.2

[4] This yields a birthrate of 20.3 per 1,000; the Health Department reported a birthrate for the city in 1951 of 20.4.

[5] Some enrollees may have had to use the maternity services in public hospitals for financial reasons because the indemnity for the hospital charges provided by their hospital insurance was insufficient to meet the cost.

Table XIII–1. Month of pregnancy in which patient came under medical care, H.I.P. enrollees and New York City sample, 1951

MONTH OF PREGNANCY IN WHICH PATIENT FIRST SAW A DOCTOR	H.I.P. ENROLLEES		NEW YORK CITY SAMPLE	
	Number	*Percent*	*Number*	*Percent*
Total	*177*	100.0	*276*	100.0
Second	84	47.5	111	40.3
Third	65	36.7	92	33.3
Fourth	16	9.0	29	10.5
Fifth	6	3.4	18	6.5
Sixth	1	0.6	10	3.6
Seventh	3	1.7	2	0.7
Eighth	—	—	1	0.4
Ninth	—	—	1	0.4
Not reported	2	1.1	12	4.3

percent of the H.I.P. enrollees were seen by their physicians, H.I.P. and non-H.I.P., during the first trimester of their pregnancy; the corresponding figure for the New York City sample is 73.6 percent. The returns indicated that the H.I.P. enrollees had received an average of 10.5 physician visits before delivery; the New York City women, an average of 9.3.

The factor of education of the head of the household seemed to have some effect on the receipt of prenatal care. In the H.I.P. sample the patients in families headed by a person with less than nine years of schooling completed reported an average of 9.8 physician visits in the prenatal period. Those in households headed by a person with nine to 12 years of schooling reported an average of 10.1 such visits, and those in the highest education class an average of 11.0 physician visits. In the New York City sample these averages were 8.9, 9.3, and 9.8, respectively.

Ever since the publication of the study of maternal mortality in New York City,[6] there has been consistent pressure on physicians and hospitals to raise the standards of obstetric care in this community. The very great reduction in those maternal deaths that the Academy's study labeled as preventable is telling evidence of the effectiveness of the measures taken to protect the lives of maternity patients. But that does not constitute the only goal in the improvement of obstetric services. It is highly important that the mother's future health should be safeguarded and, if possible, improved, and that the baby be delivered alive and in good health.

In this survey two questions on prenatal care were aimed at a rough evaluation of the quality of the care currently in practice. These questions asked whether the patient had "usually" been weighed and whether a urine sample was "usually" taken. It was also asked whether the patient had had at least one pelvic examination during the pregnancy. These questions, it was hoped, would shed some light on the fruitfulness of the efforts that have been made to raise standards of care in the general population and on differences, if any, between the care received by the H.I.P. enrollees and the women in the New York City sample.

The replies to the questions were arranged to yield a classification of four categories of prenatal care:

1. The first two components were "usually" present and at least one pelvic examination was made;

2. Some, but not all, of the components were reported positively;

3. None of the components was reported positively;

4. One or more of the components was not reported.

The results of the classification for the two samples appear in Table XIII–2. This shows further detail as to age[7] and whether or not the mother herself was the respondent.

It will be seen from these figures that 91.5 percent of the H.I.P enrollees were in the first class (90.3 of the respondents) and 87.3 of the women in the New York City sample, with almost the

[6] New York Academy of Medicine, Committee on Public Health Relations, *Maternal Mortality in New York City: A Study of All Puerperal Deaths, 1930–1932*. New York, The Commonwealth Fund, 1933.

[7] The patterns of age distribution are significant in that they conform to those found in other analyses for H.I.P. enrollees who were delivered and for the distribution of mothers in the New York City population. Higher proportions of the H.I.P. mothers are in the older age groups than obtain for the city. George Baehr, and Neva R. Deardorff, "Maternity Service Under the Health Insurance Plan of Greater New York," *American Journal of Public Health*, Vol. 41, No. 11, November Supp. 1951, pp. 44–54.

Table XIII–2. Maternity patients with prenatal examinations in Class 1,[1] H.I.P. enrollees and New York City sample, 1951, by age and respondent status

AGE AND RESPONDENT STATUS OF WOMEN INVOLVED	H.I.P. ENROLLEES			NEW YORK CITY SAMPLE		
	Total	*In prenatal examination Class 1*[1]		*Total*	*In prenatal examination Class 1*[1]	
		Number	Percent		Number	Percent
Total	*177*	*162*	91.5	*276*	*241*	87.3
Patient as respondent	*144*	*130*	90.3	*191*	*167*	87.4
15 to 29	61	53	83.3	117	100	85.5
30 to 44	83	77	92.8	74	67	90.5
Other as respondent	*33*	*32*	[2]	*85*	*74*	87.1
15 to 29	16	16	[2]	56	50	89.3
30 to 44	17	16	[2]	24	20	[2]
Not reported	—	—	—	5	4	[2]

[1] Patients in Class 1 were those who, when seen, had "usually" been weighed and had a urine sample taken and had had at least one pelvic examination during pregnancy.

[2] Percentage not calculated, base less than 50.

same percentage for respondents in that sample. This difference is not large, nor is it significant.

Inquiry was made as to the postpartum care that these patients had received. Table XIII–3 summarizes the replies elicited by the questions on this subject. Again, there is further analysis on age of patient and whether or not the patient was the respondent at the interview.

It would appear from these data that an appreciably higher proportion of the H.I.P. patients than of the New York City sample received a postpartum examination. This difference is greater for the group of cases in which the patient was the respondent and in which presumably the reporting conditions were conducive to greater accuracy than when some other member of the household was the respondent. For these self-reported cases the difference was 12.2 percentage points, or an excess in the rates of about 15 percent. The difference was especially marked for the young women under 30, for whom the excess reached 21 percent.

Table XIII–3. Maternity patients with postpartum examinations, H.I.P. enrollees and New York City sample, 1951, by age and respondent status

AGE AND RESPONDENT STATUS OF WOMEN INVOLVED	H.I.P. ENROLLEES			NEW YORK CITY SAMPLE		
	Total	*With postpartum examination*		*Total*	*With postpartum examination*	
		Number	Percent		Number	Percent
Total	*177*	*162*	91.5	*276*	*232*	84.1
Patient as respondent	*144*	*136*	94.4	*191*	*157*	82.2
15 to 29	61	57	93.4	117	90	76.9
30 to 44	83	79	95.2	74	67	90.6
Other as respondent	*33*	*26*	[1]	*85*	*75*	88.2
15 to 29	16	13	[1]	56	50	89.3
30 to 44	17	13	[1]	24	21	[1]
Not reported	—	—	—	5	4	[1]

[1] Percentage not calculated, base less than 50.

These figures would imply that by and large, comparable standards of care are in effect as between H.I.P. patients and most of the women in the city sample. In both groups, a large proportion of the patients are getting care that conforms to prevailing medical requirements for the proper supervision of patients. But it also appears that for postpartum care more of the H.I.P. patients than of the women in the general population were under the more adequate type of supervision.

Before leaving the subject of maternity care, it is well to see whether the factor of education of the head of the household figured in the situation. It has already been noted that the average number of physician visits in the prenatal period varied directly with this socioeconomic index. For this purpose the data on type of prenatal care and on postpartum examination are given in Tables XIII–4 and XIII–5. The data are those for all maternity cases, whether or not the patient was the respondent.

Although in these two analyses the numbers are so small in each of the education groups as to subject the results to considerable sampling error, it is worth noting (Table XIII–4) that for the education groups in the H.I.P. sample, the proportion of women with Class 1 prenatal examinations consistently advanced with education, while in the New York City sample the reverse is found.[8] For postpartum examinations the H.I.P. enrollees showed virtually no difference for education

[8] It will be recalled that the Academy's study of maternal mortality found that the mortality rates were not correlated with economic level.

Table XIII–4. Maternity patients with prenatal examinations in Class 1, H.I.P. enrollees and New York City sample, 1951, by education of head of household

YEARS OF SCHOOLING COMPLETED BY HEAD OF HOUSEHOLD	H.I.P. ENROLLEES			NEW YORK CITY SAMPLE		
	Total	*In prenatal examination Class 1*		*Total*	*In prenatal examination Class 1*	
		Number	Percent		Number	Percent
Total	*177*	*162*	91.5	*276*	*241*	87.3
Less than 9	27	23	[1]	65	58	89.2
9 to 12	77	71	92.2	141	123	87.2
More than 12	71	67	94.4	61	51	83.6
Not reported	2	1	[1]	9	9	[1]

[1] Percentage not calculated, base less than 50.

Table XIII–5. Maternity patients with postpartum examinations, H.I.P. enrollees and New York City sample, 1951, by education of head of household

YEARS OF SCHOOLING COMPLETED BY HEAD OF HOUSEHOLD	H.I.P. ENROLLEES			NEW YORK CITY SAMPLE		
	Total	*With postpartum examination*		*Total*	*With postpartum examination*	
		Number	Percent		Number	Percent
Total	*177*	*162*	91.5	*276*	*232*	84.1
Less than 9	27	24	[1]	65	50	76.9
9 to 12	77	71	92.2	141	122	86.5
More than 12	71	65	91.2	61	52	85.2
Not reported	2	2	[1]	9	8	[1]

[1] Percentage not calculated, base less than 50.

groups. In the New York City sample, however, there were fairly wide differences, with fewer women in the lowest education group receiving such services.

Health Examinations: General Background

Of the services aimed at preventive care, particularly in the early detection of the onset of the insidious chronic diseases, the periodic health examination, or the general health check-up, is generally regarded as of first importance. The routine examination of young children, together with their immunizations for the transmissible diseases, is a cornerstone of an effective public health program. No such systematic programs have developed for adults, probably because under the usual conditions people are inclined to wait until some condition of sickness is so painful or alarming as to induce them to call a physician. But with medical care of the type offered by H.I.P., the framework for the securing of such examinations is in some degree modified. People can go to their physicians for such examinations as a benefit paid for by their premium, and they can also see their physician for any condition, however slight, without being deterred by any fee. Since almost everyone has small physical defects or minor illnesses that appear from time to time, a way is opened for him to see his doctor who can check his general health as these minor conditions are attended to. Once a chronic disease appears, the patient is expected to present himself for regular check-ups irrespective of acute exacerbations of his condition. But such check-ups are not periodic health examinations within the usual connotations of the term. The patient sees the doctor, not for the purpose of the discovery of unsuspected disease but for general health guidance in arresting the condition that he knows he has. It is true that other conditions etiologically unrelated to the condition of which he is aware are sometimes discovered, but that does not change the essential nature of the reason for his seeing the doctor.

As reported in an earlier chapter, the H.I.P. has from the beginning required every physician in every medical group to report currently[9] on the number of health check-ups that he has made, and the Division of Research and Statistics has worked diligently to compile accurate figures on this phase of the program; but it has proven a difficult statistical procedure. It has been the policy of the Division to ask the doctors to report as health examinations only those instances in which persons without known chronic disease and without symptoms of which they were aware presented themselves for a health check-up. In other words, any mention by the patient of symptoms of disease removed the visit from the category of a health examination to one for diagnosis and treatment. Under these very strict reporting conditions in 1951, when there was a gross enrollment

[9] See Med. 10 Report Form and 1951 Report on Utilization of H.I.P. enrollees (documents available at H.I.P.) for further discussion of this problem in the reporting of physician services within the H.I.P.

of 297,400 different persons aged two years or more, a total of 43,463 "health examinations" were reported, or 14.6 per 100 persons "exposed" (16.5 per 100 enrollee years).

Household Survey Findings on School, Employment, and Insurance Examinations, and on General Check-Ups

The Household Survey gave opportunity to approach this subject from the point of view of patients and to find out how many in the H.I.P. population and in the New York City sample thought that they and the other members of their households had had such examinations within the eight-week period. On the schedule it was asked, "Did anyone in the household have a physical check-up or a routine health examination by a doctor during the last eight weeks?" If this was answered in the affirmative, the respondent was asked three more questions: why was the physical check-up made (school, employment, insurance, general, or "other," with further explanation of this); the components of the examination (medical history, height and weight, temperature, pulse, blood pressure, blood sample from finger, blood sample from arm, urinalysis, chest x-ray or fluoroscopy, vision test, hearing test, rectal examination, and, in women, vaginal examination); and the date of the examination.

A total of 896 such examinations were reported as received during the eight-week period by persons in the H.I.P. population of 8,040 enrollees —a ratio of 11.1 percent. For the New York City sample, 1,309 such examinations were reported— 9.7 percent of the population. This included the infant population as well as other children and adults.

At once the question arises as to the purposes for which examinations were made for the people in the two samples. Were there differences in the types of examinations? Table XIII–6 shows the rates at which the persons in the samples received examinations of the several types.

It is noteworthy that the rates for two types of examinations, the first and the last—the miscellaneous group—are almost the same. But the two types of special public health interest—general

Table XIII–6. Health examination rates per 100 persons, H.I.P. enrollees and New York City sample, eight-week period, by type of examination

TYPE OF HEALTH EXAMINATION	H.I.P. ENROLLEES		NEW YORK CITY SAMPLE	
	Number	*Rate per 100 persons*	*Number*	*Rate per 100 persons*
Total	*896*	11.1	*1,309*	9.7
School, employment, and insurance	159	2.0	289	2.1
General check-up	537	6.7	734	5.4
Prenatal and post-partum	76	0.9	99	0.7
Other or not reported	124	1.5	187	1.4

check-ups and maternity care—are slightly higher for the H.I.P. enrollees.

These rates cannot be converted into annual rates of persons having health examinations for at least two reasons. There is first a seasonal factor to be taken into account. In March, especially, physicians are very busy in the care of sick persons. At this time elective services are often deferred until the doctors are less pressed for time. A more troublesome problem is the receipt by infants of repeated check-ups during their first year; it is difficult to make allowance for this condition. (See Table XIII–9 for rates for physical check-ups of the several age groups.)

Components of Health Examinations

For the purpose of probing the content of these examinations reported by respondents, two tabulations have been made: (1) one for the school, employment, and insurance examinations and (2) one for the general health check-up.[10] These refer simply to the reported presence or absence of each of the specified components.

There is little or no basis for expecting differences between the two samples in the components of the first group of examinations, since for H.I.P. enrollees these examinations may be made by doctors retained by schools, employers, and insurance companies, and even in the case of examinations by H.I.P. physicians the requirements may be specified by the organization demanding the

[10] Important components of the prenatal examinations in 1951 are briefly analyzed in the section on prenatal care earlier in this chapter.

Table XIII–7. Percentage of school, employment, and insurance examinations, H.I.P. enrollees and New York City sample, eight-week period, by specified component

COMPONENT OF HEALTH EXAMINATION	H.I.P. ENROLLEES		NEW YORK CITY SAMPLE	
	Total examinations	*Percentage with specified component*	*Total examinations*	*Percentage with specified component*
Total	*159*	—	*289*	—
Medical history	107	67.3	215	74.4
Height and weight	134	84.4	234	81.0
Temperature	55	34.6	126	43.6
Pulse	87	54.7	194	67.1
Blood pressure	93	58.5	170	58.8
Blood sample—finger	38	23.9	69	23.9
Blood sample—arm	19	12.0	48	16.6
Urinalysis	46	28.9	90	31.1
Chest x-ray or fluoroscopy	58	36.5	129	44.6
Vision test	72	45.3	190	65.7
Hearing test	65	40.9	156	54.0
Rectal examination	18	11.3	48	16.6
Vaginal examination	2	1.3	5	1.7

examination. It is not surprising, therefore, to find that the pattern of the proportions with each of the components was similar for the two samples (Table XIII–7), or even that higher proportions of the examinations received by persons in the general population show the presence of a given component than seemed to be the case for the H.I.P. enrollees. Temperature, pulse, chest x-ray or fluoroscopy, vision and hearing tests showed the widest variation in rates between the two samples; these were all in favor of the general population.

We come now to the components of the health examinations that were classed as general check-ups (Table XIII–8). Again, the proportions found in the case of each component were similar in several instances. Medical histories were taken a little more frequently in the general population, but this could have come about because in the H.I.P. population the patient's medical history

Table XIII–8. Percentage of general check-ups, H.I.P. enrollees and New York City sample, eight-week period, by specified component

COMPONENT OF HEALTH EXAMINATION	H.I.P. ENROLLEES		NEW YORK CITY SAMPLE	
	Total examinations	*Percentage with specified component*	*Total examinations*	*Percentage with specified component*
Total	*537*	—	*734*	—
Medical history	321	59.8	477	65.0
Height and weight	449	83.3	608	82.8
Temperature	229	42.6	310	42.2
Pulse	307	57.2	425	57.9
Blood pressure	289	53.8	385	52.5
Blood sample—finger	127	23.6	125	17.0
Blood sample—arm	82	15.3	67	9.1
Urinalysis	171	31.8	191	26.0
Chest x-ray or fluoroscopy	179	33.3	231	31.5
Vision test	113	21.0	132	18.0
Hearing test	101	18.8	114	15.5
Rectal examination	51	9.5	85	11.6
Vaginal examination	36	6.7	79	10.8

could already have been on file with the medical group. Samples of blood and urine were taken somewhat more frequently for the H.I.P. patients; vision and hearing tests were made a little more frequently for them. On the other hand, rectal examinations and vaginal examinations were made more frequently in the check-ups for the general population. In the case of the latter this probably arises from the fact that the proportion of females in the general population given examinations considerably exceeded the proportion of males—a ratio of males to females of 44 to 56. In the H.I.P. population the ratio was almost exactly 50–50.

Health Examination Rates, by Age and Education of Household Head

The age distribution for persons with general check-ups in the two populations is shown in Table XIII–9.

Table XIII–9. Percentage of persons with general check-up, H.I.P. enrollees and New York City sample, eight-week period, by age

AGE	H.I.P. ENROLLEES			NEW YORK CITY SAMPLE		
	Total persons	*With health examinations*		*Total persons*	*With health examinations*	
		Number	Per cent		Number	Per cent
Total	*8,040*	537	6.7	*13,558*	734	5.4
Under 5	798	172	21.6	1,392	287	20.6
5 to 14	1,435	59	4.1	2,095	74	3.5
15 to 44	3,489	180	5.1	5,757	194	3.4
45 to 64	2,082	115	5.5	2,961	119	4.0
65 and over	195	10	5.1	903	39	4.3
Not reported	41	1	[1]	450	21	4.7

[1] Percentage not calculated, base less than 50.

From this it becomes evident that the receipt of health examinations in the H.I.P. population exceeded that in the general population consistently throughout the age classes. The largest difference was found for the persons aged 15 to 44, and the next largest one for those aged 45 to 64.

It remains to look at the receipt of general check-ups in terms of the education of the head of the household. The data for the two samples appear in Table XIII–10.

The difference between the H.I.P. population and the New York City population in the lowest education class is suggestive of the possible effect of membership in H.I.P. upon persons at the lower level of the socioeconomic scale.

Table XIII–10. Percentage of persons with health examinations, H.I.P. enrollees and New York City sample, eight-week period, by education of head of household

YEARS OF SCHOOLING COMPLETED BY HEAD OF HOUSEHOLD	H.I.P. ENROLLEES			NEW YORK CITY SAMPLE		
	Total	*With health examinations*		*Total*	*With health examinations*	
		Number	Per cent		Number	Per cent
Total	*8,040*	*537*	6.7	*13,558*	*734*	5.4
Less than 9	2,506	136	5.4	5,698	206	3.6
9 to 12	3,047	167	5.5	5,068	326	6.4
More than 12	2,278	225	9.9	2,071	170	8.2
Not reported	209	9	4.3	721	32	4.4

Summary

1. The concept of preventive health services encompasses both those directed toward environmental hygiene and personal services. The latter include those intended wholly to prevent disease, such as immunizations, and those which, through early diagnosis and treatment, prevent the more serious effects of illness of all kinds. In New York City the public health authorities have carried on aggressive programs in the first of these fields since the turn of the century, and in the second for at least a generation. While the Health Department does not supply care for the ill, it has actively engaged in health education and has aided private physicians in their care of patients by providing technical services of various kinds. The City of New York through its hospital system cares for patients with transmissible diseases and offers both in-patient and out-patient services to the medically indigent population, as do many voluntary institutions which provide both health education and medical care. On the whole, New York City can be said to have been a highly health-conscious community long before H.I.P. came into existence.

2. The H.I.P. program has from the beginning offered to its subscribers a battery of personal services for the prevention of disease. Its special contribution to this field was conceived to lie in

the close integration of the preventive services with the medical services for the care of illness through its provision of family doctors and pediatricians. It was thought that these doctors, working, when indicated, with the specialists in the medical groups, would enhance the effectiveness of health education and of efforts to prevent and arrest disease. A program of health education urging subscribers to use their privileges for preventive health care had been in operation from the start of the Plan.

3. The Household Survey included several lines of inquiry bearing on various kinds of preventive care. These questions were related to general aspects of medical care and to some specific procedures. The data in earlier chapters on general conditions of medical care in the two samples showed that more H.I.P. enrollees had contacts with physicians, had family doctors, had pediatric care for their children, and received dental attention, than did the general population. If these conditions carry any implications for early diagnosis and health education at the hands of doctors, it would seem that the H.I.P. enrollees were receiving more health care and guidance than were their counterparts in the general population.

4. While the H.I.P. enrollees in need of maternity care showed some advantage over those in the general population, the differences were not great; they were, however, consistently present. Both samples showed high percentages with health care that seemed to be substantially good.

5. Although the periodic general health check-up is regarded as one of the main devices in the field of personal prevention, its strategic importance is somewhat modified in the framework of a comprehensive system of prepaid medical care which encourages people to come to their physicians with conditions for which they might not otherwise seek medical care, and to come early upon the appearance of any symptoms. Unless they are unusually well, they see their physicians for minor illnesses and thereby come under medical observation without waiting for an annual or a periodic check-up. It might well be that there would actually be fewer instances in such a population of persons who technically qualified as presenting themselves for a check-up. In the case of the two samples here under scrutiny it was found that during the eight-week period the H.I.P. enrollees reported a somewhat higher rate of examinations than was reported for the New York City sample. The differences between the samples in rates were greatest for the persons in families in the lowest education group. In both groups the rates increased with education.

Appendices

APPENDIX A

Schedules Used in the Household Survey

COMMITTEE TO STUDY HEALTH AND MEDICAL CARE IN NEW YORK CITY

With the Assistance of Alfred Politz Research, Inc.

of

The City of New York

Interviewer ______________________________
Name Code

NAME ______________________________

ADDRESS ______________________________

APT. NO. OR LOCATION ______________________________

NOTES (Specify the appropriate schedule number and question number for any notes you make. Circle the appropriate question number if you make notes.)

SCHEDULE 1

LIST EVERY PERSON who usually lives in this household across the page in question 1 below. Use a separate column for each person. If there are more than six persons in this household, use another sheet, transcribing the study number and renumbering column heads. **Make no entries in shaded boxes.**

Interviewer ☐ ☐ 1 2

HOW MANY PEOPLE LIVE HERE?..........................

12 13 14 15 12 13 14 15

1. (a) WHAT IS THE NAME OF THE HEAD OF THIS HOUSEHOLD? Enter his or her name in the first column. (b) WHAT ARE THE NAMES OF ALL OTHER PERSONS WHO LIVE HERE? Use a separate column for each person, and list their names in the following order: Wife of head Unmarried sons and daughters (in order of decreasing age) Married sons and daughters and their families Other relatives Other persons who live in, such as lodgers, roomers, maids, and their relatives. (c) Circle the number of the person giving the information.	LAST NAME 1 FIRST NAME AND INITIAL	LAST NAME FIRST NAME AND INITIAL

NOW ASK THE QUESTIONS BELOW FOR EACH PERSON. Enter th

2. RELATIONSHIP — Enter relationship of person to head of household. For example: Head Daughter Lodger Wife Grandson Lodger's wife		(16) Relationship HEAD	(16) Relationship
3. SEX — Circle 1 or 2 for each person.		(17) 1 Male 2 Female	(17) 1 Male 2 Female
4. DATE OF BIRTH — Enter month and year.		Mo............... Year............... (18) (19)	Mo............... Year............... (18) (19)
5. WHAT WAS .... DOING MOST OF LAST WEEK — WORKING, KEEPING HOUSE, GOING TO SCHOOL, LOOKING FOR WORK, OR SOMETHING ELSE? Ask only for persons born before March 1938. Circle appropriate number for each person.		(20) 1 Working 2 Looking for work 3 Keeping house 4 Going to school 5 Permanently unable to work 6 Something else (specify) (21) (22)	(20) 1 Working 2 Looking for work 3 Keeping house 4 Going to school 5 Permanently unable to wo 6 Something else (specify) (21) (22)
6. I'M NOW GOING TO ASK A FEW QUESTIONS ABOUT THE HEALTH OF EACH MEMBER OF THIS HOUSEHOLD. WE'LL START WITH THEIR CONDITION YESTERDAY. Circle the appropriate number for each person for each question.	a. WAS ANYBODY IN THIS HOUSEHOLD SICK YESTERDAY?	1 YES (fill out Q. 1 and 2 on white memorandum. Check NOT ASKED for b, c, d below.) 2 NO (ask b)	1 YES (fill out Q. 1 and 2 on white memorandum. Check NOT ASKED for b, c, d below.) 2 NO (ask b
	b. WAS ANYBODY IN THIS HOUSEHOLD SUFFERING FROM AN ACCIDENT OR INJURY YESTERDAY? Include only injuries or accidents whose effects lasted more than 24 hours.	1 YES (fill out Q. 1 and 2 on white memorandum. Check NOT ASKED for c, d below.) 2 NO (ask c) 3 NOT ASKED	1 YES (fill out Q. 1 and 2 on white memorandum. Check NOT ASKED for c, d below.) 2 NO (ask c 3 NO ASK
	c. DID ANYBODY IN THIS HOUSEHOLD HAVE ANY SPECIAL SYMPTOMS YESTERDAY THAT LASTED FOR AT LEAST 24 HOURS?	1 YES (fill out Q. 1 and 2 on white memorandum. Check NOT ASKED for d below.) 2 NO (ask d) 3 NOT ASKED	1 YES (fill out Q. 1 and 2 on white memorandum. Check NOT ASKED for d below.) 2 NO (ask d 3 NO ASK
	d. DID ANYBODY IN THIS HOUSEHOLD SEE A DOCTOR OR DENTIST YESTERDAY FOR ANY REASON?	1 YES (fill out Q. 1 and 2 on white memorandum.) 2 NO 3 NOT ASKED	1 YES (fill out Q. 1 and 2 on white memorandum.) 2 NO 3 NO ASK

Sub sample

☐ ☐
3 4

Study Number

☐ ☐ ☐ ☐ ☐
5 6 7 8 9

10 11

12 13 14 15	12 13 14 15	12 13 14 15	12 13 14 15
LAST NAME 3	LAST NAME 4	LAST NAME 5	LAST NAME 6
FIRST NAME AND INITIAL	FIRST NAME AND INITIAL	FIRST NAME AND INITIAL	FIRST NAME AND INITIAL

nswers for each person in the column in which you have written his name.

(16) Relationship	(16) Relationship	(16) Relationship	(16) Relationship
(17) 1 Male 2 Female	(17) 1 Male 2 Female	(17) 1 Male 2 Female	(17) 1 Male 2 Female
Mo.......... Year.......... (18) (19)	Mo.......... Year.......... (18) (19)	Mo.......... Year.......... (18) (19)	Mo.......... Year.......... (18) (19)
(20) 1 Working 2 Looking for work 3 Keeping house 4 Going to school 5 Permanently unable to work 6 Something else (specify) (21) (22)	(20) 1 Working 2 Looking for work 3 Keeping house 4 Going to school 5 Permanently unable to work 6 Something else (specify) (21) (22)	(20) 1 Working 2 Looking for work 3 Keeping house 4 Going to school 5 Permanently unable to work 6 Something else (specify) (21) (22)	(20) 1 Working 2 Looking for work 3 Keeping house 4 Going to school 5 Permanently unable to work 6 Something else (specify) (21) (22)
YES (fill out Q. 1 and 2 on white memorandum. Check NOT ASKED for b, c, d below.) 2 NO (ask b)	1 YES (fill out Q. 1 and 2 on white memorandum. Check NOT ASKED for b, c, d below.) 2 NO (ask b)	1 YES (fill out Q. 1 and 2 on white memorandum. Check NOT ASKED for b, c, d below.) 2 NO (ask b)	1 YES (fill out Q. 1 and 2 on white memorandum. Check NOT ASKED for b, c, d below.) 2 NO (ask b)
YES (fill out Q. 1 and 2 on white memorandum. Check NOT ASKED for c, d below.) 2 NO (ask c) 3 NOT ASKED	1 YES (fill out Q. 1 and 2 on white memorandum. Check NOT ASKED for c, d below.) 2 NO (ask c) 3 NOT ASKED	1 YES (fill out Q. 1 and 2 on white memorandum. Check NOT ASKED for c, d below.) 2 NO (ask c) 3 NOT ASKED	1 YES (fill out Q. 1 and 2 on white memorandum. Check NOT ASKED for c, d below.) 2 NO (ask c) 3 NOT ASKED
YES (fill out Q. 1 and 2 on white memorandum. Check NOT ASKED for d below.) 2 NO (ask d) 3 NOT ASKED	1 YES (fill out Q. 1 and 2 on white memorandum. Check NOT ASKED for d below.) 2 NO (ask d) 3 NOT ASKED	1 YES (fill out Q. 1 and 2 on white memorandum. Check NOT ASKED for d below.) 2 NO (ask d) 3 NOT ASKED	1 YES (fill out Q. 1 and 2 on white memorandum. Check NOT ASKED for d below.) 2 NO (ask d) 3 NOT ASKED
YES (fill out Q. 1 and 2 on white memorandum.) 2 NO 3 NOT ASKED	1 YES (fill out Q. 1 and 2 on white memorandum.) 2 NO 3 NOT ASKED	1 YES (fill out Q. 1 and 2 on white memorandum.) 2 NO 3 NOT ASKED	1 YES (fill out Q. 1 and 2 on white memorandum.) 2 NO 3 NOT ASKED

7. NOW I'D LIKE TO ASK THE SAME QUESTIONS ABOUT EACH PERSON'S HEALTH DURING THE LAST EIGHT WEEKS. Ask a, b, c, d, e and f for *all* persons. Use calendar to show eight week period, which ends with date of first visit. Omit all conditions covered in 6 above.	a. WAS ANYBODY IN THIS HOUSEHOLD SICK AT ANY TIME DURING THE LAST EIGHT WEEKS BECAUSE OF A CONDITION NOT ALREADY MENTIONED?	1 YES (fill out Q. 1 and 2 on white memorandum, then ask b.) 2 NO (ask b)	1 YES (fill out Q. 1 and 2 on white memorandum, then ask b.) 2 NO (ask b)
	b. DID ANYBODY IN THIS HOUSEHOLD HAVE AN ACCIDENT OR INJURY DURING THE LAST EIGHT WEEKS NOT ALREADY MENTIONED? Include only injuries and accidents whose effects lasted more than 24 hours.	1 YES (fill out Q. 1 and 2 on white memorandum, then ask c.) 2 NO (ask c)	1 YES (fill out Q. 1 and 2 on white memorandum, then ask c.) 2 NO (ask c)
	c. DID ANYBODY IN THIS HOUSEHOLD HAVE ANY OF THE FOLLOWING CONDITIONS DURING THE LAST EIGHT WEEKS? Hand card to informant and read list slowly. Circle the numbers next to each symptom mentioned and enter them in Q. 1 on Schedule 2. If any symptom has already been mentioned circle the numbers next to that symptom but enter them in the same space on the white memorandum in which you have already entered "6" or "7". Use a separate column on white memorandum for each condition checked.	7c-1 Rashes, itching or other skin trouble 7c-2 Flat feet or other foot trouble 7c-3 Backaches 7c-4 Rectal bleeding 7c-5 Markedly overweight 7c-6 Constipation or other bowel trouble 7c-7 Marked weight loss (not due to dieting) 7c-8 Complaints or difficulties due to change of life 7c-9 Irregular or painful menstrual periods (For each circled symptom fill out Q. 1 and 2 on white memorandum, then ask d.)	7c-1 Rashes, itching or other skin trouble 7c-2 Flat feet or other foot trouble 7c-3 Backaches 7c-4 Rectal bleeding 7c-5 Markedly overweight 7c-6 Constipation or other bowel trouble 7c-7 Marked weight loss (not due to dieting) 7c-8 Complaints or difficulties due to change of life 7c-9 Irregular or painful menstrual periods (For each circled symptom fill out Q. 1 and 2 on white memorandum, then ask d.)
	d. DID ANYBODY IN THIS HOUSEHOLD HAVE A PHYSICAL CHECK-UP OR A ROUTINE HEALTH EXAMINATION BY A DOCTOR DURING THE LAST EIGHT WEEKS? Do not include check-ups for conditions mentioned above.	1 YES (fill out Q. 1 and 22 on white memorandum, then ask e.) 2 NO (ask e)	1 YES (fill out Q. 1 and 22 on white memorandum, then ask e.) 2 NO (ask e)
	e. DID ANYBODY IN THIS HOUSEHOLD SEE A DOCTOR OR A DENTIST FOR ANY OTHER REASON DURING THE PAST EIGHT WEEKS?	1 YES (fill out Q. 1 and 2 on white memorandum, then ask f.) 2 NO (ask f)	1 YES (fill out Q. 1 and 2 on white memorandum, then ask f.) 2 NO (ask f)
	f. WHAT IS THE TOTAL NUMBER OF TIMES .... SAW A DOCTOR OR DENTIST DURING THE LAST EIGHT WEEKS?	....Times	....Times
8. NOW JUST TWO QUESTIONS ABOUT LAST YEAR, THAT IS, 1951. Ask of all persons. For "yes" answers fill out Q. 1 and 2 on colored memorandum, even for conditions previously mentioned in Q. 6 and 7.	a. DID ANYBODY IN THIS HOUSEHOLD SPEND AT LEAST ONE NIGHT IN A HOSPITAL DURING 1951?	1 YES (fill out Q. 1 and 2 on colored memorandum, then ask b.) 2 NO (ask b)	1 YES (fill out Q. 1 and 2 on colored memorandum, then ask b.) 2 NO (ask b)
	b. DID ANYBODY IN THIS HOUSEHOLD HAVE AN ILLNESS OR OTHER MEDICAL CONDITION (not mentioned in 8a) THAT MADE HIM SPEND SEVEN OR MORE DAYS IN BED IN 1951?	1 YES (fill out Q. 1 and 2 on colored memorandum.) 2 NO	1 YES (fill out Q. 1 and 2 on colored memorandum.) 2 NO

NOW COMPLETE ALL COLUMNS O

FILL IN THE REMAINDER OF ALL ILLNESS AND MEDICA

	(23)	*(23)*
9. (a) I HAVE HERE A CARD WITH THE NAMES OF VARIOUS AILMENTS. WILL YOU TELL ME WHETHER ANYONE IN THIS HOUSEHOLD HAS ONE OF THESE AILMENTS? Hand card to informant and read list through slowly. Circle each ailment present. (b) For all ailments circled ask DID .... SEE A DOCTOR ABOUT THIS CONDITION AT ANY TIME DURING 1951? Circle 1 or 2 for each ailment present.	None of these *(24)* Circle each ailment present — Seen by a Doctor Asthma *(24)* 1 Yes 2 No Diabetes *(25)* 1 Yes 2 No Hardening of the arteries *(26)* 1 Yes 2 No Stroke *(27)* 1 Yes 2 No High blood pressure *(28)* 1 Yes 2 No Heart disease *(29)* 1 Yes 2 No Rheumatism or arthritis *(30)* 1 Yes 2 No Varicose veins *(31)* 1 Yes 2 No Tuberculosis *(32)* 1 Yes 2 No	None of these *(24)* Circle each ailment present — Seen by a Doctor Asthma *(24)* 1 Yes 2 N Diabetes *(25)* 1 Yes 2 N Hardening of the arteries *(26)* 1 Yes 2 N Stroke *(27)* 1 Yes 2 N High blood pressure *(28)* 1 Yes 2 N Heart disease *(29)* 1 Yes 2 N Rheumatism or arthritis *(30)* 1 Yes 2 N Varicose veins *(31)* 1 Yes 2 N Tuberculosis *(32)* 1 Yes 2 N

1 YES (fill out Q. 1 and 2 on white memorandum, then ask b.) 2 NO (ask b)	1 YES (fill out Q. 1 and 2 on white memorandum, then ask b.) 2 NO (ask b)	1 YES (fill out Q. 1 and 2 on white memorandum, then ask b.) 2 NO (ask b)	1 YES (fill out Q. 1 and 2 on white memorandum, then ask b.) 2 NO (ask b)
1 YES (fill out Q. 1 and 2 on white memorandum, then ask c.) 2 NO (ask c)	1 YES (fill out Q. 1 and 2 on white memorandum, then ask c.) 2 NO (ask c)	1 YES (fill out Q. 1 and 2 on white memorandum, then ask c.) 2 NO (ask c)	1 YES (fill out Q. 1 and 2 on white memorandum, then ask c.) 2 NO (ask c)
7c-1 Rashes, itching or other skin trouble 7c-2 Flat feet or other foot trouble 7c-3 Backaches 7c-4 Rectal bleeding 7c-5 Markedly overweight 7c-6 Constipation or other bowel trouble 7c-7 Marked weight loss (not due to dieting) 7c-8 Complaints or difficulties due to change of life 7c-9 Irregular or painful menstrual periods (For each circled symptom fill out Q. 1 and 2 on white memorandum, then ask d.)	7c-1 Rashes, itching or other skin trouble 7c-2 Flat feet or other foot trouble 7c-3 Backaches 7c-4 Rectal bleeding 7c-5 Markedly overweight 7c-6 Constipation or other bowel trouble 7c-7 Marked weight loss (not due to dieting) 7c-8 Complaints or difficulties due to change of life 7c-9 Irregular or painful menstrual periods (For each circled symptom fill out Q. 1 and 2 on white memorandum, then ask d.)	7c-1 Rashes, itching or other skin trouble 7c-2 Flat feet or other foot trouble 7c-3 Backaches 7c-4 Rectal bleeding 7c-5 Markedly overweight 7c-6 Constipation or other bowel trouble 7c-7 Marked weight loss (not due to dieting) 7c-8 Complaints or difficulties due to change of life 7c-9 Irregular or painful menstrual periods (For each circled symptom fill out Q. 1 and 2 on white memorandum, then ask d.)	7c-1 Rashes, itching or other skin trouble 7c-2 Flat feet or other foot trouble 7c-3 Backaches 7c-4 Rectal bleeding 7c-5 Markedly overweight 7c-6 Constipation or other bowel trouble 7c-7 Marked weight loss (not due to dieting) 7c-8 Complaints or difficulties due to change of life 7c-9 Irregular or painful menstrual periods (For each circled symptom fill out Q. 1 and 2 on white memorandum, then ask d.)
1 YES (fill out Q. 1 and 22 on white memorandum, then ask e.) 2 NO (ask e)	1 YES (fill out Q. 1 and 22 on white memorandum, then ask e.) 2 NO (ask e)	1 YES (fill out Q. 1 and 22 on white memorandum, then ask e.) 2 NO (ask e)	1 YES (fill out Q. 1 and 22 on white memorandum, then ask e.) 2 NO (ask e)
1 YES (fill out Q. 1 and 2 on white memorandum, then ask f.) 2 NO (ask f)	1 YES (fill out Q. 1 and 2 on white memorandum, then ask f.) 2 NO (ask f)	1 YES (fill out Q. 1 and 2 on white memorandum, then ask f.) 2 NO (ask f)	1 YES (fill out Q. 1 and 2 on white memorandum, then ask f.) 2 NO (ask f)
..........Times	..........Times	..........Times	..........Times
1 YES (fill out Q. 1 and 2 on colored memorandum, then ask b.) 2 NO (ask b)	1 YES (fill out Q. 1 and 2 on colored memorandum, then ask b.) 2 NO (ask b)	1 YES (fill out Q. 1 and 2 on colored memorandum, then ask b.) 2 NO (ask b)	1 YES (fill out Q. 1 and 2 on colored memorandum, then ask b.) 2 NO (ask b)
1 YES (fill out Q. 1 and 2 on colored memorandum.) 2 NO	1 YES (fill out Q. 1 and 2 on colored memorandum.) 2 NO	1 YES (fill out Q. 1 and 2 on colored memorandum.) 2 NO	1 YES (fill out Q. 1 and 2 on colored memorandum.) 2 NO

WHITE AND COLORED MEMORANDA

ARE MEMORANDA BEFORE ASKING THE FOLLOWING QUESTIONS.

(23)	(23)	(23)	(23)
None of these (24)	None of these (24)	None of these (24)	None of these (24)

Circle each ailment present		Seen by a Doctor		Circle each ailment present		Seen by a Doctor		Circle each ailment present		Seen by a Doctor		Circle each ailment present		Seen by a Doctor	
Asthma	(24)	1 Yes	2 No	Asthma	(24)	1 Yes	2 No	Asthma	(24)	1 Yes	2 No	Asthma	(24)	1 Yes	2 No
Diabetes	(25)	1 Yes	2 No	Diabetes	(25)	1 Yes	2 No	Diabetes	(25)	1 Yes	2 No	Diabetes	(25)	1 Yes	2 No
Hardening of the arteries	(26)	1 Yes	2 No	Hardening of the arteries	(26)	1 Yes	2 No	Hardening of the arteries	(26)	1 Yes	2 No	Hardening of the arteries	(26)	1 Yes	2 No
Stroke	(27)	1 Yes	2 No	Stroke	(27)	1 Yes	2 No	Stroke	(27)	1 Yes	2 No	Stroke	(27)	1 Yes	2 No
High blood pressure	(28)	1 Yes	2 No	High blood pressure	(28)	1 Yes	2 No	High blood pressure	(28)	1 Yes	2 No	High blood pressure	(28)	1 Yes	2 No
Heart disease	(29)	1 Yes	2 No	Heart disease	(29)	1 Yes	2 No	Heart disease	(29)	1 Yes	2 No	Heart disease	(29)	1 Yes	2 No
Rheumatism or arthritis	(30)	1 Yes	2 No	Rheumatism or arthritis	(30)	1 Yes	2 No	Rheumatism or arthritis	(30)	1 Yes	2 No	Rheumatism or arthritis	(30)	1 Yes	2 No
Varicose veins	(31)	1 Yes	2 No	Varicose veins	(31)	1 Yes	2 No	Varicose veins	(31)	1 Yes	2 No	Varicose veins	(31)	1 Yes	2 No
Tuberculosis	(32)	1 Yes	2 No	Tuberculosis	(32)	1 Yes	2 No	Tuberculosis	(32)	1 Yes	2 No	Tuberculosis	(32)	1 Yes	2 No

10. IS .... COVERED BY ANY OF THE FOLLOWING TYPES OF HEALTH INSURANCE: BLUE CROSS? ANY OTHER HOSPITAL INSURANCE? HIP, THAT IS, THE HEALTH INSURANCE PLAN OF GREATER NEW YORK? ANY OTHER INSURANCE TO COVER DOCTOR'S CARE? Ask specifically for each type of insurance and circle 1 or 2 for each type of insurance. Do not include Workmen's Compensation.	(33) (34) Blue Cross 1 Yes 2 No Other hospital 1 Yes 2 No HIP 1 Yes 2 No Other insurance for doctor's care (specify): 1 Yes 2 No	(33) (34) Blue Cross 1 Yes 2 No Other hospital 1 Yes 2 No HIP 1 Yes 2 No Other insurance for doctor's care (specify): 1 Yes 2 No
11. DID .... SEE A DOCTOR FOR ANY REASON DURING 1951? If Yes, HOW MANY TIMES? Circle 1 or X. Enter number of times.	(35) 1 YES X NO (36-37) ....Times	(35) 1 YES X NO (36-37) ....Times
12. IS .... NOW MARRIED, WIDOWED, DIVORCED, SEPARATED OR NEVER-MARRIED? Circle appropriate number for each person.	(38) 1 Married 3 Divorced 2 Widowed 4 Separated 5 Never-married	(38) 1 Married 3 Divorced 2 Widowed 4 Separated 5 Never-married
13. WHAT IS THE HIGHEST SCHOOL GRADE .... EVER COMPLETED? Enter the number of *completed* grades, not counting kindergarten, for each person. Example: for a junior in high school enter 10; for an adult who completed two years of college, enter 14.	(39-40) ....Highest school grade	(39-40) ....Highest school grade
14. Ask this question only for persons circled 1 or 2 in question 5 (working, or looking for work). If looking for work, describe last full-time job or business. a. WHAT KIND OF WORK WAS...................... DOING? For example: sales clerk, teacher, auto mechanic.	(41) ....Occupation	(41) ....Occupation
b. WHAT KIND OF BUSINESS OR INDUSTRY WAS .... WORKING IN? For example: retail store, city government (specify department), auto repair shop.	(42) ....Industry	(42) ....Industry
c. FOR WHOM DID .... WORK?	(43) 1 Private employer, 2 Government } Ask d 3 Own business, 4 Without pay in family business } Skip to 15	(43) 1 Private employer, 2 Government } Ask d 3 Own business, 4 Without pay in family business } Skip to 15
If answer to c is "Private employer" or "Government", d. DOES .... RECEIVE ANY PAY FOR DAYS WHEN HE STAYS AWAY FROM WORK BECAUSE OF ILLNESS? (Exclude State disability coverage.) Circle appropriate number.	(44) 1 Yes, full pay 2 Yes, part pay 3 No, no pay	(44) 1 Yes, full pay 2 Yes, part pay 3 No, no pay

(45) 1 (45)

(46) (47)

T U R N

(33) (34) Blue Cross 1 Yes 2 No Other hospital 1 Yes 2 No HIP 1 Yes 2 No Other insurance for doctor's care (specify): 1 Yes 2 No	(33) (34) Blue Cross 1 Yes 2 No Other hospital 1 Yes 2 No HIP 1 Yes 2 No Other insurance for doctor's care (specify): 1 Yes 2 No	(33) (34) Blue Cross 1 Yes 2 No Other hospital 1 Yes 2 No HIP 1 Yes 2 No Other insurance for doctor's care (specify): 1 Yes 2 No	(33) (34) Blue Cross 1 Yes 2 No Other Hospital —1 Yes 2 No HIP 1 Yes 2 No Other insurance for doctor's care (specify): 1 Yes 2 No
(35) 1 YES X NO (36-37) ....Times	(35) 1 YES X NO (36-37) ....Times	(35) 1 YES X NO (36-37) ....Times	(35) 1 YES X NO (36-37) ....Times
(38) 1 Married 3 Divorced 2 Widowed 4 Separated 5 Never-married	(38) 1 Married 3 Divorced 2 Widowed 4 Separated 5 Never-married	(38) 1 Married 3 Divorced 2 Widowed 4 Separated 5 Never-married	(38) 1 Married 3 Divorced 2 Widowed 4—Separated 5 Never-married
(39-40) ....Highest school grade	(39-40) ....Highest school grade	(39-40) ....Highest school grade	(39-40) ....Highest school grade
(41) ....Occupation	(41) ....Occupation	(41) ....Occupation	(41) ....Occupation
(42) ....Industry	(42) ....Industry	(42) ....Industry	(42) ....Industry
(43) 1 Private employer } Ask d 2 Government } 3 Own business } Skip to 15 4 Without pay in family business }	(43) 1 Private employer } Ask d 2 Government } 3 Own business } Skip to 15 4 Without pay in family business }	(43) 1 Private employer } Ask d 2 Government } 3 Own business } Skip to 15 4 Without pay in family business }	(43) 1 Private employer } Ask d 2 Government } 3 Own business } Skip to 15 4 Without pay in family business }
(44) 1 Yes, full pay 2 Yes, part pay 3 No, no pay	(44) 1 Yes, full pay 2 Yes, part pay 3 No, no pay	(44) 1 Yes, full pay 2 Yes, part pay 3 No, no pay	(44) 1 Yes, full pay 2 Yes, part pay 3 No, no pay
(45)	(45)	(45)	(45)

AND NOW JUST A FEW QUESTIONS ABOUT THE ENTIRE HOUSEHOLD

15. If the household contains one or more children born after March 1946, DO YOU HAVE A SPECIAL DOCTOR FOR CHILDREN? Circle 1 or X.	(48) 1 YES ↓ X NO (skip to Q. 17)
16. If Q. 15 is answered Yes	(49)
(a) WHAT IS HIS NAME?	Name: ....
(b) WHAT IS HIS ADDRESS?	Address: ....
(c) WHEN IS THE LAST TIME ANY OF THE CHILDREN SAW HIM?	Month........ Year........ (50) (51) (52)
17. DO YOU HAVE A DOCTOR YOU USUALLY CALL IN CASE OF ILLNESS FOR OTHER FAMILY MEMBERS? Circle 1 or X.	(53) 1 YES ↓ X NO (skip to Q. 19)
18. If Q. 17 is answered Yes	(54)
(a) WHAT IS HIS NAME?	Name: ....
(b) WHAT IS HIS ADDRESS?	Address: ....
(c) WHEN IS THE LAST TIME ANY FAMILY MEMBER SAW HIM?	Month........ Year........ (55) (56) (57) (58)
19. Race of Informant. Circle 1, 2 or 3.	(59) 1 White 2 Negro 3 Other (specify)
20. IN WHAT STATE OR FOREIGN COUNTRY WAS THE HEAD OF THIS HOUSEHOLD BORN?	State or foreign country (60) ....
21. WERE THERE ANY DEATHS IN THIS HOUSEHOLD DURING 1951? Circle 1 or X.	(61) 1 YES ↓ X NO (skip to Q. 23)
22. If Q. 21 is answered Yes, WHAT WAS THE RELATIONSHIP OF THE DECEASED TO THE HEAD OF HOUSEHOLD?	(62) .... Relationship
WHAT WAS THE AGE AND SEX OF THE DECEASED? Enter age at death and circle 1 or 2.	(63-64) ....Years (65) 1 Male 2 Female
23. HOW MANY ROOMS ARE THERE IN THIS DWELLING UNIT? Do not count bathroom.	(66-67) ....Rooms
HOW MANY ARE USED FOR SLEEPING PURPOSES?	(68) ....Sleeping rooms
24. IS THE TOILET SHARED WITH ANY OTHER HOUSEHOLD? Circle 1 or 2.	(69) 1 Yes, shared with another household 2 No, not shared
25. DO YOU HAVE CENTRAL HEATING? Circle 1 or 2.	(70) 1 YES 2 NO

26. I'M NOW GOING TO HAND YOU A CARD WITH DIFFERENT ANNUAL INCOME CLASSES ON IT. WILL YOU TELL ME THE LETTER OF THE INCOME CLASS IN WHICH THIS FAMILY FALLS? Circle appropriate number.	(71)	1 A $1,000 or less 1 B $1,001 — $2,000 2 C $2,001 — $3,000 3 D $3,001 — $4,000 4 E $4,001 — $5,000 5 F $5,001 — $6,500 6 G $6,501 — $8,000 7 H $8,001 and over 8 Unknown
27. WHAT IS THE RELIGION OF THE HEAD OF THIS HOUSEHOLD? Circle appropriate number.	(72)	1 Catholic 2 Protestant 3 Jewish 4 Other (specify)

VISIT NO.	DATE	HOUR	VISIT NO.	DATE	HOUR	
(73) 1			6			
2			7			
3			8			
4			9			
5			0			

(74) (75) (76)

SCHEDULE 2

ILLNESS AND MEDICAL CARE MEMORANDUM

SHEET..............

OF..............

This form is to be filled out for each person recorded as YES in one or more of the boxes in questions **6** or **7** on Schedule 1. USE A SEPARATE SHEET FOR EACH PERSON. Use a separate column on this sheet for each distinct medical condition reported. For example, if a person had a cold yesterday and a sprained ankle earlier in the eight week period, use a separate column for each condition. **If more columns are necessary use another sheet,** transcribing the study and individual number and last and first name. **Make no entries in shaded boxes.**

STUDY No. ☐☐☐☐☐ 1 2 3 4 5   6 7

INDIVIDUAL No......................LAST NAME...FIRST NAME......................................

1. Enter the number and letter of the question on Schedule 1, which led you to the illness memorandum.	(8) (9) (If 7d, skip to Q. 22)	(8) (9) (If 7d, skip to Q. 22)
2. WHAT WAS THE MATTER? Enter informant's own words.	(10) (11) (12) Now go back to Schedule 1	(10) (11) (12) Now go back to Schedule 1
3. WHEN DID THIS CONDITION START? Enter date, or circle "Before 8 week period."	Before 8 week period or Mo.................. Day.................. (13) (14) (15)	Before 8 week period or Mo.................. Day.................. (13) (14) (15)
4. WHEN DID IT END OR IS IT STILL PRESENT? Enter date. If the condition was still present at the time of the first visit, circle "still present".	Mo.................. Day.................. still present (16) (17)	Mo.................. Day.................. still present (16) (17)

DISABILITY DURING THE LAST EIGHT WEEKS

5. DID THIS CONDITION KEEP .... CONFINED TO THE HOUSE OR AWAY FROM WORK (if normally working) AWAY FROM SCHOOL (if normally at school) FROM DOING HOUSEWORK (if normally a housewife) DURING THE LAST EIGHT WEEKS? Circle 1 or X	(18) 1 YES ↓ X NO (skip to Q. 13)	(18) 1 YES ↓ X NO (skip to Q. 13)
6. If Yes to Q. 5, HOW MANY DAYS DURING THE LAST EIGHT WEEKS DID THIS CONDITION KEEP............ CONFINED TO THE HOUSE OR AWAY FROM WORK (if normally working) AWAY FROM SCHOOL (if normally at school) FROM DOING HOUSEWORK (if normally a housewife) Enter actual number of days, or circle "entire eight week period".	(19-20) ....days (skip to Q. 8) or entire eight week period ↓	(19-20) ....days (skip to Q. 8) or entire eight week period ↓
7. If answer to Q. 6 is "entire eight week period" WHEN DID THIS CONDITION START KEEPING............ CONFINED TO THE HOUSE OR AWAY FROM WORK (if normally working) AWAY FROM SCHOOL (if normally at school) FROM DOING HOUSEWORK (if normally a housewife) Enter month and year.	Mo............ Year............ (21) (22)	Mo............ Year............ (21) (22)
8. DID............ SPEND ANY TIME IN BED BECAUSE OF THIS CONDITION DURING THE LAST EIGHT WEEKS? Circle 1 or X.	(23) 1 YES ↓ X NO (skip to Q. 13)	(23) 1 YES ↓ X NO (skip to Q. 13)
9. If Yes to Q. 8, HOW MANY DAYS DID............ SPEND IN BED BECAUSE OF THIS CONDITION DURING THE LAST EIGHT WEEKS?	(24-25) ....days	(24-25) ....days

HOSPITAL CARE DURING LAST EIGHT WEEKS

10. DID............ SPEND ONE OR MORE NIGHTS IN A HOSPITAL BECAUSE OF THIS CONDITION DURING THE LAST EIGHT WEEKS? Circle 1 or X.	(26) 1 YES ↓ **10** X NO (skip to Q. 13)	(26) 1 YES ↓ **10** X NO (skip to Q. 13)
11. If Yes, to Q. 10, WHAT KIND OF ROOM DID............ OCCUPY? Circle 1, 2, 3 or 4.	(27) 1 Private Room 2 Semiprivate Room 3 Ward 4 Other (specify)	(27) 1 Private Room 2 Semiprivate Room 3 Ward 4 Other (specify) ....
12. If Yes to Q. 10, HOW MANY NIGHTS DID............ SPEND IN THE HOSPITAL BECAUSE OF THIS CONDITION DURING THE LAST EIGHT WEEKS?	(28-29) ....nights	(28-29) ....nights
13. DID .... MAKE ANY VISITS TO A HOSPITAL CLINIC OR OUT-PATIENT DEPARTMENT BECAUSE OF THIS CONDITION DURING THE LAST EIGHT WEEKS? Circle 1 or X.	(30) 1 YES ↓ X NO (If Q. 10 not asked or answered No, skip to Q. 16) (If Yes to Q. 10, skip to Q. 15)	(30) 1 YES ↓ X NO (If Q. 10 not asked or answered No, skip to Q. 16) (If Yes to Q. 10, skip to Q. 15)
14. If Yes to Q. 13, HOW MANY VISITS DID............ MAKE BECAUSE OF THIS CONDITION DURING THE LAST EIGHT WEEKS?	(31-32) ....visits	(31-32) ....visits
15. If Yes to Q. 10 or 13, WHAT WAS THE NAME AND ADDRESS OF THE HOSPITAL? (If more than one, indicate additional names and addresses in notes).	Name Address (33) (34) (35)	Name Address (33) (34) (35)

DOCTOR'S AND DENTIST'S CARE DURING THE LAST EIGHT WEEKS

16. DID .... SEE OR TALK TO A DOCTOR OR DENTIST ABOUT THIS CONDITION DURING THE LAST EIGHT WEEKS? Circle appropriate number.	(36) 1 Yes, saw a doctor 2 Yes, saw a dentist 3 Yes, saw a doctor and dentist 4 Talked with doctor over telephone but did not see him (skip to Q. 20) 5 No, no contact (no further questions in this column.)	(36) 1 Yes, saw a doctor 2 Yes, saw a dentist 3 Yes, saw a doctor and dentist 4 Talked with doctor over telephone but did not see him (skip to Q. 20) 5 No, no contact (no further questions in this column.)
17. If Yes to Q. 16 (1, 2 or 3) HOW LONG AFTER THE DEVELOPMENT OF THIS CONDITION DID............ WAIT BEFORE CALLING THE DOCTOR (OR DENTIST)?	(37-38) ....days	(37-38) ....days

18. If Yes to Q. 16 (1, 2 or 3) HOW MANY TIMES DID .... SEE THE DOCTOR (OR DENTIST) DURING THE LAST EIGHT WEEKS ABOUT THIS CONDITION? (If two or more conditions received attention in a single visit, so that the visit is duplicated in two or more columns, indicate in notes.) HOW MANY OF THESE WERE OFFICE VISITS? HOW MANY HOME VISITS? HOW MANY WERE AT THE HOSPITAL?	Number of times: Total (39-40) .... At office (41-42) .... At home (43-44) .... At hospital, Total (45-46) .... In-patient (47-48) .... Out-patient (49-50)	Number of times: Total (39-40) .... At office (41-42) .... At home (43-44) .... At hospital, Total (45-46) .... In-patient (47-48) .... Out-patient (49-50) ....
19. If Yes to Q. 16 (1, 2 or 3) DID THE DOCTOR'S (OR DENTIST'S) TREATMENT FOR THIS CONDITION INCLUDE SURGERY DURING THE LAST EIGHT WEEKS? Circle 1 or X.	(51) 1 YES X NO If Yes, indicate nature. (52) (53) (54)	(51) 1 YES X NO If Yes, indicate nature. (52) (53) (54)
20. WHAT IS THE NAME AND ADDRESS OF THE DOCTOR (OR DENTIST) WHO TOOK CARE OF ....? If more than one doctor (or dentist) for this condition, indicate additional names and addresses in notes.	Name: Address: (55)	Name: Address: (55)
21. DID INSURANCE COVER ANY PART OF THE COST OF MEDICAL CARE FOR THIS CONDITION? Circle Yes or No. a. If Yes, WHAT PART OF THE COST WAS COVERED BY INSURANCE? Circle 1, 2, 3, 4 or 5. b. If No, WAS THIS BECAUSE .... HAS NO INSURANCE OR BECAUSE THERE WERE NO COSTS? Circle 6 or 7.	YES (ask a) NO ask (b) (56) 1 Doctor's care only 2 Hospitalization only 3 Hospitalization and surgery only 4 Hospitalization, surgery and doctor's care 5 Other (specify) .... 6 No insurance 7 No costs	YES (ask a) NO ask (b) (56) 1 Doctor's care only 2 Hospitalization only 3 Hospitalization and surgery only 4 Hospitalization, surgery and doctor's care 5 Other (specify) .... 6 No insurance 7 No costs

IF QUESTION 7d ON SCHEDULE 1 WAS ANSWERED YES FILL OUT THE QUESTIONS BELOW

22. WHY DID .... SEE A DOCTOR FOR A PHYSICAL CHECK-UP? (Do not include check-ups for conditions already mentioned in Q. 6 and 7 on Schedule 1) Circle appropriate number.	(57) 1 School 2 Employment 3 Insurance 4 General check-up 5 Other (explain in notes) Now go back to Schedule 1	(57) 1 School 2 Employment 3 Insurance 4 General check-up 5 Other (explain in notes) Now go back to Schedule 1
23. DID THE EXAMINATION INVOLVE TAKING A COMPLETE MEDICAL HISTORY? HEIGHT AND WEIGHT? TEMPERATURE? PULSE? BLOOD PRESSURE? A BLOOD SAMPLE? URINE ANALYSIS? CHEST X-RAY OR FLUOROSCOPY? VISION TEST? HEARING TEST? RECTAL EXAMINATION? (and for women) VAGINAL EXAMINATION? Hand card to informant and circle 1 or 2 for each item.	Medical history (58) 1 Yes 2 No Height & weight (59) 1 Yes 2 No Temperature (60) 1 Yes 2 No Pulse (61) 1 Yes 2 No Blood pressure (62) 1 Yes 2 No Blood sample: from finger (63) 1 Yes 2 No from arm (64) 1 Yes 2 No Urine analysis (65) 1 Yes 2 No Chest x-ray or fluoroscopy (66) 1 Yes 2 No Vision test (67) 1 Yes 2 No Hearing test (68) 1 Yes 2 No Rectal exam. (69) 1 Yes 2 No Vaginal exam. (women) (70) 1 Yes 2 No (71) (72)	Medical history (58) 1 Yes 2 No Height & weight (59) 1 Yes 2 No Temperature (60) 1 Yes 2 No Pulse (61) 1 Yes 2 No Blood pressure (62) 1 Yes 2 No Blood sample: from finger (63) 1 Yes 2 No from arm (64) 1 Yes 2 No Urine analysis (65) 1 Yes 2 No Chest x-ray or fluoroscopy (66) 1 Yes 2 No Vision test (67) 1 Yes 2 No Hearing test (68) 1 Yes 2 No Rectal exam. (69) 1 Yes 2 No Vaginal exam. (women) (70) 1 Yes 2 No (71) (72)
24. WHAT WAS THE DATE OF THE EXAMINATION?	Mo.......... Day..........	Mo.......... Day..........

SCHEDULE 3

ILLNESS AND MEDICAL CARE MEMORANDUM

SHEET............... OF...............

This form is to be filled out for each person recorded as YES in one or more of the boxes in question **8** on Schedule 1. USE A SEPARATE SHEET FOR EACH PERSON. Use a separate column on this sheet for each distinct medical condition reported. For example, if a person had an appendectomy and a bone fracture in 1951, use a separate column for each condition. **If more columns are necessary use another sheet,** transcribing the study and individual number. **Make no entries in shaded boxes.**

STUDY NO. ☐☐☐☐☐ (1 2 3 4 5) ▒▒ (6 7)

INDIVIDUAL NO........................ LAST NAME........................ FIRST NAME........................

1. Which part of Q. **8** on Schedule 1 led you to this memorandum? Circle 1 or 2.	(8) 1 **8a** 2 **8b**	(8) 1 **8a** 2 **8b**
2. WHAT WAS THE MATTER? Enter informant's own words.	▒▒▒ (9) (10) (11) Now go back to Schedule 1	▒▒▒ (9) (10) (11) Now go back to Schedule 1
3. **Unless** the condition is a delivery or a birth, WHEN DID THIS CONDITION START? Enter date. If condition is a delivery or a birth, skip to Q. **4**.	Mo.................. Year.................. ▒▒▒ (12) (13) (14)	Mo.................. Year.................. ▒▒▒ (12) (13) (14)
4. WHEN DID IT END OR IS IT STILL PRESENT? Enter date. If condition was still present at the time of the first visit, circle "still present."	Mo.................. Year.................. ▒▒▒ still present (15) (16) (17)	Mo.................. Year.................. ▒▒▒ still present (15) (16) (17)
5. HOW LONG DID .... STAY IN BED BECAUSE OF THIS CONDITION DURING 1951?	▒▒ ....days, or ....weeks, or ....months (18) (19)	▒▒ ....days, or ....weeks, or ....months (18) (19)

HOSPITAL CARE DURING 1951

If Head of Column Entry is **8a**, ask Q. **6**.
If Head of Column Entry is **8b**, skip to Q. **8**.

6. (a) WHAT KIND OF HOSPITAL ROOM DID.............. OCCUPY? Circle 1, 2, 3 or 4. (b) WHAT WAS THE DATE OF ADMISSION TO HOSPITAL?	(20) 1 Private room 2 Semi-private room 3 Ward 4 Other (specify) | X 8b | Mo.................. Year..................	(20) 1 Private room 2 Semi-private room 3 Ward 4 Other (specify) | X 8b | Mo.................. Year..................
7. HOW LONG DID .... STAY IN THE HOSPITAL BECAUSE OF THIS CONDITION DURING 1951?	▒▒ ....nights, or ....weeks, or ....months (21) (22)	▒▒ ....nights, or ....weeks, or ....months (21) (22)
8. DID .... MAKE ANY VISITS TO A HOSPITAL CLINIC OR OUT-PATIENT DEPARTMENT BECAUSE OF THIS CONDITION DURING 1951? Circle 1 or X.	(23) 1 YES ↓ X NO (If head of column entry is **8a**, skip to Q. **10**) (If head of column entry is **8b**, skip to Q. **11**)	(23) 1 YES ↓ X NO (If head of column entry is **8a**, skip to Q. **10**) (If head of column entry is **8b**, skip to Q. **11**)

9. If Yes to Q. 8, HOW MANY VISITS WERE MADE BECAUSE OF THIS CONDITION DURING 1951?	(24-25) .... visits	(24-25) .... visits
10. WHAT WAS THE NAME AND ADDRESS OF THE HOSPITAL? If more than one, indicate additional names and addresses in notes.	Name: Address: (26) (27) (28)	Name: Address: (26) (27) (28)
DOCTOR'S OR DENTIST'S CARE DURING 1951		
11. DID .... SEE OR TALK TO A DOCTOR OR DENTIST ABOUT THIS CONDITION? Circle appropriate number.	(29) 1 Yes, saw a doctor 2 Yes, saw a dentist 3 Yes, saw both a doctor and dentist 4 Talked with a doctor over telephone but did not see him (skip to Q. 15) 5 No, no contact (no further questions in this column)	(29) 1 Yes, saw a doctor 2 Yes, saw a dentist 3 Yes, saw both a doctor and dentist 4 Talked with a doctor over telephone but did not see him (skip to Q. 15) 5 No, no contact (no further questions in this column)
12. If Yes to Q. 11 (1, 2 or 3) HOW LONG AFTER THE DEVELOPMENT OF THIS CONDITION DID .... WAIT BEFORE CALLING THE DOCTOR (OR DENTIST)?	(30-31) ....days	(30-31) ....days
13. If Yes to Q. 11 (1, 2 or 3) HOW MANY TIMES DID .... SEE THE DOCTOR (OR DENTIST) DURING 1951 ABOUT THIS CONDITION? If two or more conditions received attention in a single visit, so that the visit is duplicated in two or more columns, indicate in notes. HOW MANY WERE OFFICE VISITS? HOW MANY HOUSE CALLS? HOW MANY AT THE HOSPITAL?	Number of Times: Total (32-33) .... At office (34-35) .... At home (36-37) .... At hospital Total (38-39) .... In-patient (40-41) .... Out-patient (42-43)	Number of Times: Total (32-33) .... At office (34-35) .... At home (36-37) .... At hospital Total (38-39) .... In-patient (40-41) .... Out-patient (42-43) ....
14. If Yes to Q. 11 (1, 2 or 3) DID THE DOCTOR'S (OR DENTIST'S) TREATMENT FOR THIS CONDITION INCLUDE SURGERY DURING 1951? Circle 1 or X.	(44) 1 YES X NO If Yes, indicate nature of surgery. (45) (46) (47)	(44) 1 YES X NO If Yes, indicate nature of surgery. (45) (46) (47)
15. WHAT IS THE NAME AND ADDRESS OF THE DOCTOR (OR DENTIST) WHO TOOK CARE OF..................? If more than one doctor (or dentist) for this condition indicate additional names and addresses in notes.	Name: Address: (48)	Name: Address: (48)
16. DID INSURANCE COVER ANY PART OF THE COST OF MEDICAL CARE FOR THIS CONDITION? Circle Yes or No. a. If Yes, WHAT PART OF THE COST WAS COVERED BY INSURANCE? Circle 1, 2, 3, 4 or 5. b. If No, WAS THIS BECAUSE .... HAS NO INSURANCE OR BECAUSE THERE WERE NO COSTS? Circle 6 or 7.	YES (ask a) NO ask (b) (49) 1 Doctor's care only 2 Hospitalization only 3 Hospitalization and surgery only 4 Hospitalization, surgery and doctor's care 5 Other (specify)................ 6 No insurance 7 No costs	YES (ask a) NO ask (b) (49) 1 Doctor's care only 2 Hospitalization only 3 Hospitalization and surgery only 4 Hospitalization, surgery and doctor's care 5 Other (specify)................ 6 No insurance 7 No costs

QUESTIONS FOR THE CONDITION OF PREGNANCY FOLLOWED BY DELIVERY
ASK THE WOMAN WHO WAS PREGNANT.

	(50)	(50)
17. IN WHAT MONTH OF YOUR PREGNANCY DID YOU FIRST SEE A DOCTOR ABOUT THIS PREGNANCY? Circle appropriate number.	Month of Pregnancy: (51) 2 3 4 5 6 7 8 9	Month of Pregnancy: (51) 2 3 4 5 6 7 8 9
18. WHEN YOU SAW THE DOCTOR, DID HE OR THE NURSE USUALLY TAKE YOUR BLOOD PRESSURE? TAKE YOUR WEIGHT? TAKE A SAMPLE OF YOUR URINE? Circle 1 or 2 for each.	Blood Pressure 1 YES 2 NO Weight 1 YES 2 NO Urine 1 YES 2 NO	Blood Pressure 1 YES 2 NO Weight 1 YES 2 NO Urine 1 YES 2 NO
19. DID THE DOCTOR AT LEAST ONCE GIVE YOU A PELVIC (Internal) EXAMINATION? Circle 1 or 2.	1 YES 2 NO (52)	1 YES 2 NO (52)
20. HOW MANY TIMES DID YOU SEE THE DOCTOR BEFORE DELIVERY? If once a month from first visit through eighth month and once a week thereafter, check the box without computing actual number of visits. If any other pattern, compute actual number of visits and enter.	Once a month from first visit through the eighth month and once a week thereafter ☐ or (53-54) ....visits	Once a month from first visit through the eighth month and once a week thereafter ☐ or (53-54) ....visits
21. DID YOU SEE THE DOCTOR AGAIN ABOUT THE PREGNANCY AFTER YOU LEFT THE HOSPITAL? Circle 1 or X.	(55) 1 YES ↓ X NO (skip to Q. 23)	(55) 1 YES ↓ X NO (skip to Q. 23)
22. If Yes to Q. 21, DID YOU RECEIVE ANOTHER PELVIC EXAMINATION AT THAT TIME? Circle 1 or 2.	(56) 1 YES 2 NO	(56) 1 YES 2 NO
23. DID THIS CHILD WEIGH MORE THAN 5½ POUNDS AT BIRTH? Circle 1 or 2.	(57) 1 YES 2 NO	(57) 1 YES 2 NO

APPENDIX B

Notes on Terms Used in Statistical Tables

Demographic, Economic, and Social Terms

H.I.P. enrollees. Persons resident in New York City drawn for the H.I.P. sample from the H.I.P. enrollment as of December 31, 1951, plus the H.I.P. enrollees found in the survey of the sample of the New York City population. The total of these persons constitutes the H.I.P. sample. It excludes non-H.I.P. members of the families of H.I.P. subscribers; hence, all persons in the H.I.P. sample are actually eligible for H.I.P. care. The non-H.I.P. members in the households of H.I.P. subscribers are called "other" in the H.I.P sample when total membership of households is shown.

New York City sample. Persons resident in New York City living in the dwelling units drawn for the area probability sample of the New York City population, minus people living in dwelling units found to be the residence of one or more H.I.P. enrollees. None of this group of persons was eligible for H.I.P. care at the time of the interview. It excludes persons confined in resident institutions in the city.

Household composition. All persons living, during the eight weeks prior to the interview, in a dwelling unit occupied by one or more H.I.P. enrollees or in a dwelling unit drawn from the New York City sample were included in the household roster. Persons absent by reason of being in a general hospital and new babies still in the hospital at the time of the interview were included. Military personnel not using the family domicile, individuals institutionalized before the eight-week period prior to the interview in other than general hospitals, visitors to the household, and college students home for vacation were excluded from the household roster. The categories used to describe the household composition include: (1) single persons, (2) husband and wife, (3) husband, wife, and one or more children under 18, (4) one parent (or substitute) with one or more children under 18, (5) parent(s) with one or more children all over 18 and not living with spouse, (6) two or more families with children under 18, (7) two or more families with no children under 18, (8) other, and (9) not reported.

Household head. (Schedule 1, Question 1). The person designated by the respondent was accepted as the head of the household. In all cases of families with both husband and wife present, preference was given to the husband.

Education. (Schedule 1, Question 13). Represented by the number of the highest school grade ever completed. Allowance was made for vocational and professional education outside of, as well as within, the regular school system.

Education of household head. In some instances in the H.I.P. sample the household head whose education was used as an indicator of the economic level of the H.I.P. enrollees in the household was not himself an H.I.P. enrollee.

Age. (Schedule 1, Question 4). The year and month of birth were recorded. The age was calculated as of February 29, 1952, for persons covered in interviews completed in March; as of March 31, 1952, for interviews completed in April; similarly in May and June.

Marital status. (Schedule 1, Question 12). Entered according to the status on the day of the interview as either married, widowed, divorced, separated, or never married.

Labor force status. (Schedule 1, Question 5). Entered for all persons born before March 1938, as the status during the week preceding the interview. The categories are: working, looking for work, and others in the labor force (including persons with a job but not at work the previous week because of illness, bad weather, temporary lay-off, and so forth); also, keeping house, going to school, permanently unable to work, and others not in the labor force (including retired, voluntarily idle, and so forth).

Occupational class. (Schedule 1, Question 14 (a) and (b)). Reported only for persons in the labor force. For those in the labor force but not working last week, the question referred to the last full-time job or business. The kind of work and the kind of business and industry were both obtained, and both were used in coding the occupational class. The first digit of the Census code was used to establish the broad occupational class. This was further condensed for presentation in the tables to seven classes.

Sick leave status. (Schedule 1, Question 14 (d)). If the person was working for a private employer or for government, the respondent was asked, "Does ——— receive any pay for days when he stays away from work because of illness? (Exclude State disability coverage.)" The answer was checked against three possibilities: "Yes, full pay"; "Yes, part pay"; and "No, no pay." In the final classification only two groups were used: "with sick leave" and "without sick leave." For self-employed persons the question was considered inapplicable. Hence, there were two sources of "not reported": unknown whether sick leave was or was not applicable, and known to be applicable but unknown whether having or not having paid sick leave. These two types of "not reported" were combined in most of the tabulations.

Income class. (Schedule 1, Question 26). This designation was restricted to eight classes: (1A, $1,000 or less; 1B, $1,001–$2,000; 2C, $2,001–$3,000; 3D, $3,001–$4,000; 4E, $4,001–$5,000; 5F, $5,001–$6,500; 6G, $6,501–$8,000 and over; and 8, not reported), and was elicited by the enumerator's statement, "I'm now going to hand you a card with different annual income classes on it. Will you tell me the letter of the income class in which this family falls?" For this question the term "family" was never clearly defined.

Race. (Schedule 1, Question 19). The interviewer reported the race of the respondent as White, Negro, or other. All members of the household were assumed to be of the same race.

Insurance Status

Insurance coverage—persons. (Schedule 1, Question 10). Entered as status on day of interview with four possibilities which are *not* mutually exclusive: Blue Cross, other hospital insurance, H.I.P., other insurance for doctor's care (specify). One person could have insurance in all four categories. A "yes" or "no" answer was to be recorded for each one. In the tables this breakdown was shown only for the New York City sample, of course, and because of incomplete schedules it was necessary to show two categories of unknown insurance coverage, individuals for whom the coverage was specifically stated to be unknown and individuals for whom the information was incompletely or incorrectly recorded. A third extra group was labeled "Incorrect information." This includes those for whom the coverage statement could be shown to be incorrect by consulting H.I.P. files. The person was sometimes described as covered by H.I.P. but was actually not covered, or was described as covered by H.I.P. but not by Blue Cross when, in fact, he must have been covered by both because he was an employee of the City.

Insurance coverage—medical conditions. (Schedule 2, Question 21 (a) and (b) and Schedule 3, Question 16 (a) and (b)). Entered as coverage for specific instances of illness occurring within the eight-week period or during 1951. See facsimile of schedule for the form in which the questions were asked.

Medical Condition and Medical Care Terms

Eight-week period. (Schedule 1, Question 7). This was interpreted to mean the eight weeks ending with the date of the interview.

Medical condition. (Schedule 1, Questions 6, 7, 8, and 9). This was conceived to be any condition arising from disease or injury or other cause for which medical care might be sought. The series of questions on Schedule 1 was intended to elicit information for designated periods of time on all such conditions, whether or not attended by a physician. Schedule 2 was intended to secure further information on all medical conditions brought to light through the questions on Schedule 1 on the day before the interview and during the eight-week period. Schedule 3 limited medical conditions to those which produced hospitalization or bed-disability of seven or more days during 1951.

Medical conditions in eight-week period. This includes medical conditions present on the day before the interview as well as all medical conditions, regardless of the question on the schedule resulting in the report, which were stated to have been present at any time during the eight-week period. It includes, therefore, illnesses that began before the eight-week period and were still present at the beginning of it.

Dental condition. (Schedule 1, Question 7 (e), supplemented by Schedule 2, Question 16, specifying dental care). This was defined as a condition for which the services of a dentist were sought or as a reported "toothache" not treated by a dentist.

Disability. (Schedule 2, Question 5). A person was classified as disabled (and a medical condition was classified as one producing disability) if the condition confined the person to the house or kept him away from work, or away from school (if normally at school), or from doing housework (if normally a housewife).

Bed-disability. Interpreted as at least one day in bed during the period of disability.

Hospitalization. A person was considered to have been hospitalized if he spent one night in a hospital.

Degree of disability. (Schedule 2, Questions 8, 10). The degrees of disability in the eight-week period were set at: (1) hospitalized; (2) disabled in bed, no hospital; (3) disabled, no bed or hospital; (4) disabled, degree unknown; (5) not disabled; (6) unknown if disabled. The degree of disability for a person was taken as the most severe degree for any medical condition experienced by that person.

Diagnostic groups. (Schedules 1, 2, and 3). For purposes of presentation the categories of the International Statistical Classification were combined into 74 groups. The code numbers included in each of the groups are listed in Appendix H, pp. 262–265, of this report.

The 74 groups were further condensed into classifications containing 41 and 16 categories, and another containing only five categories. All possible combinations of the five broadest categories, alone or in combination with one another, made up still another classification which was used for classifying persons.

The 41 and 16 groups, the five groups, and the various combinations of the five, making 31 in all, are shown in Appendix H, pp. 265–266.

Type of medical care. (Schedule 2, Questions 10, 13, 15, 16, and 20). Out of the replies to these several questions a composite classification was constructed with the following categories for the illnesses reported for the eight-week period: (1) hospitalized and private medical care established (i.e., known to have involved office and/or home visits of private physician); (2) hospitalized, but no private physician care reported; (3) no known hospitalization, private physician only (no outpatient clinic care); (4) no known hospitalization, private physician (office and/or home visits) plus other (outpatient clinic care); (5) no known hospitalization, outpatient clinic care only; and (6) no known hospitalization, type of physician care unknown.

Physical check-up. (Schedule 1, Question 7 (d), and Schedule 2, Questions 22 and 23). These questions apply to medical examinations occurring either on the day prior to the visit or within the eight-week period but not related to the medical conditions reported on Schedule 1. The interviewers and coders received special instructions designed to eliminate "check-ups" related to the care of specified conditions. These examinations were further characterized on Schedule 2 as related to (1) school, (2) employment, (3) insurance, (4) general check-up, (5) other (explain in notes). In the case of maternity patients, routine check-ups were also reported. In the final tables the categories were set out as (1) school, employment, or insurance examination, (2) general check-up or immunization only, (3) prenatal or postpartum examination, (4) routine eye examination, and (5) other, more than one type, and unknown.

APPENDIX C

Sampling Design of the Survey

Selection of Sample

H.I.P. Enrollees

The basic source from which the sample of H.I.P. households was selected is the serial listing of certificate numbers. When a household enters H.I.P. it is assigned a certificate number. These numbers are assigned consecutively and contain virtually no gaps. A sample of certificate numbers in consequence also provides a sample of the households that had ever been enrolled up to the time of sampling. The simplest method of selecting such a sample is by use of the terminal digit. Thus, a 10 percent sample of all households would be provided by the group of the households whose certificate number ends in the digit 5. A number of checks were made on the characteristics of a small preliminary sample of households selected on a digital basis to determine whether any hidden biases or unexpected gaps in the certificate number series existed. None were found. On this basis all households whose certificate number ended in 5 were selected, to yield an initial sample, and a sub-sample of this, designed to yield 5,000 households selected on the basis of the remaining digits.[1]

New York City Sample

The basic pattern used in selecting the sample of households not members of H.I.P. was, of course, quite different. Essentially the process was as follows: a sample of blocks was selected, using as the basic list machine runs listing block population then available from the 1950 Census; the commercial agency responsible for the actual conduct of the field work then prepared an initial listing of all households living in these sampled blocks; an average of five households per sampled block was then selected from this listing.

One thousand blocks, grouped into 50 strata each containing 20 blocks, were selected. (Variation among the 20 blocks within each stratum provides the basis for a simple and accurate estimate of the sampling error involved—see p. 212.) The 50 strata were determined as follows: the Borough of Richmond, which contains approximately 2 percent of the New York City population, was set up as a single stratum. For each of the remaining four boroughs the approximately 3,000 Census tracts were listed in order by percentage change in population from 1940 to 1950. In each of the boroughs, Bronx, Brooklyn, and Manhattan, the group of tracts accounting for the largest percentage change in population and for a population of approximately 156,000, were grouped to provide three more strata.[2] In Queens, with its very large population shifts in the previous decade, two such strata were set up.[3] Population increases were used in this fashion for two reasons: (*a*) areas undergoing such changes were likely to have been subject to a considerable volume of new construction and to be populated by younger families, (*b*) the 1940 characteristics on which the remaining tracts were stratified were not likely to prove useful for tracts in which large subsequent population changes had occurred.

The remaining tracts were relisted within each borough in order of the average 1940 rental (or rental value). Groups of strata with either very high or very low 1940 rentals were separated out to yield nine more strata, each containing approximately 156,000 persons.[4] The remaining tracts in each borough were placed in two broad rental groups, each of which was further subdivided into approximately contiguous groups of strata within each borough. This yielded 35 additional strata, each containing approximately 156,000 persons.

The 20 sample blocks within each of the 50

[1] There are a few unusual situations in the certificate numbering, such as the existence of a special set of numbers for members of the painters' union, which required special handling.

[2] This yielded tracts with population increases in excess of 17 percent in the Bronx, 36 percent in Brooklyn, and 23 percent in Manhattan.

[3] One with an increase in excess of 157 percent, the other at least 45 but less than 157 percent.

[4] As follows: Bronx, less than \$32 and more than \$51; Brooklyn, less than \$22 and more than \$59; Manhattan, less than \$21, \$72 to \$89, and more than \$89; Queens, less than \$33 and more than \$57.

strata were selected with probability proportionate to 1950 population. Each block containing fewer than 50 persons had previously been combined with a neighboring block to yield a group of pseudo-blocks. When a pseudo-block was selected by this sampling process, all its component blocks were included in the sample. All the households on each sampled block or psuedo-block were then listed. To select the individual households a sampling ratio was computed for each block by first calculating an expected number of households as follows:

$$\text{Expected no. h.h.'s} = \frac{5 \times \begin{array}{c}\text{1950 stratum}\\ \text{population}\end{array}}{156{,}000}\begin{pmatrix}\text{average}\\ \text{1940}\\ \text{h.h. size}\end{pmatrix} \times \frac{\begin{array}{c}\text{No. h.h.'s in}\\ \text{block listing}\end{array}}{\begin{array}{c}\text{1950 block}\\ \text{population}\end{array}}$$

The sampling ratio was then the number of households in the block listing divided by this computed expectation. If the computed value of the ratio for a particular block was 50, every 50th household in the listing for that block was selected. For blocks which had shown no marked population change between the time of the 1950 Census and the time of the block-listing, this procedure yielded approximately five households per block. For those blocks and pseudo-blocks in which new construction had been undertaken (and a few such blocks were selected in the sample) it yielded considerably more.

Field Experience

Several difficulties were encountered in the actual process of interviewing the sample selected. As a result of these difficulties the rate of response of the selected sample in the first round of enumeration appeared too low to be satisfactory. Of the approximately 5,000 non-H.I.P. households designated for the original sample only about two-thirds had been interviewed (Table C–1). Of the 3,794 active H.I.P. households, 57 percent had been interviewed. Of the 1,232 terminated H.I.P. enrollees, slightly more than a third had been interviewed.

The unsatisfactory nature of these response rates suggested the necessity of a second round of enumeration in which further efforts were made to contact and interview non-respondents. The funds allotted for this phase of the study had been exhausted, and it was not possible to resurvey the 4,000 non-respondents. The plan finally adopted involved separating the non-respondents into two groups—those for which further effort would be useless (e.g., H.I.P. enrollees who were not living at the address indicated in the H.I.P. records) and those for which further effort might be fruitful (e.g., those who had not been at home for previous calls or had refused the interview). Because of budget limitations a random sample of the second group, rather than the entire group, was selected for re-enumeration. The numbers selected are indicated in Table C–1. The organization of the field staff was changed, chiefly in the direction of providing more supervision in the field for the interviewers. It will be noted (Table C–1) that the response rate in the second round was higher than in the first, and this despite the fact that the subjects were a selected group.

Table C–1. Summary of responses in first and second rounds of enumeration, H.I.P. and non-H.I.P. households

	NUMBER OF HOUSEHOLDS		
	H.I.P.		*Non-H.I.P.*
	Active	Terminated	
Original sample	3,794	1,232	5,006
Responding, 1st round	2,152	449	3,295
Not responding, total	1,642	783	1,711
Not considered, 2nd round	231	482	177
Considered, 2nd round	1,411	301	1,534
Original sample	540	101	463
Responding, 2nd round	362	48	311

In combining the first- and second-round responses it was, of course, necessary to "blow up" the second-round responses. The blow-up ratios are easily computed from Table C–1 as:

Non-H.I.P.	$1{,}534/463 = 3.31$
H.I.P. (active)	$1{,}411/540 = 2.61$
H.I.P. (terminated)	$301/101 = 2.98$

In practice this blow-up was accomplished by duplicating punch cards. Thus, for the non-H.I.P. sample, 31 percent of the second-round respondents had their cards reproduced three additional times; 69 percent, two additional times. This procedure yielded $3{,}295 + 3.31 \times 311 = 4{,}325$ equivalent households for the non-H.I.P. sample.[5] On this basis the first- and second-round returns, when properly weighted and combined, may be

[5] This number differs from the actual number tabulated, 4,190, because of the transfer to the H.I.P. sample of all households found in the New York City sample that included one or more persons who belonged to H.I.P.

considered to provide a sample with an 86 percent response rate (4,325/5,006) for non-H.I.P. families and an 81 percent response rate (2,152 + 2.61 × 362/3,794) for active H.I.P. families.

Two questions arise: the possible bias that arises from the failure to represent 15 or 20 percent of the target populations, and the effect of the blow-up procedure on the sampling variance of the estimates. The second question is answered, at least by implication, in the following section, but before we turn to it a few remarks on the first may be in order.

The bias introduced by non-response depends on two factors—the extent to which non-respondents differ from respondents, and the magnitude of the non-response rate. The 19 and 14 percent non-response rates in the present survey are of the magnitude experienced in most carefully conducted non-government surveys. With respect to the extent to which non-respondents differ from respondents nothing definitive, of course, can be said. The following evidence may be helpful to the reader who wishes to make up his own mind on this question.

Comparison of the first- and second-round respondents discloses some small but characteristic differences between them, all apparently dependent on the fact that second-round respondents had smaller families. Thus, for the non-H.I.P. sample the households included in the first round of enumeration averaged 3.30 persons, as compared with 3.01 persons for the second round. For the H.I.P. families the comparable figures are 3.43 and 3.29. The average number of medical conditions per person was also somewhat lower for second-round respondents in both the H.I.P. and non-H.I.P. samples. Whether non-respondents also differed in this fashion is a question on which there is no direct evidence. The seasonal factor may have entered here.

A number of comparisons of the demographic and economic characteristics of the present sample and the New York City population (as shown by the 1950 Census) have been made. In general, the items on which comparison can be made are not very sensitive indicators as to whether serious biases are or are not present. The non-H.I.P. sample has the same distribution with respect to family size, relationship to head of household, marital status, color, and occupation as does the New York City population. It seems to contain more children proportionately than does the New York City population and a slightly higher percentage of persons with at least some high school education (54 percent as compared with 48). What these comparisons suggest with respect to the possible effect of the non-response rate each reader must appraise for himself.

Estimated Sampling Error

It is best to start with an example. According to Table C–2, of the 13,553[6] non-H.I.P. persons in the survey, 3,628 or 26.8 percent reported a medical condition yesterday. What is the standard error of this percentage? Had the sample been selected by using simple random sampling with the individual as the unit of sampling (an impracticable procedure, of course), we should be able to estimate this standard error from the well-known formula for such a situation, $\sqrt{pq/n}$, where $p = .268$, $q = .732$, and $n = 13{,}553$. The estimate of $p = .268$ would thus have been subject to a standard error of .004.

Because of the nature of the sampling as well as the fact that some of the 13,553 cases are the result simply of duplicating punch cards and not of independent interviews, this formula is clearly inapplicable. An estimate could be obtained, however, from the fact that the sample was selected in effect as if 20 independent samples were being selected (see p. 210). Thus, each stratum contained 20 blocks, and variation among the results for these blocks could provide the basis for estimating the error in any one stratum. Clearly, formulae could be developed which would permit an estimate of error reflecting the nature of the sampling design and of the card duplication. The use of such a formula would have involved separate summaries for each of the 1,000 blocks in the sample, an obviously costly and hence unusable procedure. An alternative, less costly but equally acceptable, procedure involved assigning the numbers 1 to 20 to each of the sample blocks in each stratum, and combining all number 1 blocks in the 50 strata to yield one sample, all number 2 blocks in the 50 strata to yield another sample, etc. This procedure yielded 20 sub-samples, the summation of which yields the present sample. Furthermore, since variation among each of these 20 samples reflects all the sources of variation to which the present sample is subject, including those occasioned by duplicating cards, it provides the basis for an acceptable estimate of standard error.

Thus, we show in Table C–2 the proportion of persons reporting a medical condition on the day preceding the interview for each of the 20 sub-

[6] Five persons were included in the survey after these analyses were made.

samples. The sample proportion .268 may be considered an average of the 20 individual proportions shown in Table C–2, and hence subject to an estimated standard error of $s/\sqrt{20}$, where s is the standard deviation of the 20 individual entries in the table. The standard error estimated on this basis is .007, of course considerably larger than the .004 obtained by assuming a sample of 13,553 independently related individuals.

Table C–2. Proportion of persons reporting medical conditions, New York City sample, day preceding interview, by sub-sample

SUB-SAMPLE NUMBER	NUMBER OF PERSONS: *Total*	*With medical conditions*	*Proportion with medical conditions*
Total	*13,553*	*3,628*	.268
1	710	232	.326
2	681	164	.241
3	782	210	.269
4	681	171	.251
5	656	170	.269
6	656	207	.315
7	621	185	.297
8	627	169	.270
9	648	156	.241
10	746	202	.271
11	748	198	.265
12	645	162	.251
13	671	151	.225
14	708	223	.315
15	688	143	.208
16	693	186	.268
17	678	190	.280
18	749	172	.230
19	586	159	.271
20	579	178	.308

Since $\sqrt{pq/n}$ can easily be computed for many entries in the present volume, the existence of a single inflation factor by which this expectation could be increased to provide a more realistic estimate of sampling error would be useful. We show in Table C–3 the ratio $\frac{s}{20} \sqrt{pq/n}$ for a series of characteristics. It will be noted that the values range between 2.1 and 0.7, with a fairly consistent tendency for the ratio to be higher for the New York City sample than for the H.I.P. sample.

For most rates that represent proportions of persons with a certain characteristic this table should provide a sufficient basis for appraising sampling error, since one need only compute $\sqrt{pq/n}$ and inflate it by an appropriate factor, Table C–3 being used as a guide in the selection of the factor. In cases where more precise estimates of error are required it may be necessary to resort to special tabulations like those of Table C–2.

In the case of rates that are not proportions

Table C–3. Comparison of actual standard error and binomial expectation for selected characteristics, H.I.P. and New York City samples

AGE AND SEX	PROPORTION OF PERSONS WITH MEDICAL CONDITIONS: *On day preceding interview*	*In eight weeks preceding interview*: Total	Dis-abling	Respira-tory
	Ratio of actual to expected, H.I.P. sample			
All persons	1.4	1.4	1.1	1.2
Male, total	1.5	1.4	1.1	1.0
0 to 4 years	1.2	1.3	1.3	1.1
15 to 44 years	1.4	1.4	1.1	1.2
Female, total	1.1	1.2	1.2	1.2
15 to 44 years	1.2	1.7	1.5	1.2
65 years and over	0.9	1.0	1.2	1.0
	Ratio of actual to expected, New York City sample			
All persons	1.9	2.0	1.7	1.6
Male, total	1.9	2.1	1.7	1.4
0 to 4 years	1.6	1.2	1.5	1.2
15 to 44 years	1.3	1.5	1.5	1.2
Female, total	1.2	1.2	1.4	1.3
15 to 44 years	1.2	1.0	1.3	1.1
65 years and over	1.6	1.4	0.7	1.2

Table C–4. Standard errors and coefficients of variation for selected averages, H.I.P. and New York City samples

AGE AND SEX	IN EIGHT WEEKS PRECEDING INTERVIEW — *Number of doctor visits per person*: Standard error of the mean	Coeff. of variation (percent)	*Number of nights in hospital per person*: Standard error of the mean	Coeff. of variation (percent)
	H.I.P. sample			
All persons	.042	4.7	.027	20.7
Male, total	.054	6.3	.048	35.5
0 to 4 years	.135	10.7	.082	55.1
15 to 44 years	.079	11.8	.015	44.9
Female, total	.047	5.2	.023	19.0
15 to 44 years	.075	7.8	.032	20.5
65 years and over	.428	42.8	.376	97.6
	New York City sample			
All persons	.029	3.4	.013	10.2
Male, total	.038	5.0	.017	16.2
0 to 4 years	.108	10.3	.080	58.7
15 to 44 years	.048	7.6	.021	28.8
Female, total	.042	4.4	.019	13.5
15 to 44 years	.058	6.6	.032	20.1
65 years and over	.150	10.9	.051	34.3

but averages, such as the number of nights in the hospital in the eight-week period per person in the sample, no theoretical expectation equivalent to $\sqrt{pq/n}$ is available. For two such rates, number of doctor visits per person and number of nights in the hospital per person in the eight-week period, we show in Table C–4 the standard error of the mean and also this standard error as a percentage of the mean, i.e., the coefficient of variation, in various population groups. The computations were based upon tabulations of data from the survey for random sub-samples of the total sample, similar to those used for estimating the standard errors for proportions.

Two types of extensions of these standard errors may be required. First, one may wish standard errors for either number of doctor visits or nights in the hospital for population groups not shown in the table, e.g., males 45 to 64. For such a purpose it is sufficient to note that the standard errors for the different population groups shown in Table C–4 vary in approximately inverse proportion to the square root of the number of persons in that population group. Secondly, one may wish standard errors for averages not shown in Table C–4, e.g., number of illnesses in the eight-week period per 100 persons. No precise method of estimation from the data presented can be suggested for this latter situation. A serviceable approximation may perhaps be obtained by noting that number of doctor visits and number of nights in the hospital are among the more variable of the averages studied, so that for rough tests of significance a conservative procedure would involve assuming coefficients of variation like these, although nights in the hospital are so variable that this may be excessively conservative. Again, more exact tests would require special tabulations.

APPENDIX D

Methodology of the Survey

Interviewers and Interviewing

Once the two samples, consisting of approximately 5,000 H.I.P. subscribers (covered at some time during the existence of the Plan) and approximately 5,000 households representative of the general population of New York City, had been selected, the actual conduct of the field work in the Household Survey was undertaken by Alfred Politz Research, Inc.[1] This organization hired the interviewers and directed their work. The training of the interviewers was the joint responsibility of the Politz staff and the staff of the Special Research Project.

The Politz organization hired 117 people at various times for interviewing in the Household Survey. Of the 46 who started at the beginning of the survey on March 3, 26 were still active on May 13 when the first phase of the interviewing was terminated (see below). Thirty-eight additional interviewers began work on March 22; and of these, 23 were still active on May 13. Thirty-three other interviewers were hired after March 22, and 23 of these were still active on May 13.

About nine-tenths of the interviewers were women, and for the most part they were married women who were not otherwise employed. A few were teachers, and there was a scattering of persons in other types of employment. Their ages ranged from 20 to 50, but most were in their thirties. With three exceptions those whose educational status was known had completed 12 or more years of school, and 38 of them had completed 16 or more years.

Each interviewer received several hours of formal class instruction after which he or she was asked to complete at home and submit two completed practice questionnaires giving actual information supplied by acquaintances and relatives. These practice questionnaires were then reviewed by members of the Project staff, and the interviewers were informed of the results of the review. Further individual instruction was given by the staff whenever necessary. All of the first schedules for the actual sample that were submitted by the interviewers were looked over particularly carefully. Written comments were given to each interviewer whenever instructions or clarifications were needed.

The interview was to be conducted with a responsible adult member of the household in every instance. Information is given in Chapter II regarding the proportions of the sampled individuals who were reported upon by themselves or a member of the immediate family (spouse or parent), by another type of relative, and by a non-relative living in the household. Owing principally to the failure of the interviewers to record in some instances which member of the household was the respondent, the relationship of the individual reported upon to the respondent is not known in about one in every eight cases.

There was no complete manual of instructions for interviewers. Problems that arose during the course of the survey were handled by means of memoranda.

Among the particular points covered in memoranda were (see Appendix A for facsimile of schedule):

1. The interpretation of Question 3 on Schedules 2 and 3: "When did this condition start?" The interviewers were told that in the case of chronic complaints for which there was an acute flare-up the answer to the question should depend on the onset of the acute symptoms which characterized the flare-up. But if the chronic complaint was one from which the household member had experienced trouble "on and off," the interviewer was instructed to circle "Before the eight-week period."

The interviewer was urged to get the respond-

[1] As so frequently happens in complex projects of this sort, the original target date for the beginning of field work, November 1951, had to be set back. Information on the utilization of the H.I.P. by subjects of the survey during the study period is available from the records of the Health Insurance Plan for 1952. This would provide a basis for evaluating some of the Household Survey results for the sample of H.I.P. families. Owing to exigencies of the budget, this comparison has yet to be made. It is hoped that this will be the subject of a special auxiliary study at a later date.

ent's story on such conditions and make notes where necessary. The same sort of rules were to be used in recording the answer to Question 17 on Schedule 2 and Question 12 on Schedule 3: "How long after the development of this condition did ——— wait before calling the doctor?"

2. In recording the answer to Question 10 on Schedule 1, Question 21 on Schedule 2, and Question 16 on Schedule 3, dealing with the insurance status of the individual and the insurance coverage, if any, for the medical care in a particular illness, the word "insurance" was to be interpreted in the broadest possible sense. Since the purpose of the question was to find out whether the household members had help in covering the costs of medical care, regardless of whether they paid the premiums themselves or not, "insurance" was to include union benefit payments, medical care provided by an employer, and so forth.

3. The interviewers were asked to be particularly careful to distinguish between medical check-ups in connection with a specific ailment and those which were for routine purposes, such as annual health examinations and examinations for insurance or employment. Question 7d on Schedule 1 was meant to include only the latter. The interviewers were instructed to ask certain questions to distinguish between the two. If the check-up turned out to be in connection with an ailment not yet recorded, they were told how to record it.

The interviewers were not told that the purpose of the survey was a comparison of H.I.P. and non-H.I.P. experience. The assignment of work was such that each interviewer had some of each type of household to interview. All that the interviewer knew was that some of the schedules were identified by an address only, while others had family names as well as addresses. (They were admonished, of course, to make no substitution for the family whose name they were given.) It was intended that this aspect of the study be kept completely a secret from the interviewers and, as far as the appearance of the schedule was concerned, there was no clue to the auspices. The Project staff members who helped to train the interviewers were not identified as being connected with H.I.P. Furthermore many of the households in the H.I.P. sample actually no longer had H.I.P. enrollees living in them. This fact helped to conceal the H.I.P. vs. non-H.I.P. comparison from the interviewers. However, there is no doubt that a few interviewers may have gotten the point, either during the training period or during the course of the interviewing.

Interviewing was done on all seven days of the week and in the evening as well as the daytime. Interviewers were instructed to keep in touch with the central office of Alfred Politz Research, Inc. at all times and were given a number to call. At first they carried credentials issued by the City Department of Health, but this led to so many telephone calls to the Health Department that the credentials were later recalled. If there were any doubts on the part of the respondent, however, regarding the legitimacy of the purposes of the survey, the interviewers could always refer the householder to a Health Department telephone number.

Special stress was placed upon completing assigned interviewing within the specified time. Careful time records, accurate to the nearest five minutes, were required. Payment of interviewers was on the basis of time spent for interviewing, travel, and other time on the study, plus public transportation costs and seven cents a mile for the use of an automobile. When initial assignments were completed, interviewers were encouraged to take on additional work providing their performance was considered satisfactory.

No limit was set to the number of revisits made in order to complete an interview after an initial non-interview. Of those missed on the first attempt, nearly 14 percent were tried six or more times. The average number of calls for all households not contacted on the first visit was 3.9.

A tabulation was made of the distribution of the interviewers' time. The total time of the interviewers amounted to an average of 145 minutes per interview. Of this, 18 minutes per schedule was used for training, review of schedules by the interviewer, and returning of completed schedules. Forty minutes per schedule went for travel time from home to the sample block or location. The remaining 87 minutes per schedule was designated as interviewing time. However, only about 55 minutes of this was spent on the interview itself, the balance of 32 minutes being for time spent in travel from dwelling unit to dwelling unit after reaching the sample block or location, for not-at-homes, and for other things.

Success of Interviewing

The problem of reaching the sample households turned out to be particularly difficult. New York City has a reputation for being a place where it is hard to find people at home. In this survey the large number of non-interviews led to the division of the interviewing into two phases. The first phase, extending from March 3 through May 13, resulted in the completion of about 6,100 of the original 10,000. Before explaining the organization of the second phase it is necessary to see why the remaining interviews could not be completed in the first round of interviewing. Table D–1 shows the distribution of households according to response and reason for non-response in the first phase.

Table D–1. Number of households, H.I.P. and New York City samples, by response to interview (first phase) and reason for non-response

RESULTS OF INTERVIEWING—1ST PHASE	NUMBER OF HOUSEHOLDS		
	Total	*H.I.P.*	*New York City*
Original sample	10,032	5,026	5,006
Number of interviews obtained	6,085	2,823	3,262
Number of interviews not obtained	3,947[1]	2,203	1,744[1]
Reason for non-response:			
Not at home after 3 or more calls	1,953	907	1,046
Total refusal	692	342	350
Partial refusal	33	11	22
Moved	701	701	—
Address problem	166	75	91
Vacant dwelling unit	79	—	79
Language problem	57	23	34
Deceased	42	42	—
Schedule not classified[2]	224[1]	102	122[1]

[1] Estimated.

[2] This tabulation was made at a time when certain schedules were still in the field and hence could not yet be classified.

Omitting the vacant dwelling units, the families of H.I.P. subscribers who were deceased, and the schedules not yet classified in the above tabulation, there were still only 6,085, or 63 percent, of the 9,687 possible schedules obtained in this first phase of the survey. It was obviously necessary to make an effort to raise this response rate in order to avoid the possibility of serious bias. However, it did not appear to be necessary to try to complete all the outstanding interviews. Three of the categories of reasons for non-response accounted for about 93 percent of all the non-responses, again excluding the vacant dwelling units, deceased-subscriber families, and schedules still in the field. These three were the "not-at-homes" (54 percent), the total refusal cases (19 percent), and the H.I.P. families that had moved from the addresses given in the H.I.P. file (20 percent). Accordingly, it was decided to attempt to complete a sample of one-third of the "not-at-homes" and refusal cases, and all of the H.I.P. families that had moved for which an address could be obtained from the Post Office. (About five-ninths of the last group were active H.I.P. subscribers' families, and the remainder were terminated families.)

For this second phase of the interviewing, 20 interviewers selected for their superior ability in obtaining interviews were used. They worked under very close supervision of three crew leaders. More care was devoted to scheduling the hour and day for follow-up interviews.

As a result of this intensive effort, 66 percent of the non-response households that had been selected for second-round interviewing were completed. This rate, it will be noted, is as high as, if not higher than, the completion rate in the first phase, despite the select nature of the cases. Of the original "not-at-homes" (meaning not at home after three or more visits) the second-phase interviewers completed 71 percent; of the previous total refusal cases they completed 63 percent; and of the families that had moved but left an address with the Post Office, 60 percent.

Thus, in the end, roughly 85 percent of the original sample of New York City and H.I.P. families were represented by completed interviews, though in some instances they were represented on a one-third sub-sample basis.

Coding and Tabulating

The first stage in the development of the tabulating program for the household survey was the drawing up by the Steering Committee of lists of specific questions that the survey tabulations must be able to answer. In drawing up this list the Committee referred to the statement of objectives of the survey (see Chapter II), which was in more general terms. These lists of questions provided the stepping-off point for the construction by the staff of the Project of a complete set of skeleton tables. The tables were submitted to the Steering Committee for review and eventually became, with only a few important changes, the specifications for the tabulating program of the survey.

For a detailed understanding of the means by which any category of the tables was obtained it would be necessary to review the procedures of coding and the many decisions that had to be made before tabulation. However, these coding rules and other decisions are too voluminous to publish in full. The research worker who needs to know in great detail how such-and-such was done can find these decisions in writing in the files of the Project. For this reason we shall note only a few of the more important coding decisions and proceed to a description of the organization of the final tables themselves.

Major Codes[2]

1. For *Occupational Classes,* the 1950 Alphabetical Index of Occupations and Industries, published by the Bureau of the Census, condensed into broad groupings.

2. For *Diagnosis,* the International Statistical Classification of Diseases, Injuries, and Causes of Death, published by the World Health Organization, combined for presentation into several different groupings as will be discussed later.

3. For *Hospitalized Surgery,* a modified version of the Classified List of Surgical Operations, Joint Armed Forces Statistical Classification, and Basic Diagnostic Nomenclature, 1949.

Diagnostic and Medical Care Coding

1. It has already been mentioned that the interviewing instructions did not call for the opening up of a column of the Illness and Medical Care Memorandum (Schedule 2) for diagnoses reported in the chronic disease check list questions (Question 9a). It was found desirable as an office procedure to fill in an additional column of Schedule 2 in each instance where no such column already existed. (If the chronic disease had already been reported in one of the earlier questions a column would have been filled out by the interviewer.) The number of medical conditions (columns of Schedule 2) that were added by this procedure amounted to 16 percent of the total in the H.I.P. sample and 22 percent of the total in the New York City sample.

The existence of disability and bed-disability was coded as unknown in these added columns but, since there had been no previous report of the condition, it was thought safe to assume that there had been no hospitalization or medical care in connection with it during the eight-week period.

It was also decided that tabulation of the chronic diseases on the check list must include all reports of those diseases regardless of what question on the schedule was responsible for eliciting the report.

2. If the medical coder believed that a condition reported in answer to one question on Schedule 1, e.g., Question 7a, was actually the same condition and the same illness as was previously reported for the same household member in answer to another question, e.g., 6d, except described in slightly different terms, the two reports were merged. Only one column of Schedule 2 was kept. For example, a report of "backache" in response to Question 6c (special symptoms yesterday) and a report of "lumbago" in response to Question 7e (seeing a doctor for any other reason in the past eight weeks) might lead to the opening up by the interviewer of two columns on the Illness and Medical Care Memorandum if the respondent did not mention specifically that these were both the same illness. If a review of the two columns by the medical coder indicated that this seemed to be one and the same illness in the same individual, the results were merged.

On the other hand, the opposite decision might also be made upon occasion. If the coder decided that one column of Schedule 2 had in it two separate illnesses or a multiple diagnosis, both occurring in the eight-week period, the information could be split into two columns, thus producing, as we shall see, two medical condition punch cards.

3. Interviewers' notes on the front of Schedule 1 describing medical conditions for which illness memoranda had not been filled out, and indications on a 1951 illness memorandum that the condition described was "still present," sometimes made it necessary for the coder to open up new columns on Schedule 2 in order to insure complete counting of illnesses in the eight-week period. The number of medical conditions added by this procedure amounted to about 2 percent of the total.

4. When more than one diagnosis was reported as having been the cause of illness during the same or overlapping periods of time in the eight-week period, no effort was made to assign one of these as the primary diagnosis and the others as contributory. Each was treated as a separate illness, and the overlapping periods of disability or days in bed were assigned to each condition. However, for tabulations in which the unit was a person rather than a medical condition it was desirable to have a non-duplicative count of days of disability and days in bed. The schedule gave the dates of beginning and ending of each illness but gave only the number of days within the eight-week period, not the actual dates, of disability and days in bed. Hence, when the dates of the beginning and end of two illnesses recorded for one individual overlapped, and some days of disability were recorded for each illness, it was recognized that there could be overlapping of days of disability. In such cases the person was recorded as having unknown duration of disability for the

[2] See Appendix B for notes on terms used in tables.

purpose of tabulations in which the person was the unit. The person was also recorded as having unknown duration if the number of days of disability for one of the two illnesses, overlapping in time, was reported as unknown or was unreported. Bed-days were treated in the same manner.

This means that the accumulated totals of known days of disability or days in bed for the various population groups tend to be an undercount of a true unduplicated count in those tables in which the person is the unit. On the other hand, those tables in which the unit is a medical condition will have some duplication in the totals, but for any one diagnostic group the days will be a fair measure of the total volume of disabling or bed-illness for that group of diagnoses.

5. Only the first three digits of the International Statistical Classification were used in coding the nature of each medical condition. Editing and interpretation on the part of the medical coders were kept to a minimum by following rather strictly the terminology of the respondent in selecting the code number. All of the available information on the three schedules, including that contained in footnotes, was used for this coding.

6. Since no distinction was made in the interview between the date of onset of an episode of illness resulting from a chronic disease and the onset of the first symptoms of the chronic disease itself, it was believed that a distinction should be made in the coding between the instances when the date of onset could be considered acceptably reliable (acute illness, accidents) and the instances where it was thought to be ambiguous (mainly chronic conditions). This was chiefly important because of the interest in the time lag between the onset of the condition and the seeking of medical care. However, in the analysis (see Chapter x) chronic conditions were discarded.

7. The total number of doctor visits for a given individual in the eight-week period was established from all columns of Schedule 2 for that individual. Interviewers had received instructions to note duplication of doctor visits for separate medical conditions, so it was possible to eliminate duplication in the coding. Although Question 7f of Schedule 1 calls for the total number of doctor or dentist visits in the eight-week period, it was the number of doctor visits as established from the Illness and Medical Care Memorandum that was used in the tabulations.

8. Unlike the procedures used for the Illness and Medical Care Memorandum (Schedule 2), the criteria for establishing a column on Schedule 3 had no relation to the existence of episodes of illness as such, or medical conditions, or doctor's care. Only a hospitalization of one night or more or an episode of disability requiring seven or more days of bed-rest could produce such a column. However, when an individual had more than one diagnostic condition recorded in relation to an episode of hospitalization or of seven or more days in bed there was no way of establishing whether each disease by itself was responsible for the episode. In such instances the episode was counted only once but in counts of diagnoses each disease was counted.

9. If more than one dental condition appeared on Schedule 2 for any individual, such conditions were combined by the medical coder into one condition. This was done because it was decided that the data obtained on Schedule 2 concerning dental care were not sufficiently descriptive to provide a reliable basis for differentiating several conditions.

10. In dealing with inconsistencies between the number of days the person was disabled during the eight-week period and the number of days the person spent in bed, the latter was considered to be the more accurate. A day in bed was also a day disabled but, of course, the reverse was not necessarily true. Hence, if the reported number of days in bed exceeded the reported number of days disabled, the number of the latter was coded as unknown.

11. No effort was made to establish whether the doctor whose name was reported on the schedule as the "family" doctor (Question 18) or the special doctor used for the children (Question 16) was a licensed physician. The reasons for this decision were that no recent medical directory was available and also that the enumerators' spelling of the doctors' names was so questionable as to make the coding of these qualifications of the doctors very costly.

12. No distinction was made in the coding of insurance coverage between insurance payments which covered only a portion of medical expenses and those which covered the full cost of medical care. (See Question 21 of Schedule 2 and Question 16 of Schedule 3.) The code "hospitalization insurance," for example, includes cases of both full and partial payment of hospital expenses by insurance benefits.

Basic Punch Cards

In mechanical processing of the survey data there were actually many different types of punch cards devised. However, there were five basic cards that originated with the three schedules.

Card Number 1 (see Appendix F for the lists of items punched on each of the five cards) was punched from the contents of Schedule 1, one card for each member of the household. Card Number 2 came from Schedule 2, one card being punched for each medical and/or dental condition during the eight-week period prior to the date of the interview. Card Number 3 consolidated the data for the person and all of his medical conditions for the eight-week period. Card Number 4 was based upon Schedule 3, and one card was punched for each period of a night or more in the hospital and each period of seven or more days of bed-illness in 1951. Card Number 5 was made for each person showing all of his reported 1951 episodes of illness or injury. Note that there is a special section of Card Number 4 for pregnancies followed by delivery in 1951.

Organization of Tabulations

The original tabulation plans envisaged four broad groups of tables:

a. Demographic, economic, and social characteristics of persons and households.
b. Morbidity characteristics of persons, of medical conditions, and of households.
c. Medical care characteristics of persons, of medical conditions, and of households.
d. Tables designed to test or evaluate the methods used in the Household Survey.

Later, when the full magnitude of these plans was completely seen and matched against the resources available for carrying them out, it became obvious that some of the tables that had been considered desirable would have to be omitted. The first tables to be eliminated were those in which the unit was the household. Although there was curiosity as to how the analysis with the household as a unit could be worked out, the special difficulties of these tables, plus the experimental nature of some of the proposed classifications and the lack of resources made them a logical choice for elimination.

At about the same time, two other decisions were made in order to simplify the tabulations. First, the persons selected in the H.I.P. sample who were no longer covered by H.I.P. at the time of the survey, about 20 percent of the entire sample, were left out of the tables. Since many of those persons had terminated their coverage because they were planning to leave town, it had proved impossible to interview a large proportion of them except at great expense. The ones who were interviewed were considered likely to be unrepresentative of the entire group of terminated H.I.P. members. The rest of the H.I.P. cases were, therefore, current H.I.P. enrollees.

Second, it was decided that the 3 or 4 percent of the persons in the original New York City sample who were in households containing one or more H.I.P. enrollees at the time of the survey would be transferred to the H.I.P. sample. Consequently, the remaining sample would be a representative sample of all persons living in New York City (exclusive of institutional population) who were not members of a household with one or more members in H.I.P. This, it was thought, would simplify the tabulations and make the comparison between H.I.P. and non-H.I.P. populations more distinct.

The final major change in the tabulating plans was the elimination of most of the tables in Group *d*—the methodological tables.

It should be said that in the exclusion of tabulations of terminated H.I.P. members and in the dropping of the methodological tables, it was hoped that the actions taken did not mean that these questions would never be investigated. A great deal of interest was expressed in both types of information and in the possibility that they might be made the subjects of separate studies.

The groupings of the remaining tables were labeled as follows:

a. Demographic data (Appendix G, Tables 1–23)
b. Data on medical conditions and disability of persons (Appendix G, Tables 24–60)
c. Medical care of persons (Appendix G, Tables 61–88)
d. Medical conditions and disability as morbidity data (Appendix G, Tables 89–116)
e. Medical care for medical conditions (Appendix G, Tables 117–146).

Almost all of the tables are divided into two parts, one labeled "H.I.P. Sample" and the other, "New York City Sample." This, of course, results from the primary importance of the comparison of H.I.P. and non-H.I.P. populations in the objectives of the survey.

Another pattern that will be found in the base tables from which the tables in this volume are derived is the subdivision of many into a Part A and a Part B. In the former, five age groups (plus a sixth group for "Age not reported") are broken down by sex in the stub of the table. In the latter each of the age groups is subdivided, not by sex but by number of years of education of the head of the household. This, it will be recalled, is the variable which was substituted for income as an indicator of broad economic levels. It is shown in three class intervals plus a category for unknown number of years of education.

A list of the base tables will be found in Appendix G.

The appendices giving definitions and morbidity codes explain terms used in the tables. Comprehension of these is essential to an understanding of the statistics presented in this survey.

Evaluation of Schedule and Interview

It has been the experience with surveys of illness and medical care utilization in the past that errors resulting from incorrect response, failure of the respondent's memory, errors on the part of the interviewer, and in the processing of the data, and lack of clarity in definitions are more difficult to control than the errors of sampling. Furthermore, the effort to obtain a clear idea of the possible magnitude of the non-sampling errors may be as great as the original data collection. The usual compromise is to check the results of the survey wherever possible against independent sources and to look for internal inconsistencies. The purpose of this examination is, of course, to determine what limitations the data have and to avoid, wherever possible, the "weak spots" in the course of analysis.

As an example of a limitation that soon became obvious in the Household Survey, mention has already been made of the data on family income. Reports of income were not obtained for about 20 percent of the families, and the term "family" in the income question was not sufficiently clearly defined. In order to avoid this "weak spot," education of the head of the household was substituted wherever income was to have been used in the analysis.

In general, however, it was possible to check the survey results for demographic and economic items in the New York City sample against an outside source—the 1950 decennial census and the report of the Health Department on births. For the H.I.P. sample the only demographic items for which a check was readily available were age and sex. The distribution of the sample by age and sex was compared with H.I.P. enrollment data, and the results are set forth in Appendix E. All that need be said here is that, with the exception of income data (for which no good check against the Census was possible but which were known to be deficient[3]), the survey's results seemed to match well.

The situation with regard to illness and medical care items is that with very few exceptions no valid checks against already existing outside sources of information are possible. This is particularly true of the New York City data. For data on the H.I.P. families in the sample checks are potentially available for the statistics on utilization of the medical care that they obtained from the H.I.P. doctors.

When we turn to an examination of the data for internal evidence of consistency, the possibilities are also limited. A series of tabulations designed to throw light upon some of the questions of response error and schedule design was considered, but there were many more subsidiary objectives suggested for the study than could be possibly carried out, and this series of tabulations had to be abandoned. Nevertheless, a few opportunities for internal comparisons are afforded in the tables prepared to serve the main objectives of the study. Moreover, the process of coding and tabulating has revealed certain limitations which should be described in this report. These limitations had to be kept in mind during the analytical phase of the study; hence, setting them down here will help to explain some of the choice of material and methods in the preceding chapters.

Before investigating these, however, we may digress briefly to satisfy our curiosity about how some of the major measures of illness and medical care utilization compared with those from another urban study. In doing this we shall not be concerned with refined comparisons but rather with the general order of magnitude of the results. Table D–2 shows seven different rates as obtained from statistics for the eight weeks preceding the interview in the New York City sample and as obtained from the five-year study conducted in the Eastern Health District of Baltimore by the Public Health Service and the Milbank Memorial Fund in the years 1938 to 1943. The rates are expressed on an annual basis, that is, the figures for the eight-week period have been multiplied by 6.5 to show the expectation over 52 weeks if the rate remained the same throughout the year. In three instances estimates for the United States have been set down for comparison.

The fact that the New York City survey was carried out at a time of year when illness rates and the utilization of medical care tend to be near their peaks undoubtedly accounts for some of the

[3] This is not to say that the sample incorrectly represented the various income groups in the population; the point is that the income information collected was not adequate for purposes of analysis.

Table D–2. Indexes of illness and medical care, New York City sample, Eastern Health District of Baltimore, and the United States

Indexes of illness and medical care (expressed per capita, on annual basis)	*New York City, spring of 1952 (eight-week period x 6.5)*	*Eastern Health District of Baltimore, 1938–1943*	*United States (see notes)*
No. days of hospitalization per person	0.90[1]	0.98	1.1[2]
No. M.D. visits per person	5.2[1]	2.5	
No. bed-days per person	5.6[1]	5.0	
No. days disabled per person	12.4[1]	15.9	
No. days disabled per person 15 to 64 years	8.7[1]	13.1	15.2[3]
No. surgical operations per person	0.09	0.083	0.06[4]
No. physical examinations, check-ups, immunizations, routine eye examinations, prenatal, postpartum, well-baby care, and similar preventive services	0.67	0.22	

[1] Rates assume that persons with unknown number of days (or number of visits) had same average number of days (or visits) as those for whom the number of days (or visits) was known.

[2] Metropolitan areas only. From Health Information Foundation survey, 1952–53.

[3] Urban only (estimated from Current Population Survey for February 1949 and September 1950).

[4] U.S. sample. Includes all "surgical procedures." From Health Information Foundation survey, 1952–53.

differences observed. The only rates that appear to differ more than can reasonably be explained by the variation in season, year, and locality are those shown for preventive services. In both surveys an effort was made to count these services completely, and so far as can be determined they both include the same items.

At any rate, this crude comparison serves one purpose, which is to show that there is no evidence of marked undercounting of illness or medical care in the eight weeks preceding the interview when compared with a carefully conducted, intensive survey in another Eastern city.

No comparison is possible between these two surveys in terms of total days of illness, since neither study collected information on this point. Nor is it possible to compare the frequency of cases of illness (or "medical conditions" as they are called in the present study) in the month or eight weeks prior to the interview. The two studies used different measures of case frequency. An opportunity for comparing the amount of the less serious illness (along with that causing disability, time in bed, or time in the hospital) which was picked up in the two studies is afforded by the measure of prevalence. In the New York City sample 27 percent of the persons in the interviewed households were reported to have some "medical condition" (any condition arising from disease or injury or other cause for which medical care might be sought) on the day prior to the interview. There were 12 different weeks (not all consecutive) in which the interviewing for the New York City sample covered households containing 500 or more persons. The prevalence measure—percentage of persons in interviewed households reported to have some "medical condition,"—varied as shown in Table D–3.

Table D–3. Percentage of persons enumerated each week of interviewing (1952), reported to have some medical condition, New York City sample

Week beginning	*Percentage*	*Week beginning*	*Percentage*
March 9	31	April 27	24
March 16	30	May 4	25
March 23	29	—	—
March 30	30	—	—
April 6	27	May 25	24
April 13	26	June 1	27
April 20	28	June 8	21

(The two periods when interviewing was carried on intensively correspond roughly to the first and second phase of interviewing described previously.)

The five-year study in the Eastern Health District of Baltimore provides a comparable measure, that is, the prevalence at the time of the interview of all illness and chronic disease not currently causing illness. The figures in Table D–4 are for months of the year corresponding to those in which the Household Survey was done.

Considering the differences in procedure, locality, and other conditions, these percentages from

Table D–4. Average percentage for selected months (1939–1942) of persons with illness or chronic conditions, Eastern Health District of Baltimore

Month	*Percentage*
March	25.82
April	24.33
May	23.92
June	23.35

the two surveys are surprisingly similar. As was apparently true of the illness reported for the eight-week period, the reporting of illness on the day prior to the interview in this project was probably as complete as in any survey prior to 1950, if not more so. In any case, it was sufficiently complete for the purpose at hand—that is, to serve as an index of the needs for medical care in the two populations under study.

Turning now to an examination of the specific illness and medical care items, it is necessary to take what may appear to be a critical viewpoint. Unless two facts are kept in mind, the review that follows will give an exaggerated impression of the number of errors made in carrying out the survey. First, much of what now seems clear by hindsight was difficult or impossible to foresee. Second, the correct decisions and successful aspects of the survey have not been listed alongside those that now appear wrong. This is an attempt at a partial post-audit for the benefit of users of the data and future investigators.

The shortcomings of the survey design and execution which are to be discussed have made necessary particularly cautious analysis in places. Yet, it is not believed that any of these shortcomings, with one possible exception which will be mentioned, have invalidated the major comparisons which the study was intended to provide.

The most convenient organization of these comments is to divide them into three parts: (1) those having to do with the design of the interview; (2) those having to do with the instructions to the interviewers and with interviewer and respondent errors; and (3) those dealing with coding and tabulating decisions.

Design of Interview

1. There was strong evidence that the schedule expected too much of the respondent in the way of knowledge of insurance coverage for the various members of the family. For example, of the known H.I.P. enrollees in the H.I.P. sample, 8.9 percent were reported as having no insurance, insurance of an unknown type, or various types of insurance not including H.I.P. Also, 35.9 percent of that sample were reported to have H.I.P. coverage without hospital insurance coverage, which is an inconsistency, since H.I.P. members are required to carry some hospital insurance. Furthermore, 16.4 percent of the H.I.P. enrollees and 10.9 percent of the New York City sample were recorded as having insurance information incompletely reported. On the whole there can be no question of the unsatisfactory quality of the insurance coverage information.

While the essential dichotomy between H.I.P. coverage and no H.I.P. coverage could be accurately made by reference to the H.I.P. files, this deficiency in the insurance data in the survey did interfere with some important aspects of the analysis.

2. The fact that Schedule 1 did not require the interviewer to open up a column of Schedule 2 each time a chronic disease was reported in Question 9a, the chronic disease check list, led to much unnecessary difficulty in the coding. The coding procedure that was followed has already been described. The number of medical conditions added as a result of the chronic disease check list was 16 percent and 22 percent of the totals in the H.I.P. and New York City samples, respectively.

The effect of this defect in the schedule design and the resulting coding conditions was that large proportions of the cases of the chronic diseases listed on the check list had to be classified as "unknown if disabled." For example, some figures on numbers of cases for "check list" chronic diseases in the two samples combined appear in Table D–5.

Table D–5. Cases of chronic diseases on chronic disease check list and cases of undetermined disability, H.I.P. and New York City samples (combined), day preceding interview

	Total cases present on the day preceding the interview	*Cases classified as "unknown if disabled"*[1]
Tuberculosis	37	20
Asthma	287	210
Diabetes	196	138
Stroke	54	30
Heart disease	493	319
Hypertension	538	424
Varicose veins	471	436
Arthritis and rheumatism	925	701

[1] This refers to disability at any time within the eight-week period.

This may be contrasted with the figures in Table D–6 for chronic diseases that were not on the check list.

Table D–6. Cases of chronic disease not on chronic disease check list and cases of undetermined disability, H.I.P. and New York City samples (combined), day preceding interview

	Total cases present on the day preceding the interview	*Cases classified as "unknown if disabled"*[1]
Neoplasms	58	8
Psychoneuroses and disorders of character, behavior, and intelligence	89	10
Ulcer of stomach or duodenum	66	13
Kyphosis, flat feet, club feet, or other deformities	270	11

[1] This refers to disability at any time within the eight-week period.

Table D–7. Average number per examination of components reported as "unknown" by respondents for themselves and for other family members (for "general check-up" physical examination only), by age and sex

AGE AND SEX	H.I.P. SAMPLE		NEW YORK CITY SAMPLE	
	Respondents	*Not respondents*	*Respondents*	*Not respondents*
15 to 44 years				
Males	1.9	2.2	0.9	0.8
Females	1.2	2.8	0.5	0.9
45 to 64 years				
Males	1.3	1.5	1.0	1.0
Females	2.4	2.6	1.8	0.5

3. In Question 23 of Schedule 2 the interviewer was to ask whether the preventive physical examination that had been reported included certain procedures. Thirteen procedures or components of the physical examination were covered; of these one applied only to women. It was foreseen that respondents might well be unable to report accurately the components of the preventive physical examinations of the various members of the family. For this reason the tabulation showing the number of times each component was mentioned as having been part of the preventive examination was made separately for examinations reported upon by the person who was examined and for those reported upon by someone other than the person examined. Some statistics from this tabulation are presented below. It was expected that respondents describing their own physical examinations would have less occasion to report that they did not know whether a particular procedure was included. This seems to have been the case in the H.I.P. sample, but the New York City sample does not show it. Furthermore, for reasons that are not clear the respondents in the New York City households seemed to have less uncertainty about the components of the examinations than did those in the H.I.P. households.

4. In Question 3 of Schedule 2 there was encountered a difficulty that has cropped up in other illness surveys in which an attempt was made to ascertain the date of onset of an illness. On Schedule 2 the question was phrased: "When did this condition start?" This wording causes the respondent no particular trouble (except for that associated with recalling dates) when the illness is of an acute nature. But when the disease runs a chronic course it may be marked by flare-ups. These may be associated with periods of inability to carry on usual activities and periods of bed-illness, or they may be episodes when symptoms become more severe and the person feels "sick" but is not disabled or confined to bed. In cases with reported flare-ups there are two dates that the respondent may give in answer to such a question as Question 3. It may be the date when the chronic condition first began to cause trouble or it may be the date of the current flare-up.

This schedule did not provide any distinction between these two types of onset for chronic conditions. The lack of such a distinction weakened the analysis at one point, since it was desired to compare the time lag between the original onset of the trouble and the calling of a doctor. In order to make possible some comparisons on this point it was necessary to introduce an additional code for each medical condition. For all acute illnesses and injuries the medical condition was classified as "onset date acceptable," while all other medical conditions were coded "onset date not acceptable." Roughly a half of the medical conditions were considered to have acceptable dates of onset. The time lag is shown for both groups, but for those with unacceptable dates of onset the interpretation of the lag is open to question.

5. Reference has been made earlier to the procedure followed in coding the number of days of disability and the number of days in bed for an individual who had two or more illnesses with overlapping dates during the eight-week period. Many of these instances of unknown number of days of disability and bed-illness could have been avoided had the schedule included a question about possible duplication in days. In case of two illnesses for the same individual, both having days of disability reported, the interviewer could have been instructed to ask whether any of the days in the second illness had already been mentioned in connection with the first.

As a result of this difficulty the days are somewhat undercounted in the series of tables in which the unit is a person. The additional days that would have been contributed by persons with unknown duration of disability or unknown duration of bed-disability must be kept in mind. The simplest assumption to make, if an estimate of the total unduplicated count of days is required, is that the persons with unknown duration had the same average duration as those with known durations. Table D–8 shows the extent of this problem.

6. The schedule provided two means of arriving at the number of doctor contacts during the eight-week period. Question 7f on Schedule 1 called for the total number of times each individual saw a doctor or a dentist during the period. Also, Schedule 2 included a section on doctor and dentist care during the last eight weeks. The interviewers were instructed to note duplication of doctor contacts for separate medical conditions, so it was possible to obtain an unduplicated count from Schedule 2 alone. In the coding the inconsistencies between these two sources were identified. (In order to do this it was necessary to subtract the number of dentist visits from the total of doctor and dentist visits in Question 7f.) There were 1,590 individuals for whom an inconsistency was found, and the decision was made to use only the data from Schedule 2, which were believed to be the more accurate. Hence, no use was finally made of the information in Question 7f.

A consistency check was also made between the number of doctor contacts in 1951 as obtained from Question 11 on Schedule 1 and the information from Schedule 3 concerning hospitalizations of a night or more and bed-illnesses of seven or more days in 1951. The replies to Question 9, Schedule 1 (the chronic disease check list), were also brought into this check. If no contact with doctors was reported in Question 11 but Schedule 3 or Question 9 did indicate doctor care in 1951, Question 11 was edited to show that there had been contact with a doctor, but in such cases the total number of doctor contacts in 1951 was coded as unknown.

Persons with an unknown number of doctor contacts in 1951 constituted 2.4 percent of the H.I.P. sample population and 2.3 percent of the non-H.I.P. sample. For the eight-week period the most nearly corresponding percentages are between 1 and 2 percent for each sample. In view of the difficulty respondents must have had in attempting to recall the total number of times each member of the household had seen a doctor during 1951, it is surprising that the percentages of unknowns for 1951 doctor contacts are as small as they are. It is fairly obvious, however, that the reporting of contacts for 1951 in Question 11 was not complete. The persons in the H.I.P. sample, for example, reported only about 3.5 contacts per person per year, while H.I.P. records for 1951 show about 5.3 physician services per person by H.I.P. doctors alone. Of these, approximately 90 percent were home or office visits, the remainder being in hospitals. Some discrepancy between the returns in the survey and the H.I.P. utilization figures in the direction here indicated is to be expected. This arises from the way in which physician services are counted by H.I.P. Every contact of an H.I.P. enrollee with an H.I.P. doctor is recorded as it occurs. Group practice techniques tend to bring the patient into contact not only with his family physician but also with several specialists at the group center and at the hospital. The informant—indeed the patient—would hardly be able to count and remember all of the services rendered by the family physician and the specialists. (The average number of contacts in 1951 in the New York City sample was approximately 3.1 per person per year.)

7. The answers to several other questions on the schedule (besides Question 7f on Schedule 1, mentioned above) have not been included in the tables listed in Appendix G. This should not necessarily be taken to mean that the data ob-

Table D–8. Persons with disabling illnesses of known and unknown duration, H.I.P. and New York City samples, eight-week period, by type of disability

TYPE OF DISABILITY IN EIGHT-WEEK PERIOD	H.I.P. SAMPLE			NEW YORK CITY SAMPLE		
	Total	*With duration unknown*		*Total*	*With duration unknown*	
		Number	Percent		Number	Percent
Persons with disabling illness	1,605	261	16	2,334	379	16
Persons with bed-illness	1,212	184	15	1,836	325	18
Persons with hospitalization	110	7	6	213	19	9

tained were not satisfactory, but it does indicate that in the last analysis these questions were considered of lesser importance in meeting the objectives of the study. The responses to the following questions have not yet been tabulated or used in the coding of items that were tabulated:

Schedule 1

- Question 21: Deaths in the household in 1951
- Question 22: Age and sex of deceased and relationship to head of household
- Question 23: Rooms in dwelling unit; rooms used for sleeping purposes

Schedule 2

- Question 7: Date disability began for conditions with onset of disability before the eight-week period
- Question 11: Kind of hospital accommodation
- Question 24: Date of physical examination

Schedule 3

- Question 6a: Kind of hospital accommodation in 1951 hospitalization
- Question 12: Time lag before consulting physician in 1951 illness
- Question 13: Place of doctor visits in 1951 illness
- Question 22: Whether pelvic examination was given at time of postpartum check-up in 1951 pregnancies
- Question 23: Indication of prematurity in infants born following 1951 pregnancies

Interviewing Instructions and Supervision; Interviewer and Respondent Errors

1. There is some evidence that the necessarily intensive training received by the interviewers at the start of the survey did not stick with them. This could have been counteracted by more and closer supervision of the interviewers, by more thorough review of the schedules before the end of the interviewing, and by the preparation of a complete written manual of instructions for the interviewers. This last step has been considered desirable in other surveys, some of them surveys that made considerably fewer demands upon the interviewers than the H.I.P. Household Survey. There has been no experiment to our knowledge that demonstrates the value of such a manual, nor do we even know that interviewers frequently consult their instructions. Nevertheless, by hindsight it now seems that the manual would have been a desirable safeguard. There was certainly difficulty that resulted directly from the failure of interviewers to record answers properly. Hence, the problems that will be mentioned below were at least partly due to this shortcoming in the survey plans.

A more obvious reason for the problems was the failure to catch and correct the recording errors during the course of the survey. The accepted method for handling recording errors is by a review of each schedule in the central office as soon as it is sent in by the interviewer. Errors, particularly persistent errors in following instructions, are called to the attention of interviewers and review is continued to make sure that the particular errors noted are no longer occurring.

We have seen how more intensive supervision helped to improve the record on the contacting of not-at-home families in the second phase of the interviewing. It goes without saying that closer supervision of the interviewing, if it were possible, would also have lessened the recording errors and omissions on the schedules.

2. The health insurance coverage question (Question 10, Schedule 1) specified four different types of health insurance. The interviewer was supposed to circle "Yes" or "No" for each type of insurance for each member of the household. The instructions for handling this question were not followed properly by a substantial number of interviewers. It was this fact, added to the difficulties that the respondent had in supplying the desired information, that resulted in large proportions of responses necessarily being coded as unknown or obviously in error. The effect of this loss of data has already been noted.

3. Instructions for the chronic disease check list (Question 9, Schedule 1) required the interviewer to circle the name of each disease reported present in each member of the household. For each circled disease the interviewer was then to ask: "Did ——— see a doctor about this condition at any time during 1951?" Depending upon the answer, a "Yes" or a "No" was to be circled opposite each disease already circled. If a member of the household had none of the diseases listed, the words "None of these" were to be circled for that individual.

This instruction seemed to give the interviewers a great deal of trouble, and the following special coding rules had to be adopted:

a. If the interviewer circled "Yes" for medical care opposite a disease title but had not circled the disease title, this was interpreted as: disease present but medical care unknown.

b. If "No" for medical care was circled opposite a disease title and the disease title itself was not circled, the existence of this disease was coded as unknown.

c. If the interviewer failed to circle "None of these" and there was no other notation at all, the existence of all the diseases on the list was coded as unknown.

The effect of the application of these rules is seen from the fact that for about 4 percent of all the individuals in each sample the presence of a given component of the question had to be coded as unknown. Similarly, for all components of the question reported as present, medical care in 1951 had to be called unknown in roughly 13 percent of each sample.

4. Response errors are to be expected in every survey. A number of the types that occurred in this survey have already been mentioned, for example, family income, insurance coverage, doctor contacts, components of physical examinations.

Errors due to failure of the respondent's memory for events that occurred in 1951 were anticipated. Some rough comparisons of frequency of doctor contacts and days of hospitalization between the eight-week period and the calendar year 1951 can be made by making proper allowance for the difference in the length of the time interval. However, natural seasonal differences in the frequency of these events make it difficult to assess quantitatively the extent of the expected underreporting for the events in the more distant 1951 period.

One further example of response error is worth noting here, if only because the identical sort of error has shown up in several other surveys. In Question 5, Schedule 1, the labor force status of each person 14 years of age or older was ascertained by asking: "What was ——— doing most of last week—working, keeping house, going to school, looking for work, or something else?" As has been the experience on other occasions when this question has been asked in an interview, a number of people in the sample were identified as "permanently unable to work." Surely, all such individuals must have a fairly serious chronic ailment or impairment of some kind! It turns out, however, that almost a quarter of those "permanently unable to work" in the New York City sample were reported to have no medical or dental condition of any kind on the day preceding the interview.[4] The chances are that in the case of respondents giving such apparently conflicting information, the interview was not successful in getting the respondent to understand the concept of disability used in the study. While no particular effort was made in this interview to probe for information about chronic conditions and impairments not currently causing disability or illness, nevertheless it was certainly intended that all instances of inability to carry on work or other usual activities owing to disease, injury, or their residuals should be reported in one or the other of the illness questions.

Coding and Tabulating

1. The coding and tabulating decisions were made with the foremost objective of the study in view, that is, the objective of providing measures of illness and medical care for two population groups such as would permit comparison of the medical care received in the groups in relation to medical care needs. The main requirements in the processing and table production, therefore (aside from the general requirements of accuracy and suitability), were that the two sets of data be treated alike and that the resulting tables be such as to throw light upon the required comparisons. In retrospect it seems that these requirements were satisfactorily met.

In the effort to meet this primary objective, however, several of the lesser objectives of the survey were to some extent neglected. These were the objectives that had to do with the presentation of data on medical care needs, services received, and quality of services in New York City. The requirements in the processing and table production for this purpose would be somewhat different. It was necessary that tables should be produced which contained estimates for New York City or which at least permitted such estimates to be easily made.

An examination of the base tables seems to indicate that they are deficient in two respects for this purpose. The first has to do with the treatment of "not reporteds."

For comparisons of H.I.P. and non-H.I.P. populations it was essential that "not reporteds" be treated the same in the two groups, and this was done. However, when a decision was to be made in a doubtful case—should this type of case be classified as "not reported" or should it be assigned according to our best judgment to one or the other of categories of known cases?—the tendency throughout was to make the cautious decision and class the cases with the "not reporteds." This was not the best decision, it now

[4] An analysis of the age of such persons might have proved enlightening.

seems, from the standpoint of the New York City estimates.

A case in point is the coding of "not reported" resulting from mishandling of the chronic disease check list question. It has been pointed out that when no diseases were reported the interviewer was supposed to circle the words "None of these." When this was not circled and there was no other entry for the question, the existence of all diseases on the list was coded as "not reported." At a slight risk such cases could have been interpreted as if the answer for all diseases had been "No." This would have been more informative from the standpoint of the New York City estimates, but it made no difference from the standpoint of H.I.P. vs. non-H.I.P. comparisons. (These "not reporteds" are now indistinguishable from others arising in a different way.)

Similar examples can be found in the treatment of "not reporteds" for doctor contacts and for the number of days of disability.

2. The second respect in which the tables now seem deficient for making New York City estimates is in the measures of illness used. It would have been more valuable if greater attention had been paid to the measures in common usage, particularly incidence. There was no obstacle to the presentation of frequencies of episodes of illness beginning during the eight-week period, separately from those that began prior to that period. At is was, the two types were not separated, and the number of medical conditions present during the eight-week period (or producing disability or bed-disability during the eight-week period) is a sort of hybrid between prevalence and incidence. It has the drawback that one cannot make even a rough guess as to what the corresponding annual rate would be, since the number of cases that began before the eight-week period is a function of the length of the interval. Again, this decision was a reasonable one from the standpoint of the H.I.P. vs. non-H.I.P. comparisons.

APPENDIX E

Comparison of Data from Samples with Data from Other Sources

Socioeconomic Data, New York City Sample and U.S. Census, 1950

A highly realistic way of assaying the representative quality of a sample is to compare the data derived from it with what is known about the universe from which it was drawn. In the case of the sample of the New York City population this can be done for a number of items, as has been reported in Appendices C and D. In the case of the H.I.P. sample only the distribution for age and sex can be compared. But in the latter case the sampling method itself goes very much farther in guarding the representative character of the sample than in the case of the New York City sample. In the case of H.I.P. households the sampling process and the size of the sample itself did not present the same hazards as the sample for the city as a whole.

The methods used in the selection of the New York City sample and the results of the enumeration and the replication processes are described in detail elsewhere. It is intended here only to present the final results as set up for the study with the corresponding data from the 1950 Census and data from other sources for the city's population. The items for which there are comparative figures from the Census, in some instances with qualifications, include size of family, relationship of family members to head of family, marital status of persons 14 years of age and over, race, nativity, educational status of persons 25 years of age and over, persons in the labor force, occupation, industry groups, family income, age and sex distribution of the population.

One fact to be remembered is that the New York City sample is drawn exclusively from the household population and cannot therefore be considered as representative of the total population of New York City. What the Census Bureau terms "quasi-households" were not covered by the survey. These include all of the population living "in houses with at least five lodgers or in hotels, institutions, labor camps or military barracks." In 1950 the total population of New York City was reported as 7,891,957 and the household population as 7,554,080. The difference (337,877) constituted the 4.3 percent of the total population in the "quasi-households."

Since these figures for the sample and the 1950 Census so largely speak for themselves, the tables showing the comparisons are presented with a minimum of comment.

Table E–1. Households, New York City sample and 1950 Census, by size

SIZE OF HOUSEHOLD	NEW YORK CITY SAMPLE		1950 CENSUS[1]	
	Number	*Percent*	*Number*	*Percent*
Total	*4,190*	100.0	*2,357,919*[2]	100.0
One person	398	9.5	250,133	10.6
Two persons	1,151	27.5	657,093	27.9
Three persons	1,029	24.5	574,480	24.4
Four persons	874	20.9	453,621	19.2
Five to six persons	613	14.6	333,600	14.1
Seven or more persons	125	3.0	88,992	3.8

[1] *U.S. Census of Population: 1950,* Vol. III, Chapter 37.
[2] Excludes quasi-households.

It appears that the sample of New York City households is an almost exact cross-section of the parent population as regards size.

The differences here shown arise from sampling variation and slightly different coding procedures, but may also reflect a change due to the expansion of housing facilities and in employment, to be discussed in a later section, in the interval between 1950 and 1952 which took out of the households some of the relatives, friends, and lodgers. Whether the differences reflect changed conditions or arise from technical procedures or both, they are not of significant magnitudes.

The larger proportion of married persons in the New York City sample than is reported for the 1950 Census probably arises from the inclusion of all persons in quasi-family groups in the Census and their underrepresentation in this survey. The

Table E–2. Persons, New York City sample and 1950 Census, by relationship to head of household

RELATIONSHIP TO HEAD OF HOUSEHOLD	NEW YORK CITY SAMPLE		1950 CENSUS[1]	
	Number	*Percent*	*Number*	*Percent*
Total	*13,558*	100.0	*7,549,295*[2]	100.0
Head	4,190	30.9	2,361,330	31.3
Wife	3,112	22.9	1,711,315	22.7
Child	4,950	36.5	2,521,410	33.4
Parent or parent-in-law	256	1.9	169,475	2.2
Other relatives	730	5.4	494,375	6.6
Unrelated persons	242	1.8	291,390	3.8
Not reported	78	0.6	—	—

[1] A 20 percent sample, *U.S. Census of Population: 1950,* Vol. II, Part 32, New York, Chapter C.

[2] Excludes persons in quasi-households.

Table E–3. Percentage distribution of persons 14 years of age and over, New York City sample and 1950 Census, by marital status

Marital status	*New York City sample*	*1950 Census*[1]
Total	100.0	100.0
Married[2]	66.9	63.9
Single	21.3	26.1
Widowed or divorced	9.0	10.0
Not reported	2.8	—

[1] *U.S. Census of Population: 1950,* Vol. III, Chapter 37.

[2] Includes married persons separated from their spouses.

Table E–4. Persons, New York City sample (classified by race of informant) and 1950 Census, by race

RACE AS ESTABLISHED	NEW YORK CITY SAMPLE		1950 CENSUS[1]	
	Number	*Percent*	*Number*	*Percent*
Total	*13,558*	100.0	*7,891,957*	100.0
White	12,095	89.2	7,116,441	90.2
Non-white	1,380	10.2	775,516	9.8
Not reported	83	0.6	—	—

[1] *U.S. Census of Population: 1950,* Vol. III, Chapter 37.

Table E–5. White persons, New York City sample and 1950 Census, by birthplace

BIRTHPLACE OF PERSONS IN WHITE POPULATION	NEW YORK CITY SAMPLE		1950 CENSUS[1]	
	Number	*Percent*	*Number*	*Percent*
Total	*12,095*	100.0	*7,116,441*	100.0
Native-born[2]	7,677	63.5	5,332,235	74.9
Foreign-born	4,288	35.4	1,784,206	25.1
Not reported	130	1.1	—	—

[1] *U.S. Census of Population: 1950,* Vol. III, Chapter 37.

[2] New York City sample: native-born includes all persons in households with heads born in the Continental United States and Puerto Rico.

Census: native-born includes all persons born in the United States, its territories or possessions, or born in a foreign country of parents who were American citizens.

institutional population would likely be deficient in the proportion of persons reported as married. The assignment of persons with marital status unknown may also have affected the Census figures.

Considering the difference in the methods of enumeration and coding, the variation shown here is inconsequential. In the New York City sample all persons in the household were assumed to be of the same race as the informant.

In the comparison of the New York City sample with the 1950 Census data for nativity, only the white population is included. The results are shown in Table E–5.

The figures for nativity are not comparable. The sample does not include as native-born, as does the Census, the white persons born in United States possessions outside the continent other than Puerto Rico. This difference in definition could have raised the figure for the native-born by 2 percentage points and correspondingly lowered the foreign-born. Also, the Census assumes that those "not reported" are native-born. But considerably more important than either of these divergencies in method is that used in the survey that projected on to all members of the family the nativity of the head. Inevitably, this exaggerates the proportion of the foreign-born, since all family members born in America with family heads born abroad are classed with the foreign-born. It is highly probable that these several conditions account for much of the discrepancy between the figures, and that no significant difference in nativity was actually present.

Exact comparisons cannot be made between the findings of this survey on schooling and the 1950 Census because the Census counted only schooling received in "regular" schools.

In this survey, education received in other types of schools, notably vocational and trade schools, was also taken into account. The differences between the two sets of figures strongly suggest that the allowance made by this survey for schooling not accepted by the Census consistently upgraded the subjects in the sample.

Comparison of the figures on the proportion of persons in the labor force for the sample of New York City households with the returns from the 1950 Census shows a very high degree of correspondence—55.0 percent of all persons enumerated in the sample as against 55.7 percent in the Census.

Because the New York City sample has so substantial a number of unreported cases (15.3 percent) for the items on industry among its representatives on the labor force, its distribution among industrial groups may be expected to differ

Table E–6. Persons 25 years and over, New York City sample and 1950 Census, by educational status

EDUCATIONAL STATUS OF PERSONS 25 YEARS OR OVER	NEW YORK CITY SAMPLE		1950 CENSUS[1]	
	Number	*Percent*	*Number*	*Percent*
Total	*8,062*	100.0	*5,178,965*	100.0
None	387	4.8	245,135	4.7
Grade school	2,912	36.1	2,217,980	42.9
High school	3,242	40.2	1,871,010	36.1
More than high school	1,143	14.2	641,805	12.4
Not reported	378	4.7	203,035	3.9

[1] *U.S. Census of Population: 1950,* Vol. III, Chapter 37.

Table E–7. Persons in labor force, New York City sample and 1950 Census, by occupation

OCCUPATION	NEW YORK CITY SAMPLE		1950 CENSUS[1]
	Number	*Percent*	*Percent*
Total	*5,635*	100.0	100.0
Professional, semi-professional workers	566	10.0	10.0
Proprietors, managers and officials (including farm) and farmers	638	11.3	11.0
Clerical and sales	1,458	25.9	26.2
Craftsmen, foremen, operatives and laborers	2,085	37.0	37.6
Domestic service	67	1.2	2.4
Other service	527	9.4	10.4
Not reported	294	5.2	2.4

[1] Twenty percent sample, *U.S. Census of Population: 1950,* Vol. III, Chapter 37.

Table E–8. Persons in labor force, New York City sample and 1950 Census, by industry in which employed

INDUSTRY	NEW YORK CITY SAMPLE		1950 CENSUS[1]
	Number	*Percent*	*Percent*
Total	*5,635*	100.0	100.0
Construction	250	4.4	4.6
Manufacturing	1,364	24.2	27.9
Transportation, communication, public utilities	507	9.0	9.3
Wholesale and retail trades	1,036	18.4	22.6
Finance, insurance, real estate, and service trades	1,375	24.4	27.5
Government, not elsewhere classified	231	4.1	4.7
Other	11	0.2	0.2
Not reported	861	15.3	3.2

[1] Twenty percent sample, *U.S. Census of Population: 1950,* Vol. III, Chapter 37.

from that reported by the Census. But it is to be noted that if the unknown cases were distributed proportionately among the several industrial groups, or the known cases only were used in the distribution, the resulting array would not depart markedly from that in the Census.

Income Data, New York City Sample and U.S. Census, 1950

The question may well be raised as to the characteristic quality of the sample of New York City families as regards family income. This doubt cannot be resolved by reference to the Census data, which relate to the year 1949. The income data on this sample were gathered by methods, described in Chapter III, which are quite different from those used by Census enumerators. The data for the two samples are there presented.

In the Census the income for each person was secured, but the returns were not combined into family incomes. Instead, for the heads of families in the 20 percent sample the informant was asked to give the income of other related members of the household and to divide it into three parts: salary or wages, net income from business or profession, and income from other sources—interest, dividends, pension, etc. It is now known that this was an "inferior collection technique" which underreported the income received. Checks with the data from the Current Population Survey and the National Income Division of the Department of Commerce revealed this condition.[1] The income figures from the Census also include those of persons in institutions and in the armed forces, who are not represented in the samples used in this survey. In view of all of these conditions there seems no possibility of using the 1950 Census data as a means of judging the representative quality of the income data on the New York City sample of households. Since there is a direct association between income, living standards, and education of the heads of families, it is thought that the latter factor is the preferable one to use in grouping families into socioeconomic classes.

For the primary purpose of this study, that is, for comparing the experience in health and medical care of H.I.P. enrollees with that of similarly situated persons not covered by H.I.P., the income data here presented were thought to be inadequate. Caution should be exercised in any use of the income data from the New York City sample given in Chapter III as a true cross-section of the family incomes for the people of New York City

[1] Herman P. Miller, "An Appraisal of the 1950 Census Income Data," *Journal of the American Statistical Association,* Vol. 48, No. 261, p. 34, March 1953.

taken as a whole. It is vulnerable for the purpose of establishing the precise percentage of families with incomes of given sizes; the unreported cases amount to almost 22 percent. It is more than probable that it is somewhat deficient in persons and families with very low incomes or with none at all, and it makes no distribution of the families with incomes above $8,000.

Table E–9. Persons, New York City sample and 1950 Census, by housing conditions

HOUSING CONDITIONS	NEW YORK CITY SAMPLE		1950 CENSUS[1]	
	Number	*Percent*	*Number*	*Percent*
Toilet facilities	*13,558*	100.0	*2,433,465*	100.0
Shared	795	5.9	87,832	3.6
Not shared	12,591	92.8	2,273,410	93.4
Not reported	172	1.3	72,223	3.0
Central heating	*13,558*	100.0	*2,433,465*	100.0
Yes	11,866	87.5	2,066,265	84.9
No[2]	1,159	8.6	247,935	10.2
Not reported	533	3.9	119,265	4.9

[1] *U.S. Census of Housing: 1950,* Vol. 1, Central Characteristics, Chapter 32, New York.

[2] Includes "not heated."

The proportion of families in the New York City sample known to have central heating does not differ greatly from that reported in the 1950 Census. A two-year lapse in a time of very active housing development doubtless affected the situation. The data on shared toilet facilities do not directly parallel those published for New York City by the Census Bureau, but the differences are not of any significance.

Age and Sex, New York City Sample and U.S. Census, 1950

When the age distribution of the members of the families in the sample of the New York City population is compared with that shown in the 1950 Census, it is found that the sample is a little overweighted with children under 15 years and short of persons aged 15 to 44 and those in the older age groups. It is known that, beyond the factor of sampling variation, lies the fact that the New York City sample underrepresented the persons in quasi-family groups. Differences in the enumeration of family members in the armed forces may also have affected the returns from the two enumerations.

In the New York City sample the females outnumber the males in a ratio of 52.5 to 47.5 percent. In the 1950 Census this imbalance is somewhat less, 51.7 females to 48.3 males. The same reasons as account for the differences in age distribution may be operating to create this divergence in sex ratio. It is conceivable that the sample gives the truer picture of the sex distribution in the population living at home in their own households.

Table E–10. Percentage distribution of persons, New York City sample and 1950 Census, by age

Age	*New York City sample*	*1950 Census*
Total	100.0	100.0
Under 5	10.3	8.4
5 to 14	15.5	12.4
15 to 44	42.5	46.7
45 to 64	21.8	24.8
65 and over	6.6	7.7
Not reported	3.3	—

1951 Birthrate, New York City Sample and New York City Health Department Data

Information about the obstetric care received for pregnancies delivered in 1951 called for in Schedule 3 brought to light a total of 276 deliveries. There is a high probability that these were live births and that stillbirths were not fully reported. In any event, the rate of deliveries was 20.4 per 1,000 in the sample of 13,558 present in the households at the time of the survey. The New York City Department of Health reported a birthrate for the city of exactly the same size for 1951. The city's rate is the ratio of live births to the estimated mid-year population.

Age and Sex, H.I.P. Enrollees and H.I.P. Records

The age distribution of the enrollees in the H.I.P. sample and the July 31, 1952, analysis of the total H.I.P. population appears in the following table.

The ratio of males to females among enrollees in the H.I.P. sample was 52.6 to 47.4. On July 31, 1952, that ratio stood at 52.0 to 48.0 in the H.I.P. records.

Table E–11. Age distribution of enrollees, H.I.P. sample and H.I.P. enrollment, July 31, 1952

Age	*Enrollees in H.I.P. sample*	*H.I.P. enrollment July 31, 1952*
Total	100.0	100.0
Under 5	9.9	10.4
5 to 14	17.8	16.6
15 to 44	43.5	44.4
45 to 64	25.9	24.8
65 and over	2.4	2.3
Not reported	0.5	1.5

APPENDIX F

Description of Content of I.B.M. Punch Cards

FIVE basic sets of punch cards were made for the data collected on the three schedules used in the Household Survey.

Card 1. Derived almost wholly from Schedule 1, it shows for *each person* his demographic and household data. It also contains the items shown on Schedule 1 relating to his health and medical care and the total number of medical and/or dental conditions reported on the other two schedules.

Card 2. Derived mainly from Schedule 2, it shows for *each medical condition* reported for the eight-week period the edited items from that schedule and also several demographic items transferred mechanically from Card 1.

Card 3. Derived mainly from Schedule 2, it shows for *each person* the data for all of the illness conditions reported for him within the eight-week period and several demographic items transferred mechanically from Card 1.

Card 4. Derived mainly from Schedule 3, it shows for *each episode of illness* reported for 1951 the data recorded on the schedule and several demographic items transferred mechanically from Card 1.

Card 5. Derived mainly from Schedule 3, it shows for *each person* the data on all episodes reported for 1951 and several demographic items transferred mechanically from Card 1.

The following lists show the items punched into the cards in each of these five sets. The categories in the several classifications appear in the tables in the body of the report and can be located by means of the index.

Card 1. Person (Schedule 1)

Identifications, Verifications, and Other Administrative Items

1. Household identification
2. Individual identification
3. Interviewer identification
4. Card number: schedule from which derived
5. Group identification (H.I.P. enrollees, others in H.I.P. households, New York City sample)
6. H.I.P. sample: date H.I.P. coverage began
7. H.I.P. sample: subsequent coverage history
8. H.I.P. sample: claim of H.I.P. coverage verified in H.I.P. records
9. H.I.P. sample: roster of household numbers verified by H.I.P. records
10. Sample segment in which household falls, e.g.,
    New York City sample—household composed of current H.I.P. members and some individuals not currently in H.I.P.
    H.I.P. sample—households composed exclusively of H.I.P. members
11. Sub-sample of New York City sample
12. Number of visits necessary to complete schedule or schedules for household
13. Date of last visit to household

Household—Characteristics

14. Number of persons
15. Type of composition
16. Average number of rooms per person
17. Average number of sleeping rooms per person
18. Number of rooms used for sleeping
19. Toilet shared
20. Central heating
21. Birthplace of head of household
22. Education of head of household
23. Race of informant
24. Income
25. Religion of head of household
26. Claim of family doctor
27. H.I.P. status of family doctor (H.I.P. enrollees)
28. Date family doctor last seen
29. Claim of special doctor for children: H.I.P. status of this doctor (H.I.P. enrollees)
30. Date special doctor last seen
31. Deaths in household in 1951
32. Age of deceased
33. Sex of deceased

Person—Characteristics

34. Relationship to head of family
35. Relationship to informant
36. Sex
37. Age—actual
38. Age—9 classes
39. Marital status
40. Highest school grade completed
41. Labor force status
42. Occupational class
43. Industry
44. Type of employer (private, government, etc.)
45. Employer's sick leave policy
46. Insurance status for medical care
47. Any doctor's care in 1951
48. Total number of doctor's visits in 1951
49. Presence of each of 9 specified chronic diseases
50. Total number of medical and/or dental conditions reported on Schedules 2 and 3
51. Total number of doctor's visits during eight-week period preceding the interview
52. Last medical group in H.I.P. (H.I.P. enrollees)

Card 2. Medical Conditions, Eight-Week Period (mainly from Schedule 2)

Identifications, Verifications, and Other Administrative Items

1. Household identification
2. Individual identification
3. Question on Schedule 1 leading to illness memorandum
4. Identification of informant for selected items
5. Sample segment in which household falls
6. First- or second-round response
7. Group identification (H.I.P. enrollee, other in H.I.P. household, New York City sample)

Household—Characteristics

8. Education of head of household

Person—Characteristics

9. Sex
10. Age—9 classes
11. Age—6 classes
12. Labor force status—11 classes
13. Labor force status—9 classes
14. Labor force status—4 classes
15. Relationship to informant

Illness

16. Indication of condition present yesterday
17. What was the matter? (3-digit diagnostic code and other classes, i.e., check-up examination, etc.)
18. Diagnostic group—74 categories
19. Diagnostic group—16 categories
20. Diagnostic component—additive code
21. Date of onset
22. Indication of acceptability of onset date
23. Number of days condition lasted
24. Disability during eight-week period ("yes," "no," etc.)
25. Number of days disabled during eight-week period
26. Time disabled, to 98 months—for persons disabled throughout entire eight-week period
27. Bed-disability ("yes," "no," etc.)
28. Days in bed during eight-week period
29. Degree of disability (e.g., disabled, no bed-disability or hospitalization, etc.)—6 classes

Medical Care

30. Hospitalized ("yes," "no," etc.)
31. Hospital accommodations (private, semi-private, etc.)
32. Number nights in hospital during eight-week period
33. Visits to hospital outpatient department ("yes," "no," etc.)
34. Number of hospital outpatient department visits
35. Name and location of hospital, clinic or dispensary
36. Type of hospital, clinic or dispensary (voluntary, municipal, proprietary, etc.)
37. Any contact with private physician or dentist during eight-week period
38. Doctor or dentist; if doctor, H.I.P. or non-H.I.P. (H.I.P. enrollees)
39. Number of days after onset before doctor was seen
40. Total number of doctor or dentist visits during eight-week period
41. Office visits to doctor or dentist during eight-week period
42. Home visits to doctor during eight-week period
43. Hospital visits (total) of doctor during eight-week period
44. Hospital visits (inpatient) of doctor during eight-week period

45. Hospital visits (outpatient) of doctor during eight-week period
46. Surgery during eight-week period ("yes," "no," etc.)
47. Surgical operation (3-digit code)
48. Insurance coverage for medical care of this condition (hospital only, doctor only, etc.)

Physical Check-Up

49. Each of 13 components ("yes," "no," etc.)
50. Total number of components included in check-up
51. Reason for check-up

Card 3. Person's Total Medical Conditions, Eight-Week Period (mainly from Schedule 2)

Identifications, Verifications, and Other Administrative Items

1. Household identification
2. Individual identification
3. Group identification (H.I.P. enrollees, New York City sample)
4. Number of Schedule 2 cards derived from Schedule 1, Question 7c

Household—Characteristics

5. Income
6. Education of head of household
7. Race of informant

Person—Characteristics

8. Relationship to head of household
9. Sex
10. Age—6 groups
11. Labor force status
12. Occupation
13. Type of employer
14. Employer's sick leave policy
15. Applicability of sick leave policy to person's employment

Medical Conditions

16. Diagnostic experience in eight-week period—31 classes
17. Number of medical conditions present yesterday
18. Number of dental conditions present yesterday
19. Number of medical conditions present in eight-week period
20. Number of dental conditions present in eight-week period
21. Degree of disability in eight-week period
22. Number of days of disability in eight-week period
23. Number of days of bed-disability in eight-week period

Medical Care—Eight-Week Period

24. Number of medical conditions for which doctor or doctor and dentist were consulted
25. Number of conditions for which dentist was consulted
26. Number of visits to dentist
27. Number of conditions for which doctor was consulted by phone only
28. Number of medical conditions with no contact with doctor or dentist
29. Number of medical conditions with medical care unknown
30. Hospitalization ("yes," "no," etc.)
31. Number of medical conditions with outpatient clinic care
32. Number of medical conditions with outpatient clinic care unknown
33. Number of medical conditions with no outpatient clinic care
34. Number of doctor visits ungrouped (Schedule 1)
35. Number of doctor visits ungrouped (Schedule 1 or Schedule 2, when there is a discrepancy)
36. Number of doctor visits, grouped—8 classes
37. Number of office visits to doctor
38. Number of doctor home visits
39. Number of medical conditions treated by H.I.P. doctor
40. Number of medical conditions treated by non-H.I.P. doctor
41. Number of medical conditions treated by H.I.P. and non-H.I.P. doctor
42. Number of medical conditions treated by doctor of unknown H.I.P. status
43. Number of hospitalizations
44. Number of nights in hospital

Insurance

45. Number of medical conditions covered by insurance for hospitalization
46. Number of medical conditions covered by insurance for hospitalization and surgery only
47. Number of medical conditions covered by insurance (hospitalization, surgery and doctor's care, doctor's care or hospitalization or doctor's care only)

Health Check-Ups

48. Number of health examinations
49. Number of check-ups for school, employment, or insurance
50. Number of general check-ups or immunization only
51. Number of prenatal or postpartum examinations
52. Number of routine eye examinations
53. Number of dental check-ups
54. Number of check-ups for other or unknown reasons

Card 4. Selected Episodes of Illness in 1951

Identifications, Verifications, and Other Administrative Items

1. Household identification
2. Individual identification
3. Group identification (H.I.P. enrollees, New York City sample)
4. Informant identification
5. Card identification (first- or second-round response)
6. Question on Schedule 1 leading to Schedule 3
7. Indication of hospitalization or seven or more days of illness in bed or both

Household—Characteristics

8. Education of head of household

Person—Characteristics

9. Sex
10. Age—9 groups
11. Age—6 groups

Illness and Medical Care

12. Diagnostic group—74 groups
13. Diagnostic group—16 groups
14. Duration of bed-disability, grouped
15. Saw a doctor or doctor and dentist for this condition ("yes," "no," etc.)
16. Total doctor visits in 1951 (Schedule 1)
17. Total doctor visits in 1951 (Schedule 1), grouped
18. H.I.P. status of doctor who treated this condition
19. Number of weeks in bed for this condition in 1951
20. Type of doctor contact for this condition
21. Number of nights in hospital for this condition in 1951
22. Number of nights in hospital, grouped, in 1951
23. Location and name of hospital
24. Type of hospital (voluntary, municipal, proprietary, etc.)
25. Number of doctor visits for this condition in 1951
26. Number of doctor visits for this condition in 1951, grouped
27. Surgery for this condition ("yes," "no," etc.)
28. Hospitalized surgery for this condition ("yes," "no," etc.)
29. Surgical operation (3-digit code)
30. Insurance for this condition

Pregnancy and Delivery in 1951

31. Month doctor first seen
32. Components of prenatal examination
33. Number of doctor visits prior to delivery
34. Number of doctor visits prior to delivery, grouped
35. Postpartum check-up
36. Postpartum pelvic examination

Card 5. Person's Record of Selected Episodes of Illness in 1951

Identifications, Verifications, and Other Administrative Items

1. Household identification
2. Individual identification
3. Group identification (H.I.P. enrollees, New York City sample)
4. Indication of hospitalization or seven or more days of illness in bed or both

Household—Characteristics

5. Education of head of household

Person—Characteristics

6. Sex
7. Age—6 groups
8. Number of doctor visits in 1951 (Schedule 1)
9. Number of doctor visits in 1951 (Schedule 1), grouped
10. Diagnostic summary (31 diagnostic classes)
11. Duration of bed-disability (weeks, actual)
12. Duration of bed-disability (weeks, grouped)

Medical Care

13. Number of times hospitalized
14. Type of hospital (voluntary, municipal, proprietary, etc.)

15. Duration of hospitalization (number of nights, actual)
16. Duration of hospitalization (number of nights, grouped)
17. Number of primary surgical operations in hospital
18. Type of first primary surgical operation
19. Type of second operation
20. Type of third operation
21. Number of incidents of seven or more days in bed at home

Insurance

22. Insurance for hospitalization
23. Number of incidents of hospitalization with insurance
24. Number of incidents of hospitalization with no insurance
25. Number of incidents of hospitalization with insurance unknown
26. Number of cards for hospitalized surgery (primary and secondary procedures)

APPENDIX G

Detailed Statistical Tables on File

BESIDES the statistical tables for the two samples —H.I.P. enrollees and the New York City sample —presented in the text of this report, the Research Project has on file a series of elaborately detailed base tables from which summaries have been drawn for the foregoing report. The exact nature of these more detailed correlations of data for these two samples are shown below. These tables are available to students and may be examined at the H.I.P Division of Research and Statistics, 625 Madison Avenue, New York City. The descriptive titles together with the stubs and the columnar headings are shown in this list. The entries fall into the following five general categories:

a. Demographic data (Tables 1–23)

b. Data on medical conditions and disability of persons (Tables 24–60)

c. Medical care of persons (Tables 61–88)

d. Medical conditions and disability as morbidity data (Tables 89–116)

e. Medical care for medical conditions (Tables 117–146)

The index at the end of the book will direct the student to the tables showing data on each item of information.

Table 1. All persons, H.I.P. enrollees and New York City sample, by age and sex

AGE (6 GROUPS)	H.I.P. ENROLLEES			NEW YORK CITY SAMPLE
	Total	*Male*	*Female*	*Same classes as for H.I.P. enrollees*

Table 2. All persons, H.I.P. enrollees and New York City sample, by education of head of household and sex

YEARS OF SCHOOLING COMPLETED BY HEAD OF HOUSEHOLD (4 GROUPS)	H.I.P. ENROLLEES			NEW YORK CITY SAMPLE
	Total	*Male*	*Female*	*Same classes as for H.I.P. enrollees*

Table 3. All persons, H.I.P. enrollees and New York City sample, by age and education of head of household

AGE (6 GROUPS)	H.I.P. ENROLLEES					NEW YORK CITY SAMPLE
		Years of schooling completed by head of household				
	Total	Less than 9	9 to 12	Over 12	Not reported	*Same classes as for H.I.P. enrollees*

Table 4. Persons aged 14 years and over, H.I.P. enrollees and New York City sample, by age, sex, and labor force status

AGE (5 GROUPS) AND LABOR FORCE STATUS (8 GROUPS)	H.I.P. ENROLLEES			NEW YORK CITY SAMPLE
	Total	*Male*	*Female*	*Same classes as for H.I.P. enrollees*

Table 5. Persons aged 14 years and over, H.I.P. enrollees and New York City sample, by education of head of household, labor force status, and sex

YEARS OF SCHOOLING COMPLETED BY HEAD OF HOUSEHOLD (4 GROUPS) AND LABOR FORCE STATUS (8 GROUPS)	H.I.P. ENROLLEES			NEW YORK CITY SAMPLE
	Total	*Male*	*Female*	*Same classes as for H.I.P. enrollees*

Table 6. Persons aged 14 years and over, H.I.P. enrollees and New York City sample, by age, labor force status, and education of head of household

AGE (5 GROUPS) AND LABOR FORCE STATUS (8 GROUPS)	H.I.P. ENROLLEES					NEW YORK CITY SAMPLE
		Years of schooling completed by head of household				*Same classes as for H.I.P. enrollees*
	Total	Less than 9	9 to 12	Over 12	Not reported	

Table 7. Persons aged 14 years and over, H.I.P. enrollees and New York City sample, by marital status, labor force status, age, and sex

MARITAL STATUS (5 GROUPS), LABOR FORCE STATUS (3 GROUPS), AND AGE (5 GROUPS)	H.I.P. ENROLLEES			NEW YORK CITY SAMPLE
	Total	*Male*	*Female*	*Same classes as for H.I.P. enrollees*

Table 8. Persons aged 14 years and over, H.I.P. enrollees and New York City sample, by marital status, labor force status, age, and education of head of household

MARITAL STATUS (5 GROUPS), LABOR FORCE STATUS (3 GROUPS), AND AGE (5 GROUPS)	H.I.P. ENROLLEES					NEW YORK CITY SAMPLE
		Years of schooling completed by head of household				*Same classes as for H.I.P. enrollees*
	Total	Less than 9	9 to 12	Over 12	Not reported	

Table 9. H.I.P. enrollees in the labor force, by occupational group, sick leave pay status, age, and sex

AGE (5 GROUPS) AND 7 OCCUPATIONAL GROUPS	TOTAL			WITH SICK LEAVE PAY			WITHOUT SICK LEAVE PAY			SICK LEAVE STATUS NOT REPORTED			SICK LEAVE INAPPLICABLE		
	T	*M*	*F*	*T*	*M*	*F*	*T*	*M*	*F*	*T*	*M*	*F*	*T*	*M*	*F*

Table 10. Same as Table 9, for New York City sample

Table 11. Persons in the labor force, H.I.P. enrollees and New York City sample, by occupational group, education of head of household, age, and sick leave pay status

YEARS OF SCHOOLING COMPLETED BY HEAD OF HOUSEHOLD (4 GROUPS), AGE (5 GROUPS), AND 7 OCCUPATIONAL GROUPS	H.I.P. ENROLLEES					NEW YORK CITY SAMPLE
	Total	*With sick leave pay*	*Without sick leave pay*	*Sick leave status not reported*	*Sick leave inapplicable*	*Same classes as for H.I.P. enrollees*

Table 12. Persons in the labor force, H.I.P. enrollees and New York City sample, by family income, age, sex, and occupational group

FAMILY INCOME (8 GROUPS), AGE (5 GROUPS), AND SEX	H.I.P. ENROLLEES		NEW YORK CITY SAMPLE
	Total	*(7 occupational groups)*	*Same classes as for H.I.P. enrollees*

Table 13. Persons in the labor force, H.I.P. enrollees and New York City sample, by family income, education of head of household, age, and occupational group

YEARS OF SCHOOLING COMPLETED BY HEAD OF HOUSEHOLD (4 GROUPS), FAMILY INCOME (8 GROUPS), AND AGE (5 GROUPS)	H.I.P. ENROLLEES		NEW YORK CITY SAMPLE
	Total	*(7 occupational groups)*	*Same classes as for H.I.P. enrollees*

Table 14. Persons aged 14 years and over, New York City sample, by labor force status, sex, and health insurance coverage

LABOR FORCE STATUS (8 GROUPS) AND SEX	TOTAL	HEALTH INSURANCE COVERAGE										
				Insurance for medical care other than H.I.P.			*Hospital insurance only*					
		No insurance	*With insurance*	Without hospital insurance	With hospital insurance not Blue Cross	With Blue Cross	Total	Blue Cross	Other than Blue Cross	*No information*	*Unknown*	*Incorrect information*

Table 15. Persons aged 14 years and over, New York City sample, by labor force status, education of head of household, and health insurance coverage

LABOR FORCE STATUS (8 GROUPS) AND YEARS OF SCHOOLING COMPLETED BY HEAD OF HOUSEHOLD (4 GROUPS)	SAME AS TABLE 14

Table 16. Persons in the labor force, New York City sample, by occupational group, sex, and health insurance coverage

7 OCCUPATIONAL GROUPS AND SEX	SAME AS TABLE 14

Table 17. Persons in the labor force, New York City sample, by occupational group, education of head of household, and health insurance coverage

7 OCCUPATIONAL GROUPS AND YEARS OF SCHOOLING COMPLETED BY HEAD OF HOUSEHOLD (4 GROUPS)	SAME AS TABLE 14

Table 18. Children under the age of 14, New York City sample, by education of head of household and health insurance coverage

YEARS OF SCHOOLING COMPLETED BY HEAD OF HOUSEHOLD (4 GROUPS)	SAME AS TABLE 14

Table 19. All persons, H.I.P. enrollees and New York City sample, by age, sex, and household composition

	H.I.P. ENROLLEES										NEW YORK CITY SAMPLE
	Total	*1*	*2*	*3*	*4*	*5*	*6*	*7*	*8*	*9*	*Same classes as for H.I.P. enrollees*
AGE (6 GROUPS) AND SEX											

Nine classes of household composition: (1) Single persons; (2) Husband and wife; (3) Husband and wife with one or more children under 18; (4) One parent or parent substitute with one or more children under 18; (5) Parent(s) with one or more children, all over 18, and not living with spouse; (6) Two or more families with children under 18; (7) Two or more families with no children under 18; (8) Other; (9) Not reported

Table 20. All persons, H.I.P. enrollees and New York City sample, by age, education of head of household, and household composition

AGE (6 GROUPS) AND YEARS OF SCHOOLING COMPLETED BY HEAD OF HOUSEHOLD (4 GROUPS)	SAME AS TABLE 19

Table 21. All persons, H.I.P. enrollees and New York City sample, by relationship to head of household and by education of head of household

RELATIONSHIP TO HEAD OF HOUSEHOLD (10 CLASSES)	H.I.P. ENROLLEES					NEW YORK CITY SAMPLE
	Years of schooling completed by head of household					
	Total	Less than 9	9 to 12	Over 12	Not reported	*Same classes as for H.I.P. enrollees*

Table 22. All persons, H.I.P. enrollees and New York City sample, by age, sex, and race of informant

AGE (6 GROUPS) AND SEX	H.I.P. ENROLLEES				NEW YORK CITY SAMPLE
	Total	*White*	*Non-white*	*Race not reported*	*Same classes as for H.I.P. enrollees*

Table 23. Households, H.I.P. and New York City samples, by race of informant, religio-cultural background, and birthplace of head of household

RACE (3 GROUPS), RELIGIO-CULTURAL BACKGROUND (5 GROUPS), AND BIRTHPLACE OF HEAD OF HOUSEHOLD (5 GROUPS)	H.I.P. HOUSEHOLDS				NEW YORK CITY SAMPLE	
	Enrollees		*Others*			
	Number	Percent	Number	Percent	*Number*	*Percent*

Table 24. All persons, H.I.P. enrollees and New York City sample, by presence or absence of medical and/or dental condition on day preceding interview, age, and sex

AGE (6 GROUPS) AND SEX	H.I.P. ENROLLEES					NEW YORK CITY SAMPLE
	Total	*With medical condition only*	*With medical and dental condition*	*With dental condition only*	*Without either*	*Same classes as for H.I.P. enrollees*

Table 25. All persons, H.I.P. enrollees and New York City sample, by presence or absence of medical and/or dental condition on day preceding interview, age, and education of head of household

AGE (6 GROUPS) AND YEARS OF SCHOOLING COMPLETED BY HEAD OF HOUSEHOLD (4 GROUPS)	SAME AS TABLE 24

Table 26. All persons aged 14 years and over, H.I.P. enrollees and New York City sample, by presence or absence of medical and/or dental condition on day preceding interview and labor force status

LABOR FORCE STATUS (8 GROUPS)	SAME AS TABLE 24

Table 27. All persons, H.I.P. enrollees and New York City sample, by presence or absence of medical and/or dental condition on day preceding interview and relationship to head of household

RELATIONSHIP TO HEAD OF HOUSEHOLD (10 CLASSES)	SAME AS TABLE 24

Table 28. All persons, H.I.P. enrollees and New York City sample, by presence or absence of medical and/or dental condition during eight-week period, age, and sex

AGE (6 GROUPS) AND SEX	SAME AS TABLE 24

Table 29. All persons, H.I.P. enrollees and New York City sample, by presence or absence of medical and/or dental condition during eight-week period, age, and education of head of household

AGE (6 GROUPS) AND YEARS OF SCHOOLING COMPLETED BY HEAD OF HOUSEHOLD (4 GROUPS)	SAME AS TABLE 24

Table 30. Persons with medical conditions, H.I.P. enrollees and New York City sample, eight-week period, by number of medical conditions reported, age, and sex

AGE (6 GROUPS) AND SEX	H.I.P. ENROLLEES						NEW YORK CITY SAMPLE
	Total	*Number of medical conditions reported*					*Same classes as for H.I.P. enrollees*
		1	2	3	4	5–9	

Table 31. Persons with medical conditions, H.I.P. enrollees and New York City sample, eight-week period, by number of medical conditions reported, age, and education of head of household

AGE (6 GROUPS) AND YEARS OF SCHOOLING COMPLETED BY HEAD OF HOUSEHOLD (4 GROUPS)	SAME AS TABLE 30

Table 32. Persons with medical conditions, H.I.P. enrollees and New York City sample, eight-week period, by degree of disability, age, and sex

AGE (6 GROUPS) AND SEX	H.I.P. ENROLLEES							NEW YORK CITY SAMPLE
	Total	*Degree of disability*						*Same classes as for H.I.P. enrollees*
		1	2	3	4	5	6	

Degree of disability: (1) Hospitalized; (2) Disabled in bed, not hospitalized; (3) Disabled but not in bed or in hospital; (4) Disabled, degree not reported; (5) Not disabled; (6) Disablement not reported

Table 33. Persons with medical conditions, H.I.P. enrollees and New York City sample, eight-week period, by degree of disability, age, and education of head of household

AGE (6 GROUPS) AND YEARS OF SCHOOLING COMPLETED BY HEAD OF HOUSEHOLD (4 GROUPS)	SAME AS TABLE 32

Table 34. Persons with medical conditions, H.I.P. enrollees and New York City sample, eight-week period, by degree of disability, age, and race

AGE (6 GROUPS) AND RACE (3 GROUPS)	SAME AS TABLE 32

Table 35. Persons aged 25 years and over with medical conditions, H.I.P. enrollees and New York City sample, eight-week period, by degree of disability, age, and education

AGE (4 GROUPS) AND YEARS OF SCHOOLING COMPLETED (4 GROUPS)	SAME AS TABLE 32

Table 36. Persons in the labor force with medical conditions, H.I.P. enrollees and New York City sample, eight-week period, by degree of disability, age, and occupational group

AGE (5 GROUPS) AND 7 OCCUPATIONAL GROUPS	SAME AS TABLE 32

Table 37. Persons aged 14 years and over with disabling medical conditions, H.I.P. enrollees and New York City sample, eight-week period, by age, labor force status, sick leave pay status, sex, and number of days disabled

AGE (5 GROUPS), LABOR FORCE STATUS (2 GROUPS), AND SICK LEAVE PAY STATUS (5 GROUPS)	H.I.P. ENROLLEES			NEW YORK CITY SAMPLE
	Total	*Duration of disability known*		
		Persons	Days	
	Total M F	Total M F	Total M F	*Same classes as for H.I.P. enrollees*

Table 38. Persons with disability of first two classes, H.I.P. enrollees and New York City sample, eight-week period, by age, sex, disability class, and duration of bed-disability

AGE (6 GROUPS) AND SEX	H.I.P. ENROLLEES									NEW YORK CITY SAMPLE
	Total			*Known to be hospitalized*			*Not known to be hospitalized*			
	All persons	Duration bed-disability known		All persons	Duration bed-disability known		All persons	Duration bed-disability known		
		Persons	Days		Persons	Days		Persons	Days	*Same classes as for H.I.P. enrollees*

Table 39. Persons with disability of first two classes, H.I.P. enrollees and New York City sample, eight-week period, by age, education of head of household, disability class, and duration of bed-disability

AGE (6 GROUPS) AND YEARS OF SCHOOLING COMPLETED BY HEAD OF HOUSEHOLD (4 GROUPS)	SAME AS TABLE 38

Table 40. Persons with medical conditions, H.I.P. enrollees and New York City sample, eight-week period, by age, sex, and diagnostic group

DIAGNOSTIC GROUP (5 LARGE GROUPS AND 25 SUB-GROUPS) AND SEX	H.I.P. ENROLLEES							NEW YORK CITY SAMPLE
	Total	*Under 5*	*5 to 14*	*15 to 44*	*45 to 64*	*65 and over*	*Not reported*	*Same classes as for H.I.P. enrollees*

Table 41. Persons with medical conditions, H.I.P. enrollees and New York City sample, eight-week period, by age, education of head of household, and diagnostic group

DIAGNOSTIC GROUP (5 LARGE GROUPS AND 25 SUB-GROUPS) AND EDUCATION OF HEAD OF HOUSEHOLD (4 GROUPS)	SAME AS TABLE 40

Table 42. Persons with medical conditions, H.I.P. enrollees and New York City sample, eight-week period, by age, race, and diagnostic group

DIAGNOSTIC GROUP (5 LARGE GROUPS) AND 25 SUB-GROUPS) AND RACE (3 GROUPS)	SAME AS TABLE 40

Table 43. Persons in the labor force with medical conditions, H.I.P. enrollees and New York City sample, eight-week period, by diagnostic group, age, and occupational group

AGE (5 GROUPS) AND DIAGNOSTIC GROUP (5 LARGE GROUPS AND 24 SUB-GROUPS)	H.I.P. ENROLLEES		NEW YORK CITY SAMPLE
	Total	*(7 occupational groups)*	*Same classes as for H.I.P. enrollees*

Table 44. Persons with reported presence of one or more diseases on chronic disease check list (Schedule 1, Question 9), H.I.P. enrollees and New York City sample, by age, sex, chronic disease, and class with multiple diagnoses

CHRONIC DISEASES (9), CLASS WITH MULTIPLE DIAGNOSES (6), AND SEX	SAME AS TABLE 40

Table 45. Persons with reported presence of one or more diseases on chronic disease check list (Schedule 1, Question 9), H.I.P. enrollees and New York City sample, by age, education of head of household, chronic disease, and class with multiple diagnoses

CHRONIC DISEASE (9), CLASS WITH MULTIPLE DIAGNOSES (6), AND YEARS OF SCHOOLING COMPLETED BY HEAD OF HOUSEHOLD (4 GROUPS)	SAME AS TABLE 40

Table 46. Persons with reported presence of more than one disease on chronic disease check list (Schedule 1, Question 9), H.I.P. enrollees and New York City sample, by combinations of diseases reported and sex

COMBINATIONS OF DISEASES REPORTED (6 BROAD CLASSES AND 84 SUB-CLASSES)	H.I.P. ENROLLEES			NEW YORK CITY SAMPLE
	Total	*Male*	*Female*	*Same classes as for H.I.P. enrollees*

Table 47. All persons, H.I.P. enrollees and New York City sample, 1951, by presence or absence of hospitalization and/or illness causing seven or more days of bed-disability not in hospital, age, and sex

AGE (6 GROUPS) AND SEX	H.I.P. ENROLLEES									NEW YORK CITY SAMPLE
				Hospitalized						
						Without other 7-day bed-illness		With other 7-day bed-illness		
	Total	*No hospital or 7-day bed-illness*	*7-day bed-illness, no hospital*	Total	Number of times hospitalized	Total	Number of times hospitalized	Total	Number of times hospitalized	*Same classes as for H.I.P. enrollees*

Table 48. All persons, H.I.P. enrollees and New York City sample, 1951, by presence or absence of hospitalization and/or illness causing seven or more days of bed-disability not in hospital, age, and education of head of household

AGE (6 GROUPS) AND YEARS OF SCHOOLING COMPLETED BY HEAD OF HOUSEHOLD (4 GROUPS)	SAME AS TABLE 47

Table 49. Persons hospitalized or with seven or more days of bed-disability not in hospital, H.I.P. enrollees and New York City sample, 1951, by hospitalization, age, sex, and duration of bed-disability

AGE (6 GROUPS), AND DURATION OF BED-DISABILITY (WEEKS; 8 CLASSES)	H.I.P. ENROLLEES			NEW YORK CITY SAMPLE
	All persons	*Hospitalized*	*Not hospitalized*	*Same classes as for H.I.P. enrollees*
	Total M F	Total M F	Total M F	

Table 50. Persons hospitalized or with seven or more days of bed-disability not in hospital, H.I.P. enrollees and New York City sample, 1951, by hospitalization, age, education of head of household, and duration of bed-disability

AGE (6 GROUPS), AND DURATION OF BED-DISABILITY (WEEKS; 8 CLASSES)	H.I.P. ENROLLEES			NEW YORK CITY SAMPLE
	All persons	*Hospitalized*	*Not hospitalized*	*Same classes as for H.I.P. enrollees*
	Years of schooling completed by head of household (4 groups)	Years of schooling completed by head of household (4 groups)	Years of schooling completed by head of household (4 groups)	

Table 51. H.I.P. enrollees hospitalized, 1951, by age, sex, type of hospital, and duration of hospital stay

AGE (6 GROUPS) AND DURATION OF HOSPITAL STAY (DAYS; 9 CLASSES)	ALL PERSONS			MUNI-CIPAL			VOLUN-TARY			PROPRIE-TARY			OTHER			NOT RE-PORTED N.Y.C.			OUTSIDE N.Y.C.			MORE THAN ONE TYPE		
	T	*M*	*F*	*T*	*M*	*F*	*T*	*M*	*F*	*T*	*M*	*F*	*T*	*M*	*F*	*T*	*M*	*F*	*T*	*M*	*F*	*T*	*M*	*F*

Table 52. Same as Table 51, for New York City sample

Table 53. Persons hospitalized, H.I.P. enrollees and New York City sample, 1951, by age, education of head of household, duration of hospital stay, and type of hospital

AGE (6 GROUPS), YEARS OF SCHOOLING COMPLETED BY HEAD OF HOUSEHOLD (4 GROUPS), AND DURATION OF HOSPITAL STAY (DAYS; 9 GROUPS)	H.I.P. ENROLLEES								NEW YORK CITY SAMPLE
		Type of hospital							
	Total	Muni-cipal	Volun-tary	Proprie-tary	Other	Not re-ported N.Y.C.	Outside N.Y.C.	More than one type	*Same classes as for H.I.P. enrollees*

Table 54. Persons hospitalized or with seven or more days of bed-disability not in hospital, H.I.P. enrollees and New York City sample, 1951, by age, sex, and diagnostic group

DIAGNOSTIC GROUP (5 LARGE GROUPS AND 15 SUB-GROUPS) AND SEX	H.I.P. ENROLLEES		NEW YORK CITY SAMPLE
	Total	*(6 age groups)*	*Same classes as for H.I.P. enrollees*

Table 55. Persons hospitalized or with seven or more days of bed-disability not in hospital, H.I.P. enrollees and New York City sample, 1951, by age, education of head of household, and diagnostic group

DIAGNOSTIC GROUP (5 LARGE GROUPS AND 15 SUB-GROUPS) AND YEARS OF SCHOOLING COMPLETED BY HEAD OF HOUSEHOLD (4 GROUPS)	SAME AS TABLE 54

Table 56. Persons with hospitalized surgery, H.I.P. enrollees and New York City sample, 1951, by age, sex, number of episodes, and type of operation

NUMBER OF EPISODES OF HOSPITALIZED SURGERY (2 GROUPS), TYPE OF OPERATION (18 CLASSES), AND SEX	SAME AS TABLE 54

Table 57. Persons with hospitalized surgery, H.I.P. enrollees and New York City sample, 1951, by age, education of head of household, number of episodes, and type of operation

NUMBER OF EPISODES OF HOSPITALIZED SURGERY (2 GROUPS), TYPE OF OPERATION (18 CLASSES), AND YEARS OF SCHOOLING COMPLETED BY HEAD OF HOUSEHOLD (4 GROUPS)	SAME AS TABLE 54

Table 58. All persons, H.I.P. enrollees and New York City sample, eight-week period, by presence or absence of medical conditions, use of symptom question (Schedule 1, Question 7c) as source of establishing one or more medical conditions, total number of medical conditions from specified source, age, and sex

AGE (6 GROUPS) AND SEX	H.I.P. ENROLLEES								NEW YORK CITY SAMPLE
	All persons	*With medical conditions*			*Without medical conditions*	*Total conditions*			*Same classes as for H.I.P. enrollees*
		Total	Source of Schedule 2			Total	Source of Schedule 2		
			One or more from 7c	None from 7c			7c	Other	

Table 59. All persons, H.I.P. enrollees and New York City sample, eight-week period, by presence or absence of medical conditions, use of symptom question (Schedule 1, Question 7c) as source of establishing one or more medical conditions, total number of medical conditions from specified source, age, and education of head of household

AGE (6 GROUPS) AND YEARS OF SCHOOLING COMPLETED BY HEAD OF HOUSEHOLD (4 GROUPS)	SAME AS TABLE 58

Table 60. All persons, H.I.P. enrollees and New York City sample, by date of interview and presence or absence of medical and/or dental condition on preceding day

DATE OF INTERVIEW (WEEK)	H.I.P. ENROLLEES					NEW YORK CITY SAMPLE
	Total	*With medical condition*	*With medical and dental condition*	*With dental condition only*	*Without either*	*Same classes as for H.I.P. enrollees*

Table 61. H.I.P. enrollees, eight-week period, by presence or absence of medical conditions, type of contact with doctor, number of doctor visits, age, and sex

AGE (6 GROUPS) AND SEX	ALL PERSONS	WITH MEDICAL CONDITIONS						WITHOUT MEDICAL CONDITIONS			
		Total	*Seen by M.D.; number of visits*		*Phone only*	*No M.D. contact*	*M.D. contact not reported*	*Total*	*With physical check-up*		*No physical check-up*
			Total	(8 classes: 1, 2, 3, 4, 5–9, 10–19, 20, not reported)					Total	Number of M.D. visits (6 classes)	

Table 62. Same as Table 61, for New York City sample

Table 63. H.I.P. enrollees, eight-week period, by presence or absence of medical conditions, type of contact with doctor, number of doctor contacts, age, and education of head of household

AGE (6 GROUPS) AND YEARS OF SCHOOLING COMPLETED BY HEAD OF HOUSEHOLD (4 GROUPS)	SAME AS TABLE 61

Table 64. Same as Table 63, for New York City sample

Table 65. Persons who saw a doctor, H.I.P. enrollees and New York City sample, eight-week period, by type of medical care, age, and sex

AGE (6 GROUPS) AND SEX	H.I.P. ENROLLEES		NEW YORK CITY SAMPLE
	Total	*Type of medical care (6 classes)*	*Same classes as for H.I.P. enrollees*

Classes of medical care: (1) Hospitalized with private M.D. care; (2) Hospitalized but no private M.D. care; (3) Private M.D. care only, not hospitalized; (4) Private M.D. care plus other (O.P.D., etc.), not hospitalized; (5) O.P.D. only; (6) Type of M.D. care unknown, not hospitalized

Table 66. Persons who saw a doctor, H.I.P. enrollees and New York City sample, eight-week period, by type of medical care, age, and education of head of household

AGE (6 GROUPS) AND YEARS OF SCHOOLING COMPLETED BY HEAD OF HOUSEHOLD (4 GROUPS)	SAME AS TABLE 65

Table 67. Persons receiving dental attention, H.I.P. enrollees and New York City sample, eight-week period, by presence or absence of dental conditions, number of dentist visits, age, and sex

AGE (6 GROUPS), REASON, IF SEEN BY DENTIST (DENTAL CONDITION OR CHECK-UP ONLY), AND SEX	H.I.P. ENROLLEES							NEW YORK CITY SAMPLE
	All persons	*Number of D.D.S. visits, eight weeks*					*Total D.D.S. visits*	*Same classes as for H.I.P. enrollees*
		0	1	2–4	5	Not reported		

Table 68. Persons receiving dental attention, H.I.P. enrollees and New York City sample, eight-week period, by presence or absence of dental conditions, number of dentist visits, age, and education of head of household

AGE (6 GROUPS), REASON, IF SEEN BY DENTIST (DENTAL CONDITION OR CHECK-UP ONLY), AND YEARS OF SCHOOLING COMPLETED BY HEAD OF HOUSEHOLD (4 GROUPS)	SAME AS TABLE 67

Table 69. H.I.P. enrollees with medical conditions, eight-week period, by maximum degree of disability within the period, total days of disability for given degrees, total number of doctor visits within the period, age, and sex

Age (6 groups) and sex shown on stub. Items in columns include:

TOTAL PERSONS

Hospitalized
- Total
- Duration hospital stay known
  - Persons
  - Days
- Duration bed-disability known
  - Persons
  - Days
- Duration disability known
  - Persons
  - Days
- Number M.D. visits known
  - Persons
  - Days

Bed-disabled—not hospitalized
- Total
- Duration bed-disability known
  - Persons
  - Days
- Duration disability known
  - Persons
  - Days
- Number M.D. visits known
  - Persons
  - Days

Disability, no bed or hospital
- Total
- Duration disability known
  - Persons
  - Days
- Number M.D. visits known
  - Persons
  - Days

Disabled, degree unknown
- Total
- Duration disability known
  - Persons
  - Days
- Number M.D. visits known
  - Persons
  - Days

Not disabled
- Total
- Number M.D. visits known
  - Persons
  - Days

Unknown if disabled
- Number M.D. visits known
  - Persons
  - Days

Table 70. Same as Table 69, for New York City sample

Table 71. H.I.P. enrollees with medical conditions, eight-week period, by maximum degree of disability within period, total days of disability for given degrees, total number of doctor visits within the period, age, and education of head of household

Age (6 groups) and education of head of household (4 groups) are shown on stub. Items in columns same as in Table 69

Table 72. Same as Table 71, for New York City sample

Table 73. Persons in hospital, H.I.P. enrollees and New York City sample, eight-week period, by age, sex, and hospital insurance status

AGE (6 GROUPS) AND SEX	H.I.P. ENROLLEES												NEW YORK CITY SAMPLE
	Total			*With hospital insurance*			*Without hospital insurance*			*Hospital insurance not reported*			*Same classes as for H.I.P. enrollees*
	All persons	Duration hospital stay known		All persons	Duration hospital stay known		All persons	Duration hospital stay known		All persons	Duration hospital stay known		
		Persons	Days		Persons	Days		Persons	Days		Persons	Days	

Table 74. Persons in hospital, H.I.P. enrollees and New York City sample, eight-week period, by age, education of head of household, and hospital insurance status

AGE (6 GROUPS) AND YEARS OF SCHOOLING COMPLETED BY HEAD OF HOUSEHOLD (4 GROUPS)	SAME AS TABLE 73

Table 75. Persons with medical conditions, H.I.P. enrollees and New York City sample, eight-week period, by age, sex, broad diagnostic groups, type of contact with doctor, and number of doctor visits

AGE (6 GROUPS), SEX, AND DIAGNOSTIC GROUP (5 LARGE GROUPS AND 25 SUB-GROUPS)	SAME AS TABLE 61 CLASSES FOR PERSONS WITH MEDICAL CONDITIONS

Table 76. Persons with medical conditions, H.I.P. enrollees and New York City sample, eight-week period, by age, education of head of household, broad diagnostic groups, type of contact with doctor, and number of doctor visits

AGE (6 GROUPS), YEARS OF SCHOOLING COMPLETED BY HEAD OF HOUSEHOLD (4 GROUPS), AND DIAGNOSTIC GROUP (5 LARGE GROUPS AND 25 SUB-GROUPS)	SAME AS TABLE 61 CLASSES FOR PERSONS WITH MEDICAL CONDITIONS

Table 77. H.I.P. enrollees who saw a doctor, eight-week period, by age, sex, H.I.P. status of doctor, and number of doctor visits

AGE (6 GROUPS) AND H.I.P. STATUS OF DOCTOR SEEN (4 GROUPS)	ALL PERSONS			NUMBER OF M.D. VISITS											
				1			*2–4*			*5 or more*			*Not reported*		
	Total	*M*	*F*	Total	M	F	Total	M	F	Total	M	F	Total	M	F

Table 78. H.I.P. enrollees who saw a doctor, eight-week period, by age, H.I.P. status of doctor, education of head of household, and number of doctor visits

SAME AS IN TABLE 77	ALL PERSONS	NUMBER OF M.D. VISITS			
		1	*2–4*	*5 or more*	*Not reported*
	[1]	[1]	[1]	[1]	[1]

[1] Four classes for number of years of schooling completed by head of household

Table 79. Persons reporting preventive health examinations, H.I.P. enrollees and New York City sample, eight-week period, by age, sex, presence or absence of specified chronic disease, and reason for physical check-up

AGE (6 GROUPS) AND SEX	H.I.P. ENROLLEES				NEW YORK CITY SAMPLE
	Without specified chronic disease		*With specified chronic disease*		*Same classes as for H.I.P. enrollees*
	Total	Reason for physical check-up (6 classes)	Total	Reason for physical check-up (6 classes)	

Reasons for physical check-up: (1) School, employment, or insurance examination; (2) General check-up or immunization only; (3) Prenatal or postpartum examination; (4) Routine eye examination; (5) Other, more than one type or unknown

Table 80. Persons reporting preventive health examinations, H.I.P. enrollees and New York City sample, eight-week period, by age, education of head of household, presence or absence of chronic disease, and reason for physical check-up

AGE (6 GROUPS) AND YEARS OF SCHOOLING COMPLETED BY HEAD OF HOUSEHOLD (4 GROUPS)	SAME AS TABLE 79

Table 81. Persons reporting one or more diseases on chronic disease check list (Schedule 1, Question 9), H.I.P. enrollees and New York City sample, 1951, by age, sex, number and type of chronic diseases reported, and number of doctor visits

AGE (6 GROUPS), SEX, AND TYPE OF CHRONIC DISEASE (ONLY ONE CHRONIC CONDITION, 9 TYPES; MORE THAN ONE, 6 COMBINATIONS)	H.I.P. ENROLLEES							NEW YORK CITY SAMPLE
	Total	*Number of doctor visits 1951*						*Same classes as for H.I.P. enrollees*
		0	1	2–4	5–9	10	Not reported	

Table 82. Persons reporting one or more diseases on chronic disease check list (Schedule 1, Question 9), H.I.P. enrollees and New York City sample, 1951, by age, education of head of household, number and type of chronic diseases reported, and number of doctor visits

AGE (6 GROUPS), YEARS OF SCHOOLING COMPLETED BY HEAD OF HOUSEHOLD (4 GROUPS), AND TYPE OF CHRONIC DISEASE (ONLY ONE CONDITION, 9 TYPES; MORE THAN ONE, 6 COMBINATIONS)	SAME AS TABLE 81

Table 83. Persons with no disease listed on chronic disease check list (Schedule 1, Question 9), H.I.P. enrollees and New York City sample, 1951, classified by age, sex, and number of doctor visits

AGE (6 GROUPS) AND SEX	SAME AS TABLE 81

Table 84. Persons with no disease listed on chronic disease check list (Schedule 1, Question 9), H.I.P. enrollees and New York City sample, 1951, by age, education of head of household, and number of doctor visits

AGE (6 GROUPS) AND YEARS OF SCHOOLING COMPLETED BY HEAD OF HOUSEHOLD (4 GROUPS)	SAME AS TABLE 81

Table 85. H.I.P. enrollees, 1951, by age, sex, type of illness, and number of doctor visits

AGE (6 GROUPS) AND SEX	H.I.P. ENROLLEES							NEW YORK CITY SAMPLE
	All persons	*Number of doctor visits in 1951*						*Same classes as for H.I.P. enrollees*
		0	1	2–4	5–9	10 or more	Not reported	
	Total[1]	Total[1]	Total[1]	Total[1]	Total[1]	Total[1]	Total[1]	

[1] Types of illness: (1) Hospitalized; (2) Seven or more days of bed-disability, not hospitalized; (3) No hospitalization or illness causing seven or more days of bed-disability

Table 86. Same as Table 85, for New York City sample

Table 87. Persons hospitalized, H.I.P. enrollees and New York City sample, 1951 by age, sex, duration of hospital stay, and hospital insurance coverage

AGE (6 GROUPS), SEX, AND DURATION OF HOSPITAL STAY (9 CLASSES)	H.I.P. ENROLLEES								NEW YORK CITY SAMPLE
	Total		*Hospital insurance*						*Same classes as for H.I.P. enrollees*
			Some		None		Not reported		
	Persons	Days	Persons	Days	Persons	Days	Persons	Days	

Table 88. Persons hospitalized, H.I.P. enrollees and New York City sample, 1951, by age, education of head of household, duration of hospital stay, and hospital insurance coverage

AGE (6 GROUPS) AND YEARS OF SCHOOLING COMPLETED BY HEAD OF HOUSEHOLD (4 GROUPS)	SAME AS TABLE 87

Table 89. Medical conditions, H.I.P. enrollees and New York City sample, day preceding interview, by age, sex, diagnosis, and degree of related disability produced at any time during eight-week period

AGE (6 GROUPS), SEX, AND DIAGNOSIS (74 GROUPS)	H.I.P. ENROLLEES							NEW YORK CITY SAMPLE
	Total	*Degree of disability*[1]						*Same classes as for H.I.P. enrollees*
		1	2	3	4	5	6	

[1] See Table 32 for code of degrees of disability.

Table 90. Medical conditions, H.I.P. enrollees and New York City sample, day preceding interview, by age, education of head of household, diagnosis, and degree of related disability produced at any time during eight-week period

AGE (6 GROUPS), YEARS OF SCHOOLING COMPLETED BY HEAD OF HOUSEHOLD (4 GROUPS), AND DIAGNOSIS (74 GROUPS)	SAME AS TABLE 89

Table 91. Medical conditions, patients aged 14 years and over, H.I.P. enrollees and New York City sample, day preceding interview, by diagnosis, labor force status, and degree of disability produced at any time during eight-week period

LABOR FORCE STATUS (8 GROUPS) AND DIAGNOSIS (74 GROUPS)	SAME AS TABLE 89

Table 92. Medical conditions, H.I.P. enrollees and New York City sample, eight-week period, by age, sex, diagnosis, and degree of related disability at any time during period

AGE (6 GROUPS), SEX, AND DIAGNOSIS (74 GROUPS)	SAME AS TABLE 89

Table 93. Medical conditions, H.I.P. enrollees and New York City sample, eight-week period, by age, education of head of household, diagnosis, and degree of related disability at any time during period

AGE (6 GROUPS), YEARS OF SCHOOLING COMPLETED BY HEAD OF HOUSEHOLD (4 GROUPS), AND DIAGNOSIS (74 GROUPS)	SAME AS TABLE 89

Table 94. Medical conditions producing disability, H.I.P. enrollees and New York City sample, eight-week period, by age, sex, diagnosis, and total days of disability during period

AGE (6 GROUPS) AND DIAGNOSIS (74 GROUPS)	H.I.P. ENROLLEES									NEW YORK CITY SAMPLE
	All disabling conditions			*Duration of disability known*						*Same classes as for H.I.P. enrollees*
				Conditions			Days			
	Total	M	F	Total	M	F	Total	M	F	

Table 95. Summarizes Table 94, omits diagnosis

Table 96. Medical conditions producing disability, H.I.P. enrollees, eight-week period, by diagnosis, age, education of head of household, and total days of related disability during period

DIAGNOSIS (74 GROUPS) AND AGE (6 GROUPS)	ALL DISABLING CONDITIONS		DURATION OF DISABILITY KNOWN			
			Conditions		*Days*	
	Total	*Years of schooling completed by head of household (4 groups)*	Total	Years of schooling completed by head of household (4 groups)	Total	Years of schooling completed by head of household (4 groups)

Table 97. Same as Table 96, for New York City sample

Table 98. Summarizes Tables 96 and 97, omits diagnosis

Table 99. Medical conditions producing bed-disability, H.I.P. enrollees and New York City sample, eight-week period, by age, sex, diagnosis, and total days of related bed-disability during period

DIAGNOSIS (74 GROUPS) AND AGE (6 GROUPS)	H.I.P. ENROLLEES									NEW YORK CITY SAMPLE
	All conditions with bed-disability			*Duration of bed-disability known*						*Same classes as for H.I.P. enrollees*
				Conditions			Days			
	Total	M	F	Total	M	F	Total	M	F	

Table 100. Summarizes Table 99, omits diagnosis

Table 101. Medical conditions producing bed-disability, H.I.P. enrollees, eight-week period, by age, education of head of household, diagnosis, and total days of related bed-disability during period

AGE (6 GROUPS) AND DIAGNOSIS (74 GROUPS)	ALL CONDITIONS		DURATION OF BED-DISABILITY KNOWN			
			Conditions		*Days*	
	Total	*Years of schooling completed by head of household (4 groups)*	Total	Years of schooling completed by head of household (4 groups)	Total	Years of schooling completed by head of household (4 groups)

Table 102. Same as Table 101, for New York City sample

Table 103. Summarizes Tables 101 and 102, omits diagnosis

Table 104. Medical conditions producing hospitalization, H.I.P. enrollees and New York City sample, eight-week period, by age, sex, diagnosis, and total days of hospitalization during period

AGE (6 GROUPS) AND DIAGNOSIS (74 GROUPS)	H.I.P. ENROLLEES									NEW YORK CITY SAMPLE
	All conditions with hospitalization			*Duration of hospitalization known*						*Same classes as for H.I.P. enrollees*
				Conditions			Days			
	Total	M	F	Total	M	F	Total	M	F	

Table 105. Summarizes Table 104, omits diagnosis

Table 106. Medical conditions producing hospitalization, H.I.P. enrollees, eight-week period, by age, diagnosis, education of head of household, and total days of hospitalization during period

AGE (6 GROUPS) AND DIAGNOSIS (74 GROUPS)	ALL CONDITIONS WITH HOSPITALIZATION		DURATION OF HOSPITALIZATION KNOWN			
	Total	*Years of schooling completed by head of household (4 groups)*	*Total conditions*	*Years of schooling completed by head of household (4 groups)*	*Total days*	*Years of schooling completed by head of household (4 groups)*

Table 107. Same as Table 106, for New York City sample

Table 108. Summarizes Tables 106 and 107, omits diagnosis

Table 109. Medical conditions producing hospitalization, H.I.P. enrollees, eight-week period, by age, sex, type of hospital, and total days of hospitalization

AGE (6 GROUPS) AND SEX	ALL CONDITIONS[1]	TYPE OF HOSPITAL					
		Municipal	*Voluntary*	*Proprietary*	*Other*	*Not reported N.Y.C.*	*Outside N.Y.C.*
		Total[1]	Total[1]	Total[1]	Total[1]	Total[1]	Total[1]

[1] Shows number of persons and days with known hospital stay

Table 110. Same as Table 109, for New York City sample

Table 111. Surgical operations, H.I.P. enrollees and New York City sample, eight-week period, by sex

OPERATION (93 CATEGORIES)	H.I.P. ENROLLEES			NEW YORK CITY SAMPLE
	Total	*Male*	*Female*	*Same classes as for H.I.P. enrollees*

Table 112. Medical conditions producing hospitalization or seven days or more of bed-disability, H.I.P. enrollees and New York City sample, 1951, by age, sex, diagnosis, and duration of bed-disability

DIAGNOSIS (73 GROUPS), AGE (6 GROUPS), AND SEX	H.I.P. ENROLLEES		NEW YORK CITY SAMPLE
	Total	*Duration of bed-disability*[1] (8 classes)	*Same classes as for H.I.P. enrollees*

[1] Classes: (1) Less than 1 week; (2) 1 week; (3) 2 weeks; (4) 3 to 4 weeks; (5) 5 to 7 weeks; (6) 8 to 11 weeks; (7) 12 or more weeks; (8) Not reported

Table 113. Medical conditions producing hospitalization or seven days or more of bed-disability, H.I.P. enrollees and New York City sample, 1951, by age, education of head of household, diagnosis, and duration of bed-disability

DIAGNOSIS (73 GROUPS), AGE (6 GROUPS), AND YEARS OF SCHOOLING COMPLETED BY HEAD OF HOUSEHOLD (4 GROUPS)	SAME AS TABLE 112

Table 114. Medical conditions producing hospitalization, H.I.P. enrollees and New York City sample, 1951, by age, sex, diagnosis, and duration of related hospitalization during year

DIAGNOSIS (73 GROUPS), AGE (6 GROUPS), AND SEX	H.I.P. ENROLLEES		NEW YORK CITY SAMPLE
	Total	*Duration of hospitalization 1951*[1] (9 classes)	*Same classes as for H.I.P. enrollees*

[1] Classes: (1) 1 night; (2) 2 nights; (3) 3 to 4 nights; (4) 5 to 6 nights; (5) 7 to 9 nights; (6) 10 to 13 nights; (7) 14 to 20 nights; (8) 21 or more nights; (9) Not reported

Table 115. Medical conditions producing hospitalization, H.I.P. enrollees and New York City sample, 1951, by age, diagnosis, education of head of household, and duration of related hospitalization during year

DIAGNOSIS (73 GROUPS), AGE (6 GROUPS), AND YEARS OF SCHOOLING COMPLETED BY HEAD OF HOUSEHOLD (4 GROUPS)	SAME AS TABLE 114

Table 116. Medical conditions present in eight-week period and those producing hospitalization or seven days or more of bed-disability, H.I.P. enrollees and New York City sample, 1951, by diagnosis

DIAGNOSTIC GROUP (74 MAIN GROUPS AND 36 SUB-GROUPS)	CODE NUMBERS (INTERNATIONAL STATISTICAL CLASSIFICATION) COMBINED IN EACH DIAGNOSTIC GROUP	EIGHT-WEEK PERIOD		1951	
		H.I.P. enrollees	*N.Y.C. sample*	*H.I.P. enrollees*	*N.Y.C. sample*

Table 117. Medical conditions, H.I.P. enrollees and New York City sample, eight-week period, by age, sex, degree of related disability, type of doctor contact, and number of doctor visits

AGE (6 GROUPS), SEX, AND DEGREE OF DISABILITY (6 GROUPS) (SEE TABLE 32)	H.I.P. ENROLLEES											NEW YORK CITY SAMPLE
	Total	*No M.D. contact*	*Telephone only*	*Doctor seen*							*M.D. care not reported*	*Same classes as for H.I.P. enrollees*
				Total	Number of M.D. visits							
					1	2–4	5–9	10	Not reported			

Table 118. Medical conditions, H.I.P. enrollees and New York City sample, eight-week period, by age, degree of disability, education of head of household, type of doctor contact, and number of doctor visits

AGE (6 GROUPS), DEGREE OF DISABILITY (6 GROUPS), AND YEARS OF SCHOOLING COMPLETED BY HEAD OF HOUSEHOLD (4 GROUPS)	SAME AS TABLE 117

Table 119. Medical conditions seen by doctor, H.I.P. enrollees, eight-week period, by age, sex, degree of disability, and place seen by doctor

Age (6 groups) and degree of disability (6 groups) shown on stub. Items in columns include:

PLACE OF DOCTOR VISIT
- Hospital (in-patient)
  - No other place known—Total
    - Male
    - Female
  - Plus other place (home and/or office and/or O.P.D.)—Total
    - Male
    - Female
- No hospital in-patient care
  - Home
    - No other place known—Total
      - Male
      - Female
    - Plus other place—Total
      - Male
      - Female
  - No known home visits
    - Office and/or O.P.D. only—Total
      - Male
      - Female
    - Unknown if office and/or O.P.D.—Total
      - Male
      - Female

Table 120. Same as Table 119, for New York City sample

Table 121. Medical conditions, H.I.P. enrollees, eight-week period, by age, sex, type of related doctor contact, maximum degree of disability within period, total days of disability of different degrees, and number of doctor visits

AGE (6 GROUPS), SEX, AND TYPE OF DOCTOR CONTACT (4 GROUPS)	SAME AS TABLE 69
Doctor contact: (1) No M.D. contact; (2) Telephone only; (3) Saw doctor; (4) M.D. care unknown	

Table 122. Same as Table 121, for New York City sample

Table 123. Medical conditions, H.I.P. enrollees, eight-week period, by age, type of related doctor contact, education of head of household, maximum degree of disability within period, total days of disability of different degrees, and number of doctor visits

AGE (6 GROUPS), YEARS OF SCHOOLING COMPLETED BY HEAD OF HOUSEHOLD (4 GROUPS), AND TYPE OF DOCTOR CONTACT (4 GROUPS)	SAME AS TABLE 69

Table 124. Same as Table 123, for New York City sample

Table 125. Medical conditions, H.I.P. enrollees, eight-week period, by age, sex, diagnosis, type of doctor contact, and number of doctor visits

AGE (6 GROUPS), SEX, AND DIAGNOSIS (74 GROUPS)	ALL MEDICAL CONDITIONS	SAME AS TABLE 61 CLASSES FOR GROUP WITH MEDICAL CONDITIONS

Table 126. Same as Table 125, for New York City sample

Table 127. Medical conditions, H.I.P. enrollees, eight-week period, by age, diagnosis, education of head of household, type of doctor contact, and number of doctor visits

AGE (6 GROUPS), DIAGNOSIS (74 GROUPS), AND YEARS OF SCHOOLING COMPLETED BY HEAD OF HOUSEHOLD (4 GROUPS)	ALL MEDICAL CONDITIONS	SAME AS TABLE 61 CLASSES FOR GROUP WITH MEDICAL CONDITIONS

Table 128. Same as Table 127, for New York City sample

Table 129. Medical conditions receiving doctor's care, H.I.P. enrollees, eight-week period, by age, sex, diagnosis, and insurance coverage

AGE (6 GROUPS) AND DIAGNOSIS (74 GROUPS)	CONDITIONS IN ALL PERSONS			SOME INSURANCE COVERAGE			NO INSURANCE			NO COSTS			INSURANCE NOT REPORTED		
	Total	*M*	*F*	*Total*	*M*	*F*	*Total*	*M*	*F*	*Total*	*M*	*F*	*Total*	*M*	*F*

Table 130. Same as Table 129, for New York City sample

Table 131. Medical conditions receiving doctor's care, H.I.P. enrollees, eight-week period, by age, diagnosis, education of head of household, and insurance coverage

AGE (6 GROUPS) AND DIAGNOSIS (74 GROUPS)	CONDITIONS IN ALL PERSONS	SOME INSURANCE COVERAGE	NO INSURANCE	NO COSTS	INSURANCE NOT REPORTED
	[1]	[1]	[1]	[1]	[1]

[1] Years of schooling completed by head of household (4 groups)

Table 132. Same as Table 131, for New York City sample

Table 133. Medical conditions receiving doctor's care, H.I.P. enrollees, eight-week period, by age, sex, diagnosis, acceptability of reported date of onset, and time lag in doctor contact

AGE (6 GROUPS), SEX, AND DIAGNOSIS (74 GROUPS)	ONSET DATE ACCEPTABLE		ONSET DATE NOT ACCEPTABLE	
	Total	*Time lag in doctor contact (days)—(8 classes)*[1]	*Total*	*Time lag in doctor contact (days)—(8 classes)*[1]

[1] Classes: (1) Less than one day; (2) One day; (3) Two to three days; (4) Four to six days; (5) Seven to thirteen days; (6) Fourteen to twenty days; (7) Twenty-one days and over; (8) Not reported

Table 134. Same as Table 133, for New York City sample

Table 135. Medical conditions receiving doctor's care, H.I.P. enrollees, eight-week period, by age, diagnosis, education of head of household, acceptability of date of onset, and time lag in doctor contact

AGE (6 GROUPS), DIAGNOSIS (74 GROUPS), AND YEARS OF SCHOOLING COMPLETED BY HEAD OF HOUSEHOLD (4 GROUPS)	SAME AS TABLE 133

Table 136. Same as Table 135, for New York City sample

Table 137. Medical conditions receiving doctor's care, H.I.P. enrollees, eight-week period, by age, sex, diagnosis, and H.I.P. status of physician

AGE (6 GROUPS) AND DIAGNOSIS (16 GROUPS)	ALL CONDITIONS			TREATED BY											
				H.I.P. doctor only			*H.I.P. and other M.D.*			*Other M.D. only*			*M.D. not reported*		
	Total	*M*	*F*	Total	M	F	Total	M	F	Total	M	F	Total	M	F

Table 138. Medical conditions receiving doctor's care, H.I.P. enrollees, eight-week period, by age, diagnosis, education of head of household, and H.I.P. status of physician

AGE (6 GROUPS), DIAGNOSIS (16 GROUPS)	SAME AS TABLE 137 FOR H.I.P. STATUS OF DOCTOR, BUT SUBSTITUTES EDUCATION OF HEAD OF HOUSEHOLD FOR SEX

Table 139. Medical conditions producing hospitalization or seven days or more of bed-disability, H.I.P. enrollees and New York City sample, 1951, by age, sex, diagnosis, and number of related doctor visits

AGE (6 GROUPS), SEX, AND DIAGNOSIS (74 GROUPS)	H.I.P. ENROLLEES									NEW YORK CITY SAMPLE
	Total	*Number of M.D. visits*							*Total M.D. visits*	*Same classes as for H.I.P. enrollees*
		0	1	2–4	5–9	10–19	20	Not reported		

Table 140. Medical conditions producing hospitalization or seven days or more of bed-disability, H.I.P. enrollees and New York City sample, 1951, by age, education of head of household, diagnosis, and number of related doctor visits

AGE (6 GROUPS), YEARS OF SCHOOLING COMPLETED BY HEAD OF HOUSEHOLD (4 GROUPS) AND DIAGNOSIS (74 GROUPS)	SAME AS TABLE 139

Table 141. Medical conditions producing hospitalization or seven or more days of bed-disability, H.I.P. enrollees, 1951, by age, sex, diagnosis, and H.I.P. status of physician

AGE (6 GROUPS) AND DIAGNOSIS (16 GROUPS)	SAME AS TABLE 137

Table 142. Medical conditions producing hospitalization or seven days or more of bed-disability, H.I.P. enrollees, 1951, by age, education of head of household, diagnosis, and H.I.P. status of physician

AGE (6 GROUPS) AND DIAGNOSIS (16 GROUPS)	ALL CONDITIONS	TREATED BY			
	[1]	*H.I.P. doctor only* [1]	*H.I.P. and other M.D.* [1]	*Other M.D. only* [1]	*M.D. not reported* [1]

[1] Years of schooling completed by head of household (4 groups)

Table 143. Hospitalized surgery, H.I.P. enrollees and New York City sample, 1951, by age, sex, and type of operation

TYPE OF OPERATION (133 GROUPS) AND SEX	H.I.P. ENROLLEES		NEW YORK CITY SAMPLE
	Total	*6 age groups*	*Same classes as for H.I.P. enrollees*

Table 144. Chronic diseases reported on Schedule 1, Question 9, H.I.P. enrollees and New York City sample, 1951, by age, sex, disease, and related medical care

AGE (6 GROUPS) AND CHRONIC DISEASE (9)	H.I.P. ENROLLEES												NEW YORK CITY SAMPLE
	All persons with specified disease			*Related medical care in 1951*									*Same classes as for H.I.P. enrollees*
				Yes			No			Not reported			
	T	M	F	T	M	F	T	M	F	T	M	F	

Table 145. Chronic diseases reported on Schedule 1, Question 9, H.I.P. enrollees, 1951, by age, education of head of household, disease, and related medical care

AGE (6 GROUPS) AND DISEASE (9)	ALL PERSONS WITH SPECIFIED DISEASE	RELATED MEDICAL CARE IN 1951		
		Yes	*No*	*Not reported*
	1	1	1	1

[1] Years of schooling completed by head of household (4 groups)

Table 146. Same as Table 145, for New York City sample

APPENDIX H

Categories of Disease and Medical Conditions Appearing in This Report

THE three-digit code of the International Statistical Classification was used to describe the nature of each medical condition reported on Schedules 2 and 3. The terminology of the respondent was used rather strictly in determining choice of code number, in order to keep editing or interpretation on the part of the medical coders to a minimum at this point. Since each Schedule 2 was intended to report a single medical condition, it received only *one* code number, except in the case of multiple diseases associated with hospitalization. Here, in order to avoid duplicated counts of hospitalization, provision was made for coding a secondary diagnosis and identifying it as such. The actual number of such secondary diagnoses was very small, and they were omitted from tabulations of medical conditions altogether. (Secondary diagnoses occurred in only two of 4,648 medical conditions for the H.I.P. sample, and in only 10 of the 7,485 for the New York City sample.)

After the reported medical conditions had been coded as described above, they were grouped into 74 classes as shown below. This list indicates also the size of the principal components of the summarized items as they appeared in both samples for the eight-week period and for the selected episodes of illness in 1951.

Medical conditions present in the eight-week period, and medical conditions producing hospitalization or seven or more days of bed-disability in 1951, International Statistical Classification codes, grouped into 74 diagnostic categories in persons of specified H.I.P. status

HOUSEHOLD SURVEY DIAGNOSTIC GROUP	INTERNATIONAL STATISTICAL CLASSIFICATION CODE	8 WEEKS *H.I.P.*	8 WEEKS *N.Y.C.*	1951 *H.I.P.*	1951 *N.Y.C.*
All medical conditions	All	4,648	7,485	1,025	1,673
1. Tuberculosis	001, 002, 003, 008, 009,* 012	10	28	2	12
	Not specified as arrested	7	21	2	12
	Arrested, pulmonary	3	7	—	—
2. Other infective and parasitic, except late effects of poliomyelitis, unspecified "virus" infections, and dermatophytosis	020–021, 027–096, 100–130, 132–133, 135–138	211	347	69	139
	Measles (085)	120	205	28	46
	German measles (086)	11	32	3	3
	Chicken pox (087)	28	37	14	39
	Mumps (089)	18	23	8	14
	Streptococcal sore throat (051)	14	19	10	15
	Scarlet fever (050)	8	5	3	6
	Other: syphilis (029), gonorrhea (030), food poisoning (049), erysipelas (052), septicemia (053), pertussis (056), tetanus (061), Vincent's (070), acute poliomyelitis (080), herpes zoster (088), dengue (090), infectious mononucleosis (093), other specified virus infections (096), worms (130)	12	26	3	16
3. Neoplasms	140–239	29	64	47	61
	Malignant (140–205)	3	11	2	12
	Benign (210–229)	16	33	26	21
	Unspecified (230–239)	10	20	19	28

*New ISC code number adopted; see page 265.

HOUSEHOLD SURVEY DIAGNOSTIC GROUP	INTERNATIONAL STATISTICAL CLASSIFICATION CODE	8 WEEKS *H.I.P.*	8 WEEKS *N.Y.C.*	1951 *H.I.P.*	1951 *N.Y.C.*
4. Hay fever	240	45	24	1	—
5. Asthma	241	115	189	15	28
6. Other allergies	243–245	55	57	2	1
7. Diabetes	260	65	133	4	7
8. Other endocrine and metabolic disorders except obesity; avitaminoses	250–254, 270–277, 286	20	29	12	11
	Thyroid (250–254)	14	15	12	6
	Other endocrine (270–277)	2	8	—	—
	Avitaminoses, etc. (286)	4	6	—	5
9. Obesity	287	131	191	—	—
10. Anemias and blood diseases	290–299	24	36	—	9
11. Psychoneuroses; disorders of character, behavior, and intelligence	310–326	33	60	8	10
12. Vascular lesions affecting central nervous system; late effects of such lesions	330–334, 352	14	40	3	10
13. Other disease of central nervous system, except migraine	340–351, 353, 355–357	7	19	2	3
14. Neuritis, neuralgia, sciatica	360, 362, 363, 366	20	29	7	3
15. Conjunctivitis, blepharitis, hordeolum	370–372	18	2	—	—
16. Other inflammatory eye disease	373–379	17	7	—	4
17. Refractive error	380	13	11	—	—
18. Cataract, detachment of retina, blindness	385–387, 389	1	21	5	6
19. Other eye disease	383–384, 388	14	24	6	4
20. Otitis, mastoiditis, other ear disease except deafness or deaf-mutism	390–391, 393–396	61	62	9	10
	Otitis media (391)	30	37	4	7
21. Deafness, deaf-mutism	397, 398	7	17	—	1
22. Possible heart disease	435*	6	2	—	—
23. Heart disease, except congenital	400–401, 416, 420–421, 424,* 434, 443	135	364	27	63
	Rheumatic fever, rheumatic heart disease (400–401, 416)	10	14	6	9
	Valvular, not specified as rheumatic (421)	1	4	—	—
	Arteriosclerotic (420)	8	10	5	6
	Arteriosclerotic and hypertensive (424*)	1	1	1	1
	Hypertensive (443)	14	87	3	12
	Unspecified (434)	101	248	12	35
24. Hypertension	444, 446	158	382	6	11
25. Arteriosclerosis, peripheral vascular disease	450, 453	45	182	—	1
26. Varicose veins, phlebitis	460, 463, 464	178	293	6	9
27. Hemorrhoids	461	40	36	17	18
28. Other circulatory diseases	454–455, 465, 467	10	20	8	7
29. Lymphadenitis	468	1	3	1	3
30. Acute upper respiratory infection	470–475	795	1,101	35	72
	Nasopharyngitis (470)	594	812	17	57
	Pharyngitis (472)	138	178	8	7
	Tonsillitis (473)	40	91	5	6
	Other: acute sinusitis (471), acute laryngitis (474), upper respiratory infection not otherwise specified (475)	23	20	5	2
31. Influenza, grippe	481–482, 097,* 098,* 099*	369	470	117	161
	With respiratory manifestations and unqualified (481)	107	137	42	70
	With digestive manifestations (482)	11	8	5	8
	"Virus" with respiratory manifestations (097*)	48	73	8	20
	"Virus" with digestive manifestations (098*)	17	27	7	8
	"Virus infection" not otherwise specified (099*)	186	225	55	55
32. Pneumonia	490–493	13	34	35	75
33. Bronchitis	500–502	49	65	14	29

*New ISC code number adopted; see page 265.

HOUSEHOLD SURVEY DIAGNOSTIC GROUP	INTERNATIONAL STATISTICAL CLASSIFICATION CODE	8 WEEKS H.I.P.	8 WEEKS N.Y.C.	1951 H.I.P.	1951 N.Y.C.
34. Chronic and other upper respiratory conditions	510–517	76	114	38	90
	Hypertrophied tonsils (510)	26	34	29	70
	Sinusitis (513)	27	51	1	8
35. Pleurisy, other lung disease	519, 522, 527	9	15	8	13
36. Gingivitis, teething, other buccal conditions; diseases of esophagus	532–534, 537–539	12	9	1	9
37. Ulcer of stomach or duodenum	540–541	33	39	20	16
38. Ulcerative colitis	572	7	3	5	2
39. Gastroenteritis	571	21	13	1	1
40. Gastritis, functional stomach disorders, symptoms referable to upper gastrointestinal tract	543–544, 784	60	76	1	4
41. Other and unspecified disorders of stomach	545	6	23	6	11
42. Appendicitis	550–552	7	12	32	44
43. Hernia	560–561	14	23	26	25
44. Functional disorders of intestine; symptoms referable to abdomen	573, 785	134	231	4	5
45. Other diseases of intestine (obstruction, anal fissure or abscess, adhesions, other)	570, 574–578	36	46	8	13
46. Diseases of liver, gallbladder, and pancreas	583–587	21	31	20	17
	Gallbladder (584–586)	16	29	18	15
47. Diseases of kidney, urinary tract, and bladder	590, 592, 600, 602–606, 609	21	40	12	29
48. Diseases of prostate and other male genital organs	610, 612–613, 615, 617	8	6	3	10
49. Disorders of menstruation and menopause	634–635	155	287	2	5
50. Diseases of breast; other diseases of female genital organs	620–621, 624–625, 630–633, 636–637	27	34	22	32
51. Complications of pregnancy	640, 642, 644–649	5	8	2	7
52. Abortion	650	4	5	19	24
53. Delivery without complications	660	18	46	166	260
54. Delivery with complications	674, 675, 678,* 679*	2	1	9	16
55. Complications of puerperium	682, 688–689	4	4	2	5
56. Infections of skin and subcutaneous tissue except warts (boils, cellulitis and abscess, impetigo, other local infections)	690–692, 695, 698	26	31	3	17
57. Dermatophytosis, fungus infections not otherwise specified, warts, and all other skin conditions	131, 134, 696, 700–716	167	239	5	6
58. Arthritis	720–725	129	270	11	30
59. Myositis, rheumatism	726–727	143	399	—	3
60. Disorders of back; displaced intervertebral disc, chronic sacroiliac disease, back sprains	735–736, 846–847	43	36	6	4
	Back sprain (846–847)	22	17	3	2
61. Symptoms referable to limbs or back; unspecified muscular disease	744, 787	178	276	4	15
62. Osteomyelitis; other diseases of bone and joint	730, 733–734, 737–738	4	5	3	3
63. Late effects of old injuries or of poliomyelitis; old amputations	081, 799,* 899*	47	64	8	10
64. Bunions, bursitis	740–742	31	14	14	3
65. Kyphosis, flat feet, club feet, other deformities	745–749	109	168	—	1
	Flat feet (746)	101	161	—	—
66. Congenital malformations and diseases peculiar to early infancy	750, 754–760, 763, 766, 773, 776	7	4	9	4

*New ISC code number adopted; see page 265.

HOUSEHOLD SURVEY DIAGNOSTIC GROUP	INTERNATIONAL STATISTICAL CLASSIFICATION CODE	8 WEEKS *H.I.P.*	8 WEEKS *N.Y.C.*	1951 *H.I.P.*	1951 *N.Y.C.*
67. Symptoms referable to nervous, cardio-vascular, or lymphatic systems	780–782	22	30	—	5
68. Symptoms referable to respiratory system	783	41	30	1	5
69. Nervousness and debility	790	30	52	1	3
70. Headache, migraine	354, 791	36	43	1	3
71. Other general symptoms	788	38	70	3	8
72. Other specified symptoms, senility, ill-defined morbidity	786, 789, 794–795, 798*	40	82	13	23
73. Accidental injuries	802–845, 848–996	158	260	70	120
	Fractures (802–828)	12	39	27	43
	Dislocations (831–837)	—	3	1	3
	Sprains, except back (840–845, 848)	15	31	5	5
	Head injuries (850–856)	9	23	14	13
	Open wounds (870–898, 900–908)	34	57	5	9
	Contusions, superficial injuries (910, 917, 920–929)	17	18	3	3
	Burns (940–949)	6	14	2	5
	Other specified accidents (869, 930, 935, 962, 966, 968–970, 975, 980–981, 989)	11	6	1	8
	Injury not otherwise specified 996	54	69	12	31
74. Reactions to immunization or therapeutic procedures	997–998	10	5	8	3

*New ISC code number adopted; see directly below.

**Additional International Statistical Classification Code Numbers adopted or modified for Household Survey tabulations:*

009—arrested pulmonary tuberculosis
097—"virus" infection with respiratory manifestations
098—"virus" infection with digestive manifestations
099—"virus infection" not otherwise specified
424—arteriosclerotic heart disease with hypertension
435—"possible heart disease" or murmur not otherwise specified in children
678—delivery without specified complication, but by Caesarean section
679—delivery without specified complication, stillbirth
798—administrative physician service
799—late effect of old injury
899—old amputation

Further summarization into 41 classes and subclasses was effected as shown below:

Summary classification	*74 diagnostic groups*	
Infective and parasitic diseases	1–2	
Tuberculosis		1
Other		2
Neoplasms	3	
Allergic, metabolic, endocrine, and nutritional diseases	4–9	
Asthma		5
Other allergies		4, 6
Diabetes		7
Obesity		9
Other		8
Diseases of blood and blood-forming organs	10	
Mental, psychoneurotic, and personality disorders	11	
Diseases of nervous system and sense organs	12–21	
Vascular lesions and inflammatory disorder of C.N.S.		12–14
Diseases of the ear		20, 21
Diseases of the eye		15–19
Diseases of circulatory system	22–29	
Heart disease		23
Hypertension		24
Other		22, 25–29
Diseases of respiratory system	30–35	
Acute upper respiratory infection		30
Other		31–35
Diseases of digestive tract	36–46	
Ulcer of stomach and ulcerative colitis		37–38

Summary classification	*74 diagnostic groups*	
Gastroenteritis		39
Functional disorder of stomach and intestines		40, 44
Other		36, 41–43, 45–46
Disorder of genito-urinary tract	47–50	
Disorder of menstruation and menopause		49
Other		47–48, 50
Deliveries and complications of pregnancy	51–55	
Delivery without complication		53
Other		51–52, 54–55
Diseases of skin and cellular tissue	56–57	
Diseases of bones and organs of movement	58–65	
Arthritis and rheumatism		58–59
Disorders of back and symptoms referable to limbs or back		60–61
Other		62–65
Accidental injuries	73	
All other	66–72, 74	

For some tables a condensation of the 74 basic diagnostic groups into 16 categories was constructed, as shown below. The designations to the right are the code numbers from the list of 74 categories.

1. Specified chronic disease:

Tuberculosis	1	Heart disease	23
Asthma	5	Hypertension	24
Diabetes	7	Ulcer of stomach	37
Psychoneurosis	11	Ulcerative colitis	38

2. Other infective and parasitic, as described	2
3. Respiratory	30–35
4. Allergies other than asthma	4, 6
5. Endocrine and metabolic; anemias, etc.	8, 9, 10
6. Diseases of eye and ear	15–21
7. Circulatory except heart disease	22, 25–29
8. Diseases of gastrointestinal tract, except specified chronic and neoplasms	36, 39–46
9. Genito-urinary	47–48, 49–50
10. Complications of pregnancy, abortion, delivery, complications of puerperium	51–55
11. Infections of skin and subcutaneous tissue; all skin conditions	56–57
12. Arthritis and rheumatism	58–59
13. Other diseases of and symptoms referable to musculo-skeletal system; neuritis, neuralgia, and sciatica	14, 60–65
14. Symptomatic complaints not elsewhere classified	67–72
15. Accidental injuries	73

16. Other:

Neoplasms	3
Vascular lesions affecting central nervous system	12
Other diseases of central nervous system	13
Congenital malformations, etc.	66
Reactions to immunizations, etc.	74

To describe the configurations of conditions as they are found in persons, it was necessary to develop an additive code which would show in one figure the combination of conditions reported in a given person. This code was made by grouping the 16 categories into five broad groups, each with an additive code number. These were:

Additive code number	*Disease category*	*Components from 16-class summary*
01	Specified chronic disease	1
02	Arthritis and rheumatism	12
04	Respiratory	3
10	Accidental injury	15
20	Other	2, 4–11, 13–14, 16

Out of this there could be a maximum of 31 combinations. These are listed opposite.

In some of the tables the general classes of "acute" and "chronic" conditions appear. These were built up from the 74 categories which were assigned as follows:

Acute

2 Other infective and parasitic, etc.
15 Conjunctivitis, blepharitis, hordeolum
16 Other inflammatory eye disease
20 Otitis, mastoiditis, other ear disease except deafness, etc.
29 Lymphadenitis
30 Acute upper respiratory infection
31 Influenza, grippe
32 Pneumonia
33 Bronchitis
35 Pleurisy, other lung disease
39 Gastroenteritis
42 Appendicitis
56 Infections of skin and subcutaneous tissue except warts
71 Other general symptoms (rash, fever)
73 Accidental injuries
74 Reactions to immunization or therapeutic procedures

Chronic

1 Tuberculosis
3 Neoplasms
4 Hay fever
5 Asthma
6 Other allergies
7 Diabetes
8 Other endocrine and metabolic
9 Obesity
10 Anemias, etc.
11 Psychoneuroses, etc.
12 Vascular lesions affecting C.N.S., etc.
13 Other disease of C.N.S. except migraine
14 Neuritis, neuralgia, sciatica
18 Cataract, detached retina, blindness
19 Other eye disease
21 Deafness, deaf-mutism
23 Heart disease except congenital
24 Hypertension
25 Arteriosclerosis, peripheral vascular disease
26 Varicose veins, phlebitis
27 Hemorrhoids
28 Other circulatory
34 Chronic and other upper respiratory

Code	*Classification of persons*
	I. SPECIFIED CHRONIC DISEASE
01	Chronic only
03	Chronic plus arthritis/rheumatism
07	Chronic plus arthritis/rheumatism plus respiratory
13	Chronic plus arthritis/rheumatism plus.............. accident
17	Chronic plus arthritis/rheumatism plus respiratory plus accident
23	Chronic plus arthritis/rheumatism plus........................ ....other
27	Chronic plus arthritis/rheumatism plus respiratory plus............other
33	Chronic plus arthritis/rheumatism plus...............accident plus other
37	Chronic plus arthritis/rheumatism plus respiratory plus accident plus other
05	Chronic plus.......................respiratory
15	Chronic plus.......................respiratory plus accident
25	Chronic plus.......................respiratory plus............ other
35	Chronic plus.......................respiratory plus accident plus other
11	Chronic plus...................................accident
31	Chronic plus .... accident plus other
21	Chronic plus ....other
	II. ARTHRITIS/RHEUMATISM WITHOUT SPECIFIED CHRONIC
02	Arthritis/rheumatism only
06	Arthritis/rheumatism plus respiratory
16	Arthritis/rheumatism plus respiratory plus accident
26	Arthritis/rheumatism plus respiratory plus............other
36	Arthritis/rheumatism plus respiratory plus accident plus other
12	Arthritis/rheumatism plus.............. accident
32	Arthritis/rheumatism plus.............. accident plus other
22	Arthritis/rheumatism plus..........................other
	III. RESPIRATORY WITHOUT SPECIFIED CHRONIC OR ARTHRITIS/RHEUMATISM
04	Respiratory only
14	Respiratory plus accident
34	Respiratory plus accident plus other
24	Respiratory plus............ other
	IV. ACCIDENTAL INJURY WITHOUT SPECIFIED CHRONIC, ARTHRITIS/RHEUMATISM OR RESPIRATORY
10	Accident only
30	Accident plus other
	V. OTHER
20	Other only

---

37 Ulcer of stomach or duodenum
38 Ulcerative colitis
40 Gastritis, functional stomach disorder
41 Other and unspecified disorder of stomach
43 Hernia
44 Functional disorder of intestine, etc.
45 Other disease of intestine, etc.
46 Diseases of liver, gallbladder, pancreas
47 Diseases of kidney, urinary tract, bladder
48 Diseases of prostate, other male genital
49 Disorder of menstruation, menopause
50 Diseases of breast; other female genital
58 Arthritis
59 Myositis, rheumatism
60 Disorders of back, etc.
61 Symptoms referable to limbs or back
62 Osteomyelitis; other bone and joint diseases
63 Late effects of old injuries, etc.
64 Bunions, bursitis
65 Kyphosis, etc.
66 Congenital malformations
67 Symptoms—nervous, cardiovascular, or lymphatic
68 Symptoms—respiratory
69 Nervousness
70 Headache, migraine
72 Other specified symptoms

Not assigned to acute or chronic categories

17 Refractive error
22 Possible heart disease
36 Gingivitis, teething, other buccal conditions, diseases of esophagus
51 Complications of pregnancy
52 Abortion
53 Delivery without complications
54 Delivery with complications
55 Complications of puerperium
57 Dermatophytosis, fungus infections, warts, and all skin conditions other than in 56 (acute)

Index

Index

Unbracketed numbers refer to pages in the text and the appendices in this volume. Bracketed references are to table form numbers in Appendix H. No bracketed references are given for specific diseases or conditions. All table forms with disease categories are listed under "Diagnostic data." Page references beginning with 207 will be found in the appendices setting forth definitions of terms, description of method, and discussion of methodological questions.